Advances in Solid-Phase Microextraction

Advances in Solid-Phase Microextraction

Editors

Attilio Naccarato
Antonio Tagarelli

MDPI • Basel • Beijing • Wuhan • Barcelona • Belgrade • Manchester • Tokyo • Cluj • Tianjin

Editors

Attilio Naccarato
CNR-Institute of Atmospheric
Pollution Research
Italy

Antonio Tagarelli
Università della Calabria
Italy

Editorial Office
MDPI
St. Alban-Anlage 66
4052 Basel, Switzerland

This is a reprint of articles from the Special Issue published online in the open access journal *Separations* (ISSN 2297-8739) (available at: https://www.mdpi.com/journal/separations/special_issues/solid_phase_microextract).

For citation purposes, cite each article independently as indicated on the article page online and as indicated below:

LastName, A.A.; LastName, B.B.; LastName, C.C. Article Title. *Journal Name* **Year**, *Article Number*, Page Range.

ISBN 978-3-03936-928-7 (Hbk)
ISBN 978-3-03936-929-4 (PDF)

Contents

About the Editors . . . . **vii**

Attilio Naccarato and Antonio Tagarelli
Advances in Solid-Phase Microextraction
Reprinted from: *Separations* **2020**, *7*, 34, doi:10.3390/separations7020034 . . . . **1**

Pascual Serra-Mora, Paola García-Narbona, Jorge Verdú-Andrés, Rosa Herráez-Hernández and Pilar Campíns-Falcó
Exploring New Extractive Phases for In-Tube Solid Phase Microextraction Coupled to Miniaturized Liquid Chromatography
Reprinted from: *Separations* **2019**, *6*, 12, doi:10.3390/separations6010012 . . . . **5**

Adrián Gutiérrez-Serpa, Idaira Pacheco-Fernández, Jorge Pasán and Verónica Pino
Metal–Organic Frameworks as Key Materials for Solid-Phase Microextraction Devices—A Review
Reprinted from: *Separations* **2019**, *6*, 47, doi:10.3390/separations6040047 . . . . **17**

Olga P. Ibragimova, Nassiba Baimatova and Bulat Kenessov
Low-Cost Quantitation of Multiple Volatile Organic Compounds in Air Using Solid-Phase Microextraction
Reprinted from: *Separations* **2019**, *6*, 51, doi:10.3390/separations6040051 . . . . **47**

Attilio Naccarato and Antonio Tagarelli
Recent Applications and Newly Developed Strategies of Solid-Phase Microextraction in Contaminant Analysis: Through the Environment to Humans
Reprinted from: *Separations* **2019**, *6*, 54, doi:10.3390/separations6040054 . . . . **65**

Gabriela Mafra, María Teresa García-Valverde, Jaime Millán-Santiago, Eduardo Carasek, Rafael Lucena and Soledad Cárdenas
Returning to Nature for the Design of Sorptive Phases in Solid-Phase Microextraction
Reprinted from: *Separations* **2020**, *7*, 2, doi:10.3390/separations7010002 . . . . **109**

Nicolò Riboni, Fabio Fornari, Federica Bianchi and Maria Careri
Recent Advances in In Vivo SPME Sampling
Reprinted from: *Separations* **2020**, *7*, 6, doi:10.3390/separations7010006 . . . . **131**

About the Editors

Attilio Naccarato is a researcher at the Institute of Atmospheric Pollution Research of the Italian National Research Council (CNR-IIA) and holds the position of Adjunct Professor at the University of Calabria. In recent years, most of his work has been devoted to method development for the analysis of organic and inorganic pollutants using microextraction approaches (e.g., SPME, MEPS), mass spectrometry-based techniques, and multivariate optimization by "Design of Experiment". Dr. Naccarato is involved in National and European projects aimed at monitoring the levels and studying the health concerns of persistent and emerging atmospheric pollutants including mercury in the major environmental compartments. He is also a referee for numerous international peer-reviewed journals and serves as an Associate Editor in the editorial board of Chemical Papers (Springer).

Antonio Tagarelli is Associate Professor of analytical chemistry at the Department of Chemistry and Chemical Technologies of the University of Calabria. His research interest focuses on the development and optimization of new analytical protocols for the determination of pollutants in environmental matrices and of markers of several diseases and pollutants in biological fluids. These methods are based on analytical microextraction techniques that allow minimizing the use of organic solvents (for example "Solid phase microextraction", SPME or Micro extraction by packed sorbent, MEPS), on derivatization approaches to be carried out directly in aqueous matrices and following GC-QqQ-MS analysis. Optimization of the analytical procedures involves the use of chemometric multivariate approach of experimental design.

Another research interest regards the use of specific parameters related to geographical origin of agricultural products (for example the multielement fingerprint). The experimental data are subjected to several chemometric techniques (PCA, LDA, SIMCA, ANN, PLS, etc.) in order to obtain robust and reliable statistical models for the classification of unknown samples.

Editorial

Advances in Solid-Phase Microextraction

Attilio Naccarato [1],* and Antonio Tagarelli [2],*

[1] CNR-Institute of Atmospheric Pollution Research, Division of Rende, UNICAL-Polifunzionale, I-87036 Arcavacata di Rende, CS, Italy
[2] Dipartimento di Chimica e Tecnologie Chimiche, Università della Calabria, Via P. Bucci Cubo 12/C, I-87030 Arcavacata di Rende, CS, Italy
* Correspondence: attilio.naccarato@iia.cnr.it (A.N.); a.tagarelli@unical.it (A.T.)

Received: 29 April 2020; Accepted: 26 May 2020; Published: 12 June 2020

Analysis imposes substantial challenges, especially when dealing with analytes present at trace levels in complex matrices. Although modern instrumentation has simplified analyses and made them more reliable, its use is only the last step of the whole analytical process. On the other hand, sample preparation still represents the bottleneck in many analytical methods and often requires the use of extensive protocols before instrumental analysis.

The research field of microextraction gained significance with the invention of solid-phase microextraction (SPME) in 1990 [1], which later, in 1993, became commercially available. In this technique, a small amount of extracting phase dispersed on a solid support, normally a fused-silica fiber or a metal core, is exposed to the sample, or its headspace, for a well-defined time [2,3].

Since then, SPME has become a well-established sample-prep technique for simultaneous extraction and preconcentration of compounds from a variety of matrices [4–7]. Given the simplicity, versatility, and availability of different formats, SPME addresses several challenges associated with the traditional sample preparation approaches and allows for a substantial streamlining of the analytical workflow.

Over the decades, its remarkable evolution has led to new in vivo applications [8–10], development of methods for the analysis of complex matrices [4,11–14], use of new coating materials [15–19], but also development of new devices and geometries [20,21]. Although it has been recently utilized in ambient mass spectrometry, its use in conjunction with the chromatographic approaches is now consolidated, while experimental design techniques are recommended for efficient multivariate optimization of the working variables which affect the SPME performance [3,22–24].

The *Special Issue* described below includes six contributions provided by some of the world's leading research groups and focuses on recent advances in solid-phase microextraction.

In publication time sequence, the first contribution was submitted by Prof. Rosa Herráez-Hernández and is an article from the MINTOTA Research Group lead by Prof. Pilar Campíns-Falcó at the University of Valencia [25]. In this work, the authors explore a new material functionalized with nanoparticles as a coating for In-tube SPME. They synthesized a polymer of tetraethyl orthosilicate (TEOS) and methyltriethoxysilane (MTEOS) modified with SiO_2 and TiO_2 NPs and used for the extraction of a variety of water pollutants, including pesticides and PAH, using both Capillary-LC and Nano-LC. The extraction efficiencies found with the synthesized coating were compared to those obtained with commercially available capillaries.

The second contribution is by Professor Verónica Pino and coworkers from the University of La Laguna, which present a review article focused on metal–organic frameworks (MOFs) as novel sorbent materials in solid-phase microextraction (SPME) [19]. This review offers an overview of the current state of the use of MOFs in different SPME configurations, in all cases covering extraction devices coated with (or incorporating) MOFs, with emphases in their preparation. Because of their outstanding properties, MOFs have been used in an increasing number of applications and the authors foresee a rise in their applicability in a variety of SPME devices in the next years.

The third published contribution is an article by Professor Kenessov and coworkers from the Al-Farabi Kazakh National University [26]. This work is based on a method previously proposed by the same research group for the analysis of BTEX in air using 20 mL headspace vials and standard addition calibration and SPME-GC-MS instrumentation. The research aimed to expand this method to the quantitation of more than 20 VOCs in ambient air, which is the least addressed environmental matrix with the use of SPME. The developed method is low-cost and demonstrated its effectiveness for the assay of the chosen analytes in urban air.

The fourth contribution is a review article from the editors of the special issue and is the result of the extensive collaboration between Dr. Naccarato from CNR-Institute of Atmospheric Pollution Research Professor Tagarelli from University of Calabria [4]. This paper aims to describe the recent and most impactful applications in pollutant analysis using solid-phase microextraction (SPME) technology in environmental, food, and bioclinical analysis. The purpose of this review is to highlight the role that SPME is having in contaminant monitoring through the path that goes from the environment to humans. The covered papers were published in the last five years (2014–2019), thus, providing the reader with information about the current state-of-the-art and the future potential directions of the research in pollutant monitoring using SPME.

The last two published papers are review articles regarding two SPME cutting-edge topics such as the use of natural products as sorbent material and in vivo sampling.

The former is the result of a transcontinental collaboration between Professor Carasek's group in Brazil and the Spanish group with Professor Lucena and Professor Cardenas as senior members. This paper reviews the potential of natural products as sorbents in extraction and microextraction techniques from the synergic perspectives of the two research groups working on the topic. The reuse of materials complies with the basic principles of green analytical chemistry (GAC), which provides for the reduction/minimization of the sample treatment and the use of renewable sources when possible. The article covers the use of unmodified natural materials and the modified ones to draw a general picture of the usefulness of the materials [15].

The latter paper was submitted by Professor Bianchi and is an interesting contribution from a noteworthy Italian research group [8]. In this review, the authors provide a survey of in vivo SPME applications, which cover the state-of-the-art from 2014 up to They went through the use of miniaturized devices characterized by both commercial and lab-made coatings for in vivo SPME tissue sampling, targeted to biomarker discovery or metabolomics studies. The paper pointed out how this approach can minimize adverse effects commonly present when tissue sampling is performed by ex vivo procedures, and how the use of portable instruments and the hyphenation with sensitive techniques like ambient mass spectrometry will increase the applicability of in vivo SPME.

I hope readers will judge attractive the topics covered in this *Special Issue*. In this specific historical moment, we wish to conclude this editorial with a quote from Seneca:

"Honores, monumenta, quicquid aut decretis ambition iussit aut operibus exstruxit cito subruitur, nihil non longa demolitur vetustas et movet; at iis quae consecravit sapientia nocere non potest; nulla abolebit aetas, nulla deminuet" (Seneca, De brev. vit., 15,4)

It leads us to ponder how the material desires of human ambition are deteriorated by the passage of time, while wisdom and knowledge cannot be harmed, time does not erase it, nothing can diminish it.

Enjoy reading.

Funding: This research received no external funding

Conflicts of Interest: The authors declare no conflict of interest.

References

1. Arthur, C.L.; Pawliszyn, J. Solid Phase Microextraction with Thermal Desorption Using Fused Silica Optical Fibers. *Anal. Chem.* **1990**, *62*, 2145–2148. [CrossRef]
2. Pawliszyn, J. *Handbook of Solid Phase Microextraction*; Elsevier: Waltham, MA, USA, 2012; ISBN 9780124160170.
3. Talarico, F.; Brandmayr, P.; Giulianini, P.G.; Ietto, F.; Naccarato, A.; Perrotta, E.; Tagarelli, A.; Giglio, A. Effects of metal pollution on survival and physiological responses in Carabus (Chaetocarabus) lefebvrei (Coleoptera, Carabidae). *Eur. J. Soil Biol.* **2014**, *61*, 80–89. [CrossRef]
4. Naccarato, A.; Tagarelli, A. Recent applications and newly developed strategies of solid-phase microextraction in contaminant analysis: Through the environment to humans. *Separations* **2019**, *6*, 54. [CrossRef]
5. Carasek, E.; Morés, L.; Merib, J. Basic principles, recent trends and future directions of microextraction techniques for the analysis of aqueous environmental samples. *Trends Environ. Anal. Chem.* **2018**, *19*, e00060. [CrossRef]
6. Roszkowska, A.; Miękus, N.; Bączek, T. Application of solid-phase microextraction in current biomedical research. *J. Sep. Sci.* **2019**, *42*, 285–302. [CrossRef]
7. Dinoi, A.; Cesari, D.; Marinoni, A.; Bonasoni, P.; Riccio, A.; Chianese, E.; Tirimberio, G.; Naccarato, A.; Sprovieri, F.; Andreoli, V.; et al. Inter-Comparison of Carbon Content in PM2.5 and PM10 Collected at Five Measurement Sites in Southern Italy. *Atmosphere* **2017**, *8*, 243.
8. Riboni, N.; Fornari, F.; Bianchi, F.; Careri, M. Recent advances in in vivo spme sampling. *Separations* **2020**, *7*, 6. [CrossRef]
9. Naccarato, A.; Cavaliere, F.; Tassone, A.; Brandmayr, P.; Tagarelli, A.; Pirrone, N.; Sprovieri, F.; Giglio, A. In vivo solid-phase microextraction gas chromatography-mass spectrometry (SPME-GC-MS) assay to identify epicuticular profiles across task groups of Apis mellifera ligustica workers. *J. Entomol. Acarol. Res.* **2019**, *51*, 468–481. [CrossRef]
10. Bonacci, T.; Mazzei, A.; Naccarato, A.; Elliani, R.; Tagarelli, A.; Brandmayr, P. Beetles "in red": Are the endangered flat bark beetles Cucujus cinnaberinus and C. haematodes chemically protected? (Coleoptera: Cucujidae). *Eur. Zool. J.* **2018**, *85*, 129–137. [CrossRef]
11. Huang, S.; Chen, G.; Ye, N.; Kou, X.; Zhu, F.; Shen, J.; Ouyang, G. Solid-phase microextraction: An appealing alternative for the determination of endogenous substances—A review. *Anal. Chim. Acta* **2019**, *1077*, 67–86. [CrossRef]
12. Kenessov, B.; Koziel, J.A.; Bakaikina, N.V.; Orazbayeva, D. Perspectives and challenges of on-site quantification of organic pollutants in soils using solid-phase microextraction. *TrAC—Trends Anal. Chem.* **2016**, *85*, 111–122. [CrossRef]
13. Naccarato, A.; Gionfriddo, E.; Elliani, R.; Sindona, G.; Tagarelli, A. A fast and simple solid phase microextraction coupled with gas chromatography-triple quadrupole mass spectrometry method for the assay of urinary markers of glutaric acidemias. *J. Chromatogr. A* **2014**, *1372*, 253–259. [CrossRef] [PubMed]
14. Gionfriddo, E.; Naccarato, A.; Sindona, G.; Tagarelli, A. A reliable solid phase microextraction-gas chromatography-triple quadrupole mass spectrometry method for the assay of selenomethionine and selenomethylselenocysteine in aqueous extracts: Difference between selenized and not-enriched selenium potatoes. *Anal. Chim. Acta* **2012**, *747*, 58–66. [CrossRef] [PubMed]
15. Mafra, G.; García-Valverde, M.T.; Millán-Santiago, J.; Carasek, E.; Lucena, R.; Cárdenas, S. Returning to Nature for the Design of Sorptive Phases in Solid-Phase Microextraction. *Separations* **2019**, *7*, 2. [CrossRef]
16. Naccarato, A.; Pawliszyn, J. Matrix compatible solid phase microextraction coating, a greener approach to sample preparation in vegetable matrices. *Food Chem.* **2016**, *206*, 67–73. [CrossRef] [PubMed]
17. Naccarato, A.; Gionfriddo, E.; Elliani, R.; Pawliszyn, J.; Sindona, G.; Tagarelli, A. Investigating the robustness and extraction performance of a matrix-compatible solid-phase microextraction coating in human urine and its application to assess 2–6-ring polycyclic aromatic hydrocarbons using GC–MS/MS. *J. Sep. Sci.* **2018**, *41*, 929–939. [CrossRef] [PubMed]
18. Lashgari, M.; Yamini, Y. An overview of the most common lab-made coating materials in solid phase microextraction. *Talanta* **2019**, *191*, 283–306. [CrossRef]
19. Gutiérez-Serpa, A.; Pacheco-Fernández, I.; Pasán, J.; Pino, V. Metal–Organic Frameworks as Key Materials for Solid-Phase Microextraction Devices—A Review. *Separations* **2019**, *6*, 47.

20. Sajid, M.; Khaled Nazal, M.; Rutkowska, M.; Szczepańska, N.; Namieśnik, J.; Płotka-Wasylka, J. Solid Phase Microextraction: Apparatus, Sorbent Materials, and Application. *Crit. Rev. Anal. Chem.* **2019**, *49*, 271–288. [CrossRef]
21. Psillakis, E. Vacuum-assisted headspace solid-phase microextraction: A tutorial review. *Anal. Chim. Acta* **2017**, *986*, 12–24. [CrossRef]
22. Naccarato, A.; Elliani, R.; Cavaliere, B.; Sindona, G.; Tagarelli, A. Development of a fast and simple gas chromatographic protocol based on the combined use of alkyl chloroformate and solid phase microextraction for the assay of polyamines in human urine. *J. Chromatogr. A* **2018**, *1549*, 1–13. [CrossRef] [PubMed]
23. Naccarato, A.; Tassone, A.; Moretti, S.; Elliani, R.; Sprovieri, F.; Pirrone, N.; Tagarelli, A. A green approach for organophosphate ester determination in airborne particulate matter: Microwave-assisted extraction using hydroalcoholic mixture coupled with solid-phase microextraction gas chromatography-tandem mass spectrometry. *Talanta* **2018**, *189*, 657–665. [CrossRef] [PubMed]
24. Naccarato, A.; Elliani, R.; Sindona, G.; Tagarelli, A. Multivariate optimization of a microextraction by packed sorbent-programmed temperature vaporization-gas chromatography–tandem mass spectrometry method for organophosphate flame retardant analysis in environmental aqueous matrices. *Anal. Bioanal. Chem.* **2017**, *409*, 7105–7120. [CrossRef] [PubMed]
25. Serra-Mora, P.; García-Narbona, P.; Verdú-Andrés, J.; Herráez-Hernández, R.; Campíns-Falcó, P. Exploring new extractive phases for in-tube solid phase microextraction coupled to miniaturized liquid chromatography. *Separations* **2019**, *6*, 12. [CrossRef]
26. Ibragimova, O.P.; Baimatova, N.; Kenessov, B. Low-cost quantitation of multiple volatile organic compounds in air using solid-phase microextraction. *Separations* **6**. [CrossRef]

 *separations*

Article

Exploring New Extractive Phases for In-Tube Solid Phase Microextraction Coupled to Miniaturized Liquid Chromatography

Pascual Serra-Mora, Paola García-Narbona, Jorge Verdú-Andrés, Rosa Herráez-Hernández * and Pilar Campíns-Falcó *

MINTOTA Research Group, Department of Analytical Chemistry, Faculty of Chemistry, University of Valencia, Dr Moliner 50, 46100 Burjassot, Valencia, Spain; pascual.serra@uv.es (P.S.-M.); paganar@alumni.uv.es (P.G.-N.); Jorge.Verdu@uv.es (J.V.-A.)
* Correspondence: rosa.herraez@uv.es (R.H.-H.); pilar.campins@uv.es (P.C.-F.); Tel.: +34-96-354-4978 (R.H.-H.); +34-96-354-3002 (P.C.-F.)

Received: 30 December 2018; Accepted: 14 February 2019; Published: 25 February 2019

Abstract: In-tube solid-phase microextraction (IT-SPME) coupled on-line to miniaturized liquid chromatography (LC) has emerged as a powerful tool to address a variety of analytical problems. However, in order to expand its applicability, the development of new sorbents that enhance the efficiency and specificity of the extraction is highly desirable. In this respect, the employment of capillary columns coated with sorbents functionalized with nanoparticles (NPs) replacing the loop of the injection valve (in-valve IT-SPME) is one of the most attractive options. In this work, polymers of tetraethyl orthosilicate (TEOS) and trimethoxyethylsilane (MTEOS) modified with SiO_2 and TiO_2 NPs have been synthetized and used for the extraction of a variety of water pollutants, using both Capillary-LC and Nano-LC. Compounds with different chemical structures and polarities such as the artificial sweetener saccharine, the polycyclic aromatic hydrocarbons (PAHs) naphthalene and fluoranthene, and some phenylurea and organophosphorous herbicides have been used as target analytes. The extraction efficiencies found with the synthetized capillaries have been compared to those obtained with commercially available capillaries coated with polydiphenyl-polydimethylsiloxane (PDMS), nitroterephthalic acid modified polyetilenglicol (FFAP), and polystyrene-divinylbenzene (PS-DVB) phases. The results obtained in this preliminary study showed that, although PS-DVB phase has the strongest affinity for compounds with two or more aromatic rings, the extraction with TEOS-MTEOS coatings modified with NPs is the best option for a majority of the tested compounds. Examples of application are given.

Keywords: in-tube solid phase microextraction (IT-SPME); SiO_2 nanoparticles; TiO_2 nanoparticles; capillary liquid chromatography; nano-liquid chromatography

---

1. Introduction

High extraction efficiencies, although always desirable, are essential in techniques that integrate on-line sample preparation and LC. This is the case of IT-SPME. In this modality of microextraction, the extractive phase is typically the coating of a capillary column used in replacement of the injection valve inert loop, so that the extraction takes place simultaneously with the sample loading. A subsequent change in the valve position allows the desorption and transfer of the retained analytes to the separative column by means of the mobile-phase. Today, IT-SPME is a well-established technique that has been successfully used in many fields of applications [1–3]. This technique is especially well-suited for miniaturized LC systems such as Capillary-LC (Cap-LC) and Nano-LC. This is because relatively large sample volumes can be loaded into the extractive capillary for on-line analyte enrichment overcoming the lack of sensitivity derived from the fact that only low volumes of the samples can be injected in miniaturized LC systems. The utility of IT-SPME in Cap-LC has been demonstrated through a wide variety of applications mainly in the environmental and biomedical fields [4–7] and, very recently, IT-SPME has been coupled to Nano-LC [8,9]. Substantial progress in the area can be expected through the development of new sorbents for the improved extraction of a wide variety of analytes and matrices.

In recent years, several materials have been used as sorbents for extraction and microextraction of organic compounds. Successful examples have been reported using a variety of polymers, ionic liquids, metal organic frameworks, covalent organic frameworks and different types of NPs such as carbon, metal or metal oxide NPs [10,11]. Among them, nanostructured sorbents have gained significant interest due to their inherent advantages, especially their high specific surface for interaction with the target compounds and the possibility of increasing the affinity for the analytes through a variety of interactions [12,13].

As regards solid-phase microextraction, most of the efforts made have been focused on the development of coatings for fibres [14], whereas only a few sorbents with nanomaterials for IT-SPME have been reported so far. Examples are the employment of titanium [15] or silica [16] capillaries chemically treated to produce nanostructured internal surfaces. From a different perspective, a polymeric phase can be reinforced with NPs. For example, in previous studies, we demonstrated that the functionalization of commercial polydimethylsiloxane (PDMS) coated columns with different types of carbon nanotubes (CNTs) may improve the extraction efficiency for a variety of compounds such as drugs and pollutants [5,6]. More recently, polymeric coatings of tetraethyl orthosilicate (TEOS) and trimethoxyethylsilane (MTEOS) were functionalized with SiO_2 NPs and used for the extraction of herbicides of different polarities. The presence of SiO_2 NPs increased the extraction efficiency for most of the compounds tested [7].

As a continuation of those studies, in the present work we have synthetized a TEOS-MTEOS polymer modified with TiO_2 NPs. This type of NPs has been extensively investigated in SPME with fibres and other forms of microextraction [17]. However, their application to IT-SPME is still very limited [15]. The new TEOS-MTEOS/TiO_2 NPs composite has been tested for the IT-SPME of variety of organic pollutants, and the results have been compared with those obtained with the polymer modified with SiO_2 NPs, as well as with different commercially available capillaries coated with polymers. The commercial capillaries tested were TRB 35, FFAP and PS-DVB, with coatings of 35% polydiphenyl-65% polydimethyl siloxane (PDMS), nitroterephthalic acid modified poly (ethyleneglycol) (PEG) and polystyrene-divinylbenzene (PS-DBV), respectively.

The proposed phases were tested for different types of substances. IT-SPME coupled to Cap-LC with fluorescence detection was used for the analysis of compounds with aromatic rings in their chemical structure, more specifically the artificial sweetener saccharine (emerging pollutant), and the PAHs naphthalene and fluoranthene, all of them with native fluorescence. IT-SPME coupled to Nano-LC with UV detection has been used for the study of a variety of phenylurea and organophosphorous herbicides. The chemical structures of the tested compounds and their respective octanol/water partition coefficients (K_{ow}) are listed in Table 1.

Table 1. Chemical structures and log K_{ow} of the tested compounds.

Compound	Chemical Structure	Log K_{ow}
Saccharine		0.45
Naphthalene		3.3
Fluoranthene		5.2
Fluometuron		2.2
Isoproturon		2.5
Metobromuron		2.4
Linuron		2.7
Fenamiphos		3.2
Fenitrothion		3.4
Fenthion		4.0
Bifenox		3.6

2. Materials and Methods

2.1. Chemicals

All the reagents used throughout the study were of analytical grade. Saccharin, fenitrothion bifenox, TEOS, MTEOS, PEG, SiO$_2$ NPs (5–15 nm), TiO$_2$ NPs (21 nm), NaOH and NH$_4$OH were obtained from Sigma-Aldrich (St. Louis, MO, USA). Naphthalene, fluoranthene, fluometuron, isoproturon, metobromuron, linuron, fenthion and fenamiphos were obtained from Dr. Ehrenstorfer (Augsburg, Germany). Acetone was obtained from Romil (Cambridge, UK). Acetonitrile was of HPLC grade (MWR Radnor, Philadelphia, PA, USA).

Stock standard solutions of the analytes (100 µg/mL) were prepared by dilution of the commercial reagents in acetonitrile and kept at −20 °C until use. Working solutions were prepared by dilution of the stock solutions with ultrapure water.

2.2. Apparatus and Chromatographic Conditions

2.2.1. Cap-LC

The chromatographic system consisted of an isocratic capillary pump, a high-pressure six-port valve (Rheodyne, Rohnert Park, CA, USA), a LC-Net II/ADC interface and a programmable fluorescence detector (Jasco Corporation Micro 21PU-01, Tokyo, Japan). The detector was coupled to a data system (Jasco ChromNAV Chromatography Data System) for data acquisition and calculation. The excitation/emission wavelengths were 235 nm/335 nm, 265 nm/475 nm and 250 nm/440 nm for naphthalene, fluoranthene and saccharine, respectively.

A Zorbax SB-C18 (150 mm × 0.5 mm i. d., 5 μm) column was used for the separation of the analytes. The mobile-phase was a mixture of acetonitrile-water in isocratic mode, and the flow rate was 25 μL/min. Under optimized conditions, the run times were 8 min and 10 min the analysis of saccharine and the PAHs, respectively. Solvents were filtered through 0.22 μm nylon membranes (Teknokroma, Barcelona, Spain) and degassed in an ultrasonic bath before use.

2.2.2. Nano-LC

Chromatographic analysis was performed using a Agilent 1260 Infinity nanoLC chromatograph equipped with a quaternary nano-pump, a six port micro-scale manual injector (Rheodyne), and a UV-Vis diode array detector with 80 nL nanoflow cell (Agilent, Waldbronn, Germany). The detector was coupled to a data system (Agilent, ChemStation) for data acquisition and treatment. The analytical signal was recorded between 190 nm and 400 nm and monitored at 254 nm. A Zorbax 300SB C18 (50 mm × 0.075 mm i. d., 3.5 μm particle size) analytical column (Agilent) was used for separation.

The mobile phase was a mixture of water-acetonitrile in gradient elution mode. The percentage of acetonitrile in the mobile phase was linearly increased from 30% at 0–2 min, to 100% at 8 min, and then kept constant until 13 min; finally, the acetonitrile percentage was linearly decreased to reach a percentage of 30% at 18 min, and maintained constant until the end of the run; the run time was 30 min. The flow rate was 0.5 μL/min. All solvents were filtered through 0.22 μm nylon membranes (Teknokroma) before use.

2.3. Preparation of the TEOS-MTEOS Coated Capillaries

The TEOS-MTEOS coated capillaries were prepared from segments of fused silica capillaries of 30 cm-length and 320 μm i. d. or 15-cm length and 75 μm i. d. (Análisis Vínicos, Tomelloso, Spain) for the Cap-LC and Nano-LC systems, respectively. The procedure used to synthetize the SiO$_2$ NPs reinforced coatings was previously described in detail in [8]. Briefly, the internal walls of the silica capillaries were first activated by flushing through them 1 M NaOH for 4 h at 40 °C followed by 0.1 M HCl for 30 min at room temperature; next, the capillaries were heated at 60 °C for 3 h, and finally flushed with water and dried with air. For coating of the capillaries, a mixture of 65 mg of PEG, 100 μL of TEOS (93 mg), 100 μL MTEOS (90 mg), 50 μL of water, 2 mL of 0.1 M NH$_4$OH (catalyst) and the SiO$_2$ or the TiO$_2$ NPs were placed in a glass vial; the amount of NPs in the resulting mixture was 0.05 mg/mL. After vortexing for 1 min, the resulting homogenous dispersion was used to fulfill the preconditioned capillaries. Then, the capillaries were heated at 40 °C for 2 h and aged overnight (14–15 h) at 120 °C.

2.4. IT-SPME Conditions

For IT-SPME coupled to Cap-LC, segments of different commercially available GC columns of 30 cm length and 320 μm i. d. were used as extractive capillaries for IT-SPME, namely TRB 35, ZB-FFAP and PS-DVB, and the results were compared with those obtained with the synthesized TEOS-MTEOS reinforced with SiO$_2$ or TiO$_2$ NPs capillaries. The TRB 35 capillaries, coated with a 35% diphenyl-65% PDMS, 3 μm coating thickness, were purchased from Teknokroma (Barcelona, Spain). The ZB-FFAP (nitroterephthalic acid modified PEG), 1 μm film thickness, was supplied from Phenomenex (Torrance, CA, USA). The PS-DBV, 20 μm coating thickness, capillary was obtained from Agilent Technologies.

The extractive capillaries were used as the loop of the six-port injection valves. Samples were manually loaded into capillaries using a 500 μL precision syringe; then, the valve was changed to the injection position, so the analytes retained in the capillary were desorbed with the mobile-phase and transferred to the analytical column for separation and detection. For connecting the extractive capillaries to the valve 2.5 cm sleeve of 1/6 i. n. (340–380 μm i. d.) polyether ether ketone (PEEK) tubing, 1/6 i. n. PEEK nuts and ferrules were used. All assays were made by triplicate at ambient temperature.

2.5. Analysis of Water and Soil samples

Samples were collected at the Comunitat Valenciana region (East Spain). Water samples were river water (Xúquer river, coordinates: 39.151469, −0.239126) and ditch water (coordinates: 39.500606, −0.384912). Once collected, samples were kept at 4 °C, and filtered through 0.22 μm nylon filters (Teknokroma) just before their analysis. Aliquots of 200 μL of the filtered samples were processed by Cap-LC under the optimized conditions.

For the analysis of soil, a soil sample collected from agricultural zone was dried at ambient temperature and then sieved (≤2 mm). Accurately weight portions (0.3 g) were spiked with a mixture of naphthalene and fluoranthene at concentrations of 15 and 12 μg/g, respectively, and extracted with 1.3 mL of acetone at 30 °C in an ultrasonic bath for 30 min. After centrifugation at 5000 rpm for 10 min, the supernatant was removed and filtered with 0.22 μm nylon filters (Teknokroma). The filtered extracts were evaporated to dryness and then reconstituted with 1 mL of ultrapure water. Finally, 200 μL of the reconstituted extracts were processed by under the optimized conditions. All assays were made by triplicate at ambient temperature.

3. Results

3.1. IT-SPME Coupled to Cap-LC

3.1.1. Mobile Phase Composition

Different extractive phases were evaluated for the extraction of three fluorescent compounds differenig in the number of benzene rings in their structure, sacharine, naphtalene and fluoranthene, with 1, 2 and 4 rings, respectively (see Table 1). Capillary columns with different kinds of coatings are commercially available which are compatible with the dimensions of Cap-LC. Among them, in this study columns with coatings containing phenyl groups were selected, as these phases have proved to be effective in the retention of aromatic compounds via π-π interactions [7]. Capillary columns coated with PDMS modified with diphenyl groups (TRB-35), PEG modified with nitroterephtalic acid (FFAP) and polystyrene-divinylbenzene (PS-DVB) were tested, and the results were compared with those obtained with the TEOS-MTEOS reinforced with the SiO_2 or TiO_2 NPs coated capillaries.

Preliminary assays carried out under a variety of conditions demonstrated that not only the extraction efficiencies (evaluated as the corresponding peak areas) but also the retention times and peak shapes were highly dependent on the composition of the mobile-phase delivered though the capillary for the desorption of the analytes. For example, saccharine could be rapidly desorbed and transferred from all the capillaries tested even when water was used as the mobile phase, which can be explained by its high polarity (see Table 1). In contrast, when eluents with high percentages of water were used for fluoranthene (the most apolar compound) the desorption from some capillaries did not take place within suitable times (<5 min) and the resulting peaks were too wide, particularly with the PS-DVB coated capillary. For this reason, and in order to study separately the extraction efficiency from the chromatographic separation, the analytical column was removed from the system (the injection valve was directly connected to the detector). The eluent compositions selected were

100% water for saccharine in the TRB, FFAP and PS-DVB columns, 100% acetonitrile for fluoranthene in the PS-DVB capillary, and 50:50 for the rest of assays.

3.1.2. Study of the Extraction Efficiency

The extraction efficiency for the different capillaries tested was studied by processing increasing volumes of standard solutions of the analytes (50–400 μL), under the elution conditions indicated above and without the chromatographic column. Although the absolute recoveries were not obtained, the efficiency of the different capillaries tested was compared though the measurement of the peak areas obtained for the target compounds with them [5–8]. The peak areas obtained for the three compounds tested are depicted in Figure 1.

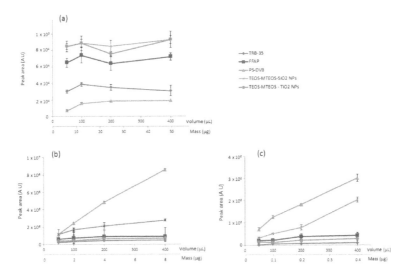

Figure 1. Effect of the sample volume (or mass of analyte introduced into the system) on the responses obtained with the different extractive capillary coatings tested for (**a**) saccharine (125 μg/mL), (**b**) naphthalene (20 μg/mL) and (**c**) fluoranthene (1 μg/mL).

As observed from the above figure, the results obtained for saccharine were significantly different to those observed for naphthalene and fluoranthene. In all of the extractive phases tested, increasing the sample volume from 50 μL to 100 μL led to an increment of the peak areas of saccharine, but a further increment of the sample volume did not increase the responses. In contrast, the peak areas registered for naphthalene and fluoranthene increased as the volume of sample processed was increased within the tested interval. For the two compounds, the increment of peak areas was particularly marked with the capillaries that provided the highest analyte responses, PS-DVB and TEOS-MTEOS modified with SiO$_2$ NPs; with these two extractive phases a nearly linear relationship between the sample volume and the peak areas was observed. For the rest of the capillaries, the increment was much more modest.

For a given sample volume, highest peak areas were obtained for saccharine with the TEOS-MTEOS capillaries modified with SiO$_2$ and TiO$_2$ NPs; no significant differences between these two capillaries were found. This suggests that the hydrogen bonding and dipole-dipole interactions that can be established between the NPs and the amino groups of the analyte are the predominant mechanisms of interaction between the extractive coatings and the analyte molecules. Among the phases with aromatic rings, the FFAP coated capillary provided the highest responses. This can be explained by the electrostatic interactions that can be established between the amino group of the analyte and the nitro groups of the nitroterephthalic acid coating (with positive charge on the nitrogen and negative on the oxygen atoms).

Naphthalene and fluoranthene are expected to interact with the TEOS-MTEOS extractive phase mainly by hydrophobic interactions, and also by π-π interactions with the TRB, FFAP and PS-DVB phases. As observed from Figure 1, the PS-DVB provided much higher extraction efficiencies than the TRB and FFAP capillaries. This can be explained by differences on the film thickness, which was much higher for the PS-DVB. In fact, even the TEOS-MTEOS SiO_2 NPs reinforced polymer coating provided higher responses than the TRB and FFAP coated capillaries. As regards the two types of particles used for the reinforcement of the TEOS-MTEOS polymer, the SiO_2 NPs provided higher responses, which suggested that the resulting composite had a higher specific area for interaction, as neither naphthalene nor fluoranthene have functional groups capable of establishing interactions other than hydrophobic interactions.

3.1.3. Reproducibility and Specificity

In order to study the reproducibility, three consecutive injections of the tested compounds were affected in the chromatographic system (with the separative column placed between the IT-SPME device and the detector) and using a sample volume of 200 μL. As an example, in Figure 2a are shown the chromatograms obtained for naphthalene and fluoranthene. The relative standard deviations (RSDs) were calculated from the peak areas measured for each compound ((standard deviation/mean area) × 100). The values found with the synthetized capillaries are summarized in Table 2, which also shows the values obtained for the commercial capillary that provided best extraction efficiency for each compound.

Table 2. Reproducibility obtained by IT-SPME–Cap-LC with the trimethoxyethylsilane (TEOS-MTEOS) capillaries functionallized with nanoparticles (NPs) and the commercial capillary that gave the best extraction rate for each compound (n = 3); volume of sample processed, 200 μL.

Compound	Concentration(μg/mL)	Extractive Phase	RDS (%)
Saccharine	125	TEOS-MTEOS/SiO_2 NPs	6
		TEOS-MTEOS/TiO_2 NPs	4
		FFAP	9
Naphthalene	20.0	TEOS-MTEOS/SiO_2 NPs	4
		TEOS-MTEOS/TiO_2 NPs	9
		PS-DVB	8
Fluoranthene	1.0	TEOS-MTEOS/SiO_2 NPs	4
		TEOS-MTEOS/TiO_2 NPs	7
		PS-DVB	2

The results of Table 2 show that the synthetized TEOS-MTEOS reinforced with NPs capillaries provided reproducibility suitable and comparable to that achieved with commercial capillaries. No significant differences on the reproducibility obtained between the two synthetized capillaries were found

The specificity was also tested for two different matrices of interest in the environmental field, in order to investigate whether matrix components could interfere with the identification or quantification of the analytes. The samples selected were water (ditch and river water) and the extract obtained from a soil sample (0.3 g) treated with 1.2 mL of acetone in an ultrasonic bath, and the PAHs naphthalene and fluoranthene were selected as model compounds. The water samples were filtered before being loaded into the chromatographic system, whereas the extract of soil was evaporated to dryness, and then reconstituted with water and filtered before being processed. In Figure 2b are shown the chromatograms obtained for some of the samples assayed using the optimized IT-SPME conditions (PS-DVB capillary).

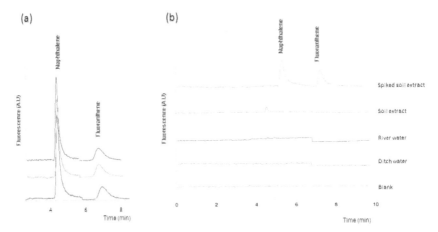

Figure 2. Chromatograms obtained under optimized conditions for (**a**) three successive injections of a standard solution containing 2.5 μg/mL of naphthalene and 0.18 μg/mL of fluoranthene; (**b**) a blank (nanopure water), ditch and river water, and for the extract obtained for a soil sample, and the same soil spiked with naphthalene and fluoranthene. Volume of working solution processed, 200 μL.

As observed in the above figure, no significant differences between the registers obtained for nanopure water and for the water samples were observed. Thus, the specificity for this kind of samples was considered satisfactory. A minor peak was observed in the solid extract; the intensity of such peak was much lower in the spiked soil sample. These differences could most probably be minimized by reducing the soil particle size. Nevertheless, as the aforementioned peak eluted at a retention time different to those of the analytes, it was concluded that the specificity for the solid extracts was also suitable.

3.2. IT-SPME Coupled to Nano-LC

The number of capillaries with suitable dimensions for coupling IT-SPME to Nano-LC is still very low. For this reason, only the extraction efficiency of TEOS-MTEOS modified with SiO_2 NPs and TiO_2 NPs could be tested and compared. Different herbicides were tested as the target compounds (Table 1).

Preliminary tests showed that the desorption of the extracted analytes from the capillaries could be effected under a wide variety of eluent compositions; therefore, this study was carried out with the IT-SPME connected to the analytical column. As for Cap-LC, an increment volume had a positive effect on peak areas for a majority of the tested compounds; increasing responses were observed up to sample volumes of 500 μL, although a further increment to 750 μL had no a positive effect on peaks areas. This is illustrated, in Figure 3, which shows the effect of the sample volume on peak areas when processing different sample volumes with the TiO_2 NPs modified coating.

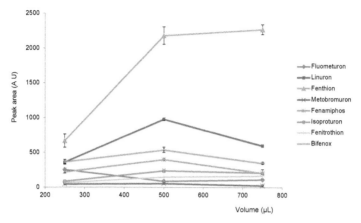

Figure 3. Variation of the peak areas with the sample volume with the TEOS-MTEOS extractive phase reinforced with TiO$_2$ NPs. Concentration assayed, 25 ng/mL for linuron and 10 ng/mL for the rest of compounds.

Consequently, a sample volume of 500 µL was selected to compare the extraction efficiency of the two capillaries tested. The results obtained are depicted in Figure 4.

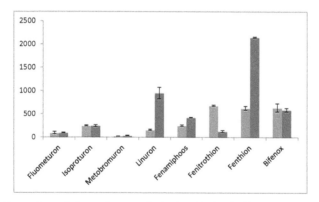

Figure 4. Comparison of the peak areas obtained with the TEOS-MTEOS coated capillaries functionalized with SiO$_2$ NPs and TiO$_2$ NPs. Concentrations assayed, 25 ng/mL for linuron and 10 ng/mL for the rest of compounds.

In view of the chemical structures of the tested compounds (Table 1), the retention of the analytes on the extractive phase can be considered the result of hydrophobic, polar and, in some cases, hydrogen bonding interactions. Since all the tested compounds have similar K_{ow} coefficients (see Table 1) functional groups are expected to play a key role in the extraction. In fact, the results of Figure 4 show that even compounds with very similar chemical structure exhibit quite different affinity for the two extractive phases. For example, whereas for the phenylureas fluometuron, isoproturon and metobromuron both phases provided similar extraction rates, linuron showed much stronger affinity for the TiO$_2$ NPs functionalized phase. The main difference between the latter compound and the other members of the family is the presence of an additional substituent in the aromatic ring. The presence of two contiguous substituents with partial negative charges was suggested as the reason for the strong affinity of phthalate esters for TiO$_2$ surfaces by Banitaba et al. [18]. The reason given by the authors was that this conformation allows the establishment of mono and bidentate interactions between the negatively charged substituents and the TiO$_2$ sites. The presence of the two electronegative halogen substituents in the linuron molecule would facilitate a similar interaction with the TEOS-MTEOS/TiO$_2$ NPs phase, thus explaining the high extraction rate found for this herbicide.

On the other hand, different studies have demonstrated the strong affinity of TiO$_2$ for compounds containing phosphate groups [15,19]. The results of Figure 4 indicate that TiO$_2$ NPs are a better option for fenamiphos and fenthion. However, the extraction efficiency for fenitrothion is superior with the SiO$_2$ NPs modified phase. This can be explained by the presence of the nitro group on the analyte molecule, which facilitates their interaction with the ionized silica NPs of the coating via dipole-dipole interaction mechanism. This is in agreement with the results found for bifenox, also with a nitro substituent, as the extraction efficiency is also better with the SiO$_2$ NPs composite.

4. Discussion

In this work, the extraction capabilities of different commercially available capillaries (TRB 35, FFAP and PS-DVB) have been tested and compared with those of two polymeric coatings reinforced with NPs, using different pollutants with aromatic rings and Cap-LC. For the highly polar compound saccharine, the TEOS-METOS phase reinforced with NPs is the best option. This is because, besides hydrophobic interactions, the analyte can establish electrostatic interaction with the coating. For the analysis of the aromatic hydrocarbons naphthalene and fluoranthene the PS-DVB coated capillary is recommended. This capillary provided extraction rates much higher than those achieved with the other capillaries; this can be, at least, partially attributed to the thickness of the coating. A relatively high acetonitrile content in the mobile-phase was necessary for the rapid desorption and transfer of the retained analytes from the capillary to the analytical column. In principle, the specificity was also suitable for the analysis of these pollutants in environmental matrices such as water and soil extracts, but further studies would be required to optimized and validate the entire method. In this sense, substantial improvement of the sensibility can be expected by increasing the sample volume (see Figure 1). However, with this extractive capillary, the eluent composition required may be a limitation for the chromatographic separation if compounds with more than four aromatic rings (highly apolar) are going to be processed.

Although less effective for the extraction of naphthalene and fluoranthene, the TEOS-MTEOS capillary reinforced with SiO$_2$ NPs is a good alternative, particularly for compounds with functional groups capable of establishing dipole-dipole or hydrogen bonding interactions.

The number of capillaries that can be used for IT-SPME coupled on-line to Nano-LC is even more limited. In the present study, we have tested and compared TEOS-MTEOS phases modified with SiO$_2$ or with TiO$_2$ NPs. The extraction rates were highly dependent on the chemical structure of the analytes. The extraction efficiency was generally better with the TiO$_2$ functionalized capillary for most of the tested compounds. However, the SiO$_2$ NPs showed stronger interaction with compounds having nitro groups. Both capillaries allowed the direct analysis of the tested herbicides at ng/mL, illustrating the potential of IT-SPME-Nano-LC for the analysis of organic pollutants. It has to be noted that, throughout our study, we used TEOS-MTEOS capillaries synthetized in different batches and no significant differences in their performance was found, which is in agreement with previously reported results [8,20].

The results of this study may help to select the extractive phase according to the characteristics of the targeted compounds. Nevertheless, extending the study to new types of substances is still necessary, particularly in Nano-LC systems.

Author Contributions: P.G.-N. performed part of the experiments; the rest of authors designed and performed part of the experiments, analyzed the data and wrote the paper.

Funding: This research was funded by EU FEDER and the Spanish Agencia Española de Investigación (AEI)(project CTQ2017-90082-P), and the Generalitat Valenciana (PROMETEO 2016/109) for the financial support received. P. S.-M. expresses his grateful to the EU FEDER and the Spanish AEI for his pre-doctoral grant.

Conflicts of Interest: The authors declare no conflicts of interest. The funders had no role in the design of the study; in the collection, analyses, or interpretation of data; in the writing of the manuscript, or in the decision to publish the results.

References

1. Moliner-Martínez, Y.; Herráez-Hernández, R.; Verdú-Andrés, J.; Molins-Legua, C.; Campíns-Falcó, P. Recent advances of in-tube solid phase microextraction. *Trends Anal. Chem.* **2015**, *71*, 205–213. [CrossRef]
2. Fernández-Amado, M.; Prieto-Blanco, M.C.; López-Mahía, P.; Muniategui-Lorenzo, S. Strengths and weaknesses of in-tube solid-phase microextraction: A scoping review. *Anal. Chim. Acta* **2016**, *906*, 41–57. [CrossRef] [PubMed]
3. Serra-Mora, P.; Moliner-Martínez, Y.; Molins-Legua, C.; Herráez-Hernández, R.; Verdú-Andrés, J.; Campíns-Falcó, P. Trends in online in-tube solid phase microextraction. In *Comprehensive Analytical Chemistry*; Elsevier: Amsterdam, The Netherlands, 2017; pp. 427–461, ISSN 0166-526X.
4. Jornet-Martínez, N.; Serra-Mora, P.; Moliner-Martínez, Y.; Herráez-Hernández, R.; Campíns-Falcó, P. Evaluation of carbon nanotubes functionalized polydimethylsiloxane based coatings for in-tube solid phase microextraction coupled to capillary liquid chromatography. *Chromatography* **2015**, *2*, 515–528. [CrossRef]
5. Moliner-Martínez, Y.; Serra-Mora, P.; Verdú-Andrés, J.; Herráez-Hernández, R.; Campíns-Falcó, P. Analysis of polar triazines and degradation products in waters by in-tube solid-phase microextraction and capillary chromatography: An environmentally friendly method. *Anal. Bioanal. Chem.* **2015**, *407*, 1485–1497. [CrossRef] [PubMed]
6. Argente-García, A.I.; Moliner-Martínez, Y.; López-García, E.; Campíns-Falcó, P.; Herráez-Hernández, R. Application of carbon nanotubes modified coatings for the determination of amphethamines by in-tube solid-phase microextraction and capillary liquid chromatography. *Separations* **2016**, *3*, 7. [CrossRef]
7. Serra-Mora, P.; Rodríguez-Palma, C.E.; Verdú-Andrés, J.; Herráez-Hernández, R.; Campíns-Falcó, P. Improving the on-line extraction of polar compounds by IT-SPME with silica nanoparticles modified phases. *Separations* **2018**, *5*, 10. [CrossRef]
8. Serra-Mora, P.; Jornet-Martínez, N.; Moliner-Martínez, Y.; Campíns-Falcó, P. In tube-solid phase microextraction-nano liquid chromatography: Application to the determination of intact and degraded polar triazines in waters and recovered struvite. *J. Chromatogr. A* **2017**, *1513*, 51–58. [CrossRef] [PubMed]
9. Jornet-Martínez, N.; Ortega-Sierra, A.; Verdú-Andrés, J.; Herráez-Hernández, R.; Campíns-Falcó, P. Analysis of contact traces of cannabis by in-tube solid-phase microextraction coupled to nanoliquid chromatography. *Molecules* **2018**, *23*, 2359. [CrossRef] [PubMed]
10. Fumes, B.H.; Silva, M.R.; Andrade, F.N.; Nazario, C.E.D.; Lanças, F.M. Recent advances and future trends in new materials for sample preparation. *Trends Anal. Chem.* **2015**, *71*, 9–25. [CrossRef]
11. Zheng, J.; Huang, J.; Yang, Q.; Ni, C.; Xie, X.; Shi, Y.; Sun, J.; Zhu, F.; Ouyang, G. Fabrications of novel solid phase microextraction coatings based on new materials for high enrichment capability. *Trends Anal. Chem.* **2018**, *108*, 135–153. [CrossRef]
12. Moliner-Martínez, Y.; Serra-Mora, P.; Verdú-Andrés, J.; Molins-Legua, C.; Herráez-Hernández, R.; Campíns-Falcó, P. Application of nanomaterials in solid and liquid microextraction. In *Analytical Microextraction Techniques*; Bentham Science Publishers: Emirate of Sharjah, United Arab Emirates, 2016; pp. 135–166.
13. Ahmadi, M.; Elmongy, H.; Madrakian, T.; Abdel-Rehim, M. Nanomaterials as sorbents for simple preparation in bioanalysis: A review. *Anal. Chim. Acta* **2017**, *958*, 1–21. [CrossRef] [PubMed]
14. Azzouz, A.; Kailasa, S.K.; Lee, S.S.; Racón, A.J.; Ballesteros, E.; Zhang, M.; Kim, K.-H. Review of nanomaterials as sorbents in solid-phase extraction for environmental samples. *Trends Anal. Chem.* **2018**, *108*, 347–369. [CrossRef]
15. Lin, B.; Li, T.; Zhao, Y.; Huang, F.-K.; Guo, L.; Feng, Y.-Q. Preparation of a TiO_2 nanoparticle-deposited capillary column by liquid phase deposition and its application in phosphopeptide analysis. *J. Chromatogr. A* **2008**, *1192*, 95–102. [CrossRef] [PubMed]
16. Li, T.; Xu, J.; Wu, J.-H.; Feng, Y.-Q. Liquid-phase deposition of silica nanoparticles into a capillary for in-tube solid-phase microextraction coupled to high-performance liquid chromatography. *J. Chomatogr. A* **2009**, *1216*, 2989–2995. [CrossRef] [PubMed]

Separations **2019**, *6*, 12

17. Xu, J.; Wu, P.; Ye, E.-C.; Yaun, B.-F.; Feng, Y.-Q. Metal oxides in sample pretreatment. *Trends Anal. Chem.* **2016**, *80*, 41–56. [CrossRef]

18. Banitaba, M.H.; Davarani, S.S.H.; Pourahadi, A. Solid-phase microextraction of phthalate esters from aqueous media by electrophoretically deposited TiO_2 nanoparticles on a stainless steel fiber. *J. Chromatogr. A* **2013**, *1283*, 1–8. [CrossRef] [PubMed]

19. Wang, S.-T.; Wang, M.-Y.; Su, X.; Yuan, B.-F.; Feng, Y.-Q. Facile preparation of SiO_2/TiO_2 composite monolithic capillary column and its application in enrichment of phosphopeptides. *Anal. Chem.* **2012**, *84*, 7763–7770. [CrossRef] [PubMed]

20. Silva, R.G.C.; Bottoli, C.B.G.; Collins, C.H. New silica gel-based monolithic column fort nano-liquid chromatography, used in the HILIC mode. *J. Chromatogr. Sci.* **2012**, *50*, 649–657. [CrossRef] [PubMed]

Review

Metal–Organic Frameworks as Key Materials for Solid-Phase Microextraction Devices—A Review

Adrián Gutiérrez-Serpa [1,†], Idaira Pacheco-Fernández [1,†], Jorge Pasán [2] and Verónica Pino [1,3,*

[1] Department of Chemistry, Analytical Division, Universidad de La Laguna, 38206 Tenerife, Spain; agutiers@ull.edu.es (A.G.-S.); ipacheco@ull.edu.es (I.P.-F.)

[2] X-ray and Molecular Lab, Department of Physics, Universidad de La Laguna, 38206 Tenerife, Spain; jpasang@ull.edu.es

[3] University Institute of Tropical Diseases and Public Health, Universidad de La Laguna, 38206 Tenerife, Spain

* Correspondence: veropino@ull.edu.es; Tel.: +34-922318990

† Those authors contributed equally to this work.

Received: 2 August 2019; Accepted: 6 September 2019; Published: 2 October 2019

Abstract: Metal–organic frameworks (MOFs) have attracted recently considerable attention in analytical sample preparation, particularly when used as novel sorbent materials in solid-phase microextraction (SPME). MOFs are highly ordered porous crystalline structures, full of cavities. They are formed by inorganic centers (metal ion atoms or metal clusters) and organic linkers connected by covalent coordination bonds. Depending on the ratio of such precursors and the synthetic conditions, the characteristics of the resulting MOF vary significantly, thus drifting into a countless number of interesting materials with unique properties. Among astonishing features of MOFs, their high chemical and thermal stability, easy tuneability, simple synthesis, and impressive surface area (which is the highest known), are the most attractive characteristics that makes them outstanding materials in SPME. This review offers an overview on the current state of the use of MOFs in different SPME configurations, in all cases covering extraction devices coated with (or incorporating) MOFs, with particular emphases in their preparation.

Keywords: solid-phase microextraction; metal–organic framework; crystalline nanostructures; nanomaterials; analytical chemistry; coatings; microextraction devices; sample preparation

---

1. Overview on Metal–Organic Framework

Metal–organic frameworks (MOFs) are solids constituted of inorganic metal ions (or metallic clusters) and organic linkers connected by coordination bonds. The metal ions act as nodes or centers and the organic linkers act as a bridge between them, forming a complex bi-dimensional or three-dimensional net. Nodes and ligands are termed secondary building units (SBUs). Depending on the coordination sphere of the inorganic SBU, the organic SBU used, and their connectivity, the topology, geometry, and properties of the resultant material will vary significantly [1–4]. Metal–organic frameworks are a subclass of the more general coordination polymers, because they include only those materials with permanent porosity.

The design and synthesis of MOFs rely on reticular chemistry. This approach allows the design of specific structures by the selection of the inorganic and organic SBUs identifying how the nodes and the linkers interact to form the network [4,5]. While the inorganic SBU dictates the node connectivity (usually as a polyhedron where the vertices are the connectivity points), the organic linker indicates the number of nodes that will be interconnected, being necessary, at least, the use of a ditopic linker (linear connector). Figure 1 shows several representative examples of MOFs structures and their respective SBUs. One of the most representative examples is the family of isoreticular metal–organic frameworks (IRMOFs). This group of MOFs present the same topology and skeleton but different functionalization and pore dimensions due to changes introduced in the organic linker, such as increasing its length or by the incorporation of different functional groups [6].

The design of a MOF implies smart selection of the SBUs. Clearly, the number of possible metal-linker combinations are countless. In fact, the Cambridge Crystallographic Data Center contains more than 75,000 different registered MOF structures [7]. There is still a variety of abbreviations to refer to different classes of MOF, without any kind of unified nomenclature: MILs—Materials of Institute of Lavoisier [8], HKUST—Hong Kong University of Science and Technology [9], UiO—University of Oslo [10], CIM—Canary Islands Material [11], or DUT—Dresden University of Technology [12]. Other nomenclatures relate with the structure and organic linker nature used, such as ZIFs—Zeolitic Imidazolate Frameworks [13] or PCN—Porous Coordination Network [14]. Given this nomenclature gap, several MOFs have more than one name, i.e., HKUST-1 = MOF-199. Taking into account the increasing number of applications of these materials, we believe that a common and unified nomenclature will arise necessarily.

The characteristics of MOFs mainly depend on the nature of the selected inorganic and organic SBUs and their connectivity. These three factors will define the geometrical disposition of the network, the pore size, the morphology of the cavities, and the channels distribution. Nevertheless, other parameters related to the synthetic conditions such as the amount of each precursor, ratios, solvents, modulators, and the synthetic method followed also exert a noticeable influence on the network [1].

The preparation of MOFs follows common strategies to obtain crystalline structures such as slow diffusion or solvent evaporation [1,3]. In the generic procedure, a solution containing the precursors (organic and inorganic SBUs) gets under favorable conditions to ensure the integrity of the SBUs and their assembly to form a network. Specifically, the slow diffusion synthesis consists on the preparation of two solutions containing each one of the MOF precursors (the metal and the linker). The two solutions get in contact and slowly diffuse forming the crystals at the interface. The evaporation strategy utilizes a saturated solution of the SBUs mixture, followed by heating to remove the solvent slowly, thus forcing the formation of the crystals. Although both methods are easy to perform, sometimes, MOF preparation requires an energy input to form the product. Therefore, the solvo(hydro)thermal synthesis emerged as a common method to obtain MOFs [1]. This procedure utilizes a solution of inorganic and organic SBUs in a Teflon-lined stainless steel autoclave, followed by heating at the adequate temperature. The reached temperature while maintaining a constant volume in the reactor generates an autogenous pressure that facilitates the formation of the crystals [3]. This method is the most common strategy to prepare MOFs. However, it is an energy intensive procedure if the MOF requires high temperature, and most of the solutions are prepared with high polar toxic solvents to ensure the solubility of the precursors such as *N,N*-dimethylformamide, *N,N*-dimethylacetamide, *N,N*-diethylformamide, etc. Nowadays, other procedures such as electrochemical, microwave-assisted, mechanochemical-assisted, and sonochemistry synthesis have emerged as environmentally friendly alternatives to prepare MOFs, while increasing the final amount obtained [15].

MOFs have become a trendy material due to their excellent properties. Most of these compounds possess a high thermal, chemical, and mechanical stability. Several MOFs present a flexible behavior, being able to expand or contract their structures as a response to an external stimulus: electromagnetic radiation, temperature, or mechanical stress. Most of these interactions relate with a host–guest phenomenon, depending if the initial synthetic solvent fills the pore (expanded) or if the pores are empty (contracted) [2].

Their current success in analytical chemistry directly links to their impressive surface areas. MOFs have the highest surface area known, with values ranging from ~150 up to ~7,000 $m^2 \cdot g^{-1}$ [16]. Nowadays, the MOF DUT-60 holds the world record regarding the highest surface area and pore volume. This MOF has a surface area of 7,800 $m^2 \cdot g^{-1}$ and a pore volume of 5.02 $cm^3 \cdot g^{-1}$ [17]. It is formed by Zn_4O^{6+} clusters and an expanded tritopic ligand 1,3,5-tris(4′-carboxy[1,1′-biphenyl]-4-yl)benzene in combination with a ditopic linker 1,4-bis-*p*-carboxyphenylbuta-1,3-diene. In general, MOFs with surface areas over 6,000 $m^2 \cdot g^{-1}$ are termed ultrahigh porosity crystalline frameworks. Their applicability is still challenging despite this property because their activation is quite complex [16]. The activation of a MOF refers to any procedure shifted to clean the non-reacted chemicals while evacuating the remaining synthetic solvent from the pores of the material. The purpose is to obtain vacant space in the crystal. This procedure can be accomplished by different strategies such us heating, application of vacuum, or even using a solvent exchange [18]. In the case of ultrahigh porosity MOFs, this evacuation can render the structure useless due to the collapse of the structure after the removal of the solvent molecules. The linkers used in these materials as organic SBUs are extended-ligands (to ensure the obtaining of larger porous), which cannot hold on the complex node-linker network once they get empty. In fact, once the cavities and pores are empty, there is more free space than material [16]. For this reason, conventional MOFs (which also have high surface areas but not comparable to those termed ultrahigh porous MOFs) have been more widely used in the majority of applications, such as gas storage [19], heterogeneous catalysis [20], sensors [21], drug delivery systems [22], energy storage devices [23], and in analytical chemistry applications [24–27].

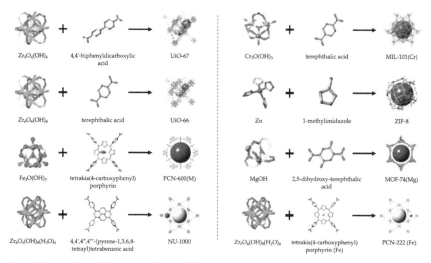

Figure 1. Examples of different metal–organic frameworks structures with their corresponding metallic clusters and organic linkers. Adapted from [18], with permission from American Chemical Society, 2017.

2. Metal–Organic Frameworks in Analytical Separations

Regarding their use in analytical chemistry separations, MOFs have been employed as stationary phases in chromatography and as sorbent materials in analytical sample preparation methods, taking advantage of their surface area, stability, and tuneability [24,28]. Figure 2 summarizes the evolution of the use of MOFs in analytical chemistry separations, focusing the attention in analytical sample preparation approaches.

The advantages offered by MOFs as stationary phases in chromatography include the pore size selectivity, the possible use of functional organic ligands as linkers that increase the specificity of the material (favoring interactions with analytes), and the separation of species due to metal affinity events. Furthermore, it is possible to achieve chiral chromatographic separations by using chiral MOFs [28]. However, their non-spherical morphology, nanoscale particle size, and (for several MOFs) a limited working pH range stability are issues requiring polishing to expand the application of MOFs as chromatographic stationary phases. Recent developments in the field focus the efforts on the synthesis of silica-based core–shell MOFs to increase the particle size while improving the homogeneity of the chromatographic stationary phase [28,29].

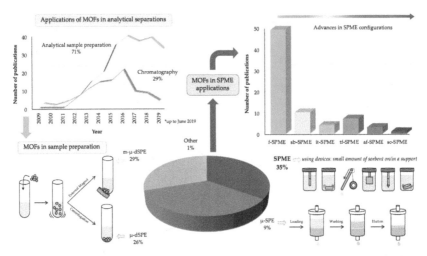

Figure 2. Summary of the number of publications reported up to date involving the use of MOFs in analytical separations, particularly in analytical sample preparation methods. For the definition of the abbreviations, refer to the list of abbreviations at the end of the article.

The use of MOFs as novel sorbent materials in a variety of analytical sample preparation methods somehow directly relates within the trends of green analytical chemistry [24]. Conventional extraction methods are time consuming and require the use of large volumes of toxic organic solvents and sample volumes. As improvements, there has been a high applicability of miniaturized analytical sample preparation methods. These novel miniaturized approaches require outstanding materials to perform with the same analytical performance as conventional materials in non-miniaturized methods. Among miniaturized sorbent-based microextraction strategies incorporating MOFs it is possible to cite: miniaturized solid-phase extraction (μ-SPE) [30], dispersive solid-phase microextraction (μ-dSPE) and its magnetic-assisted version (m-μ-dSPE) [25,31], and solid-phase microextraction (SPME) [24,32], each of which are also susceptible to be performed under different operational strategies, as shown in Figure 2.

In all cases, MOFs are utilized as porous materials to somehow ensure trapping those target molecules able to get inside their pores while interacting with the metal nodes [27,33]. Once trapped by the material, proper desorption (thermally induced or aided by desorption solvents) is performed to accomplish the analytical determination.

Another recent trend of incorporating MOFs in analytical sample miniaturized methods pursue the use of low cytotoxic MOFs, prepared following the criteria of green synthesis [34].

Initial studies of MOFs as sorbent materials were in on-line and off-line μ-SPE methods. Thus, Zhou et al. prepared a copper (II) isonicotinate MOF powder packed precolumn (1.5 cm × 4 mm) to perform an on-line extraction of polycyclic aromatic hydrocarbons (PAHs) in environmental waters [35]. Yang et al. also used a similar strategy packing ZIF-8(Zn) into a stainless-steel column for the on-line μ-SPE determination of tetracyclines in water and milk samples [36]. Regarding off-line μ-SPE, the first application reported a μ-SPE column prepared by packing MOF-5(Zn) in a polypropylene cartridge, which was used for the extraction of PAHs [37]. In a different approach, the device consisted on a polypropylene membrane bag filled with ZIF-8(Zn) powder (similar to a tea bag) instead of the most conventional cartridge. One of the most attractive characteristics of this device is the possibility of performing a vortex-assisted extraction without requiring any centrifugation step [38]. Since then, MOFs have been packed as powder into disks, cartridges, and micro-columns for their use in different analytical sample preparation applications of μ-SPE [27,39].

Separations **2019**, *6*, 47

The success of MOFs as sorbent materials in the microextraction variant that disperses the material (without utilizing any device) in the sample, μ-dSPE, lies in the simplicity of the approach. MOFs as net crystals experience dispersion (by agitation) into the sample containing the analytes. Once the MOF traps the target analytes, they are desorbed and analytically determined [25]. In addition to simplicity, the resulting method presents high extraction efficiency (given the strength of the interaction analyte-MOF during MOF dispersion), adequate preconcentration, reproducibility, and accuracy. This leads not only to the expansion of the use of neat MOFs in μ-dSPE but also to the development of novel MOF-hybrid materials and composites [25]. However, considering the use of net crystals not confined in any device of easy manipulation, in all cases a final step of centrifugation, decantation, or magnetic separation with an external magnet is required, in turn requiring more steps than expected for a truly miniaturized approach.

Pawliszyn et al. developed the first SPME device in the early 1990s. The first SPME device utilized a silica wire of 1 cm coated by polyimide as sorbent material [40]. Although the extraction of the analytes was successful, the device suffered a lack of strength and robustness. Out of this first design, different SPME configurations have been developed progressively to improve this technique [41]. This includes mainly the following SPME modes: on-fiber solid-phase microextraction (f-SPME) [42], arrow fiber solid-phase microextraction (af-SPME) [43], in-tube solid-phase microextraction (it-SPME) [44], thin-film solid-phase microextraction (tf-SPME) [45], and stir-based solid-phase microextraction, including stir-bar (sb-SPME) [46] and stir-cake solid-phase microextraction (sc-SPME). The introduction of MOFs as sorbent materials in the different SPME devices and configurations has been gradual. Thus, Figure 3 shows a timeline of the introduction of MOFs in the main different SPME configurations developed up to date [47–52].

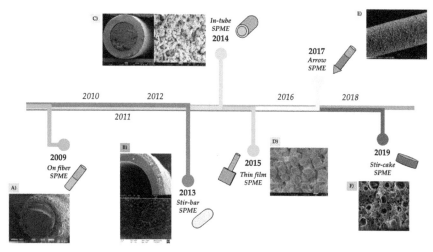

Figure 3. Timeline covering the introduction of MOFs as sorbents in the different solid-phase microextraction devices and configurations. (**A**) Adapted from [47], with permission from Elsevier, 2016. (**B**) Adapted from [48], with permission from Elsevier, 2016. (**C**) Adapted from [49], with permission from American Chemical Society, 2016. (**D**) Adapted from [50], with permission from Elsevier, 2018. (**E**) Adapted from [51], with permission from Elsevier, 2017. (**F**) Adapted from [52], with permission from Springer Nature, 2019.

This review includes a general overview on the state of the art of the use of MOFs as sorbent materials in different SPME devices (Figure 3), paying particular attention to their preparation for the different configurations.

3. MOFs in On-Fiber Solid-Phase Microextraction (f-SPME)

3.1. Overwiev on Commercial f-SPME Devices

In its more common configuration, the SPME device involves a fiber-shaped support coated with the extracting phase leading to the on-fiber SPME (f-SPME), as shown in Figure 4A. This SPME configuration normally performs in two main extraction modes: headspace (HS) SPME, in which the fiber exposes to the headspace over the sample, and direct immersion mode (DI-SPME), where the fiber immerses completely in the aqueous sample. The final desorption step can be accomplished either by placing the fiber in the inlet of a gas chromatography (GC) system (the coating resists high temperatures and the analytes volatilize and get into the GC) or by exposing the fiber to a small amount (<1 mL) of organic solvent (solubilizing analytes while preserving the coating). The thermal desorption approach is the most desirable since it leads to a solvent-free extraction method.

Currently, several brands, including Supelco (Merck) [53] and PAL from CTC Analytics (Restek) [54], supply SPME fibers coated with stationary phases of different polarities and thicknesses. All commercial stationary phases for f-SPME contain a liquid polymer, which is the main component of the coating in the case of absorbent-type fibers (polydimethylsiloxane (PDMS), polyacrylate, and polyethyleneglycol), or is the liquid bulk material in which the solid sorbent is suspended in the case of adsorbent-type stationary fibers (carboxen/PDMS, PDMS/divinylbenzene, and divinylbenzene/carboxen/PDMS).

For the preparation of commercial f-SPME devices, fused silica fibers and metal wires act as the core to support the coating material, with diameters of 100 and 128 µm, respectively [55]. Despite the fragility of fused silica, it is the preferred core for most f-SPME devices since the diameter can be highly controlled and long fibers can be coated precisely with absorbent materials during the manufacturing. Stableflex cores, consisting of fused fibers coated with a thin layer of an inert polymer, and metallic wires, composed of a flexible and thermally stable non-ferrous metal alloy, were introduced to overcome this stability issue [55]. The use of these novel substrates as cores improves the bonding of the adsorbent-type materials during the coating process, which also helps in improving the robustness and reproducibility between batches of the resulting device.

Regarding the size of the f-SPME devices, commercial fibers consists of coated cores of 1 cm. The thicknesses of the coating are up to 100 µm depending on the composition of the sorbent material [53,54]. Despite thicker coatings possibly leading to an improvement on the extraction capability of the SPME fiber, they may also require long extraction times to reach equilibrium when operating [41]. These coated cores assemble in a device that resembles a syringe to facilitate its manipulation and the automation of the methodology. It allows exposing the extracting phase to the sample by pushing the plunger forward, while the fiber experience retraction and protection by pulling the plunger back.

The f-SPME mode is the most widely-exploited approach within all the SPME configurations reported up to date (Figure 2). This success relates to its huge trade expansion in the analysis field [56–58], the existence of standard methods proposing this technique [59,60], together with the simplicity of its operation and the easiness in the preparation of these fibers in comparison with other SPME devices.

Despite the commercially available coatings allow the application of this technique for extracting a broad range of compounds, they still lack selectivity and present relatively low thermal stability [41]. In this sense, considering the interesting properties of MOFs, they have been explored as sorbent coatings for f-SPME [32].

3.2. Preparation of MOF-Based f-SPME Devices

Table ?? includes several representative examples of the reported MOF-based coatings for this SPME geometry together with other configurations [48–51,61–76]. The vast majority of reported MOF-based f-SPME devices uses the most common MOFs, such as: HKUST-1—composed of copper nodes and 1,3,5-benzenetricarboxylate struts [61,65,77–79]; UiO-66—formed by the combination of Zr clusters and 1,4-benzenedicarboxylate ligands [62,67,80,81]; MIL-type MOFs, synthesized using 1,4-benzenedicarboxylate ligands and different metal ions, including Cr [68,69,82,83], Fe [84–87], and Al [66,88]; and MOFs composed of Zn metal centers, including MOF-5 with 1,4-benzenedicarboxylate as ligand [64,89–92], and the family of ZIF MOFs containing imidazolate-based ligands [63,70,93–96]. The selection of these MOFs over others (particularly considering the vast list of possible MOFs) lies on their easy preparation and inter-batch reproducibility of their preparation, together with the fact that their characterization is thorough. To sum up, MOFs containing Zn, Zr, and trivalent metals in their structures normally present higher water and thermal stability [97,98], which makes them adequate candidates for SPME stationary phases.

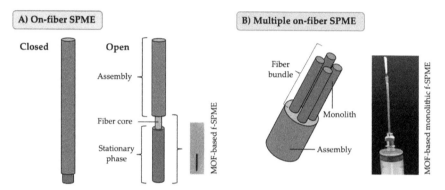

Figure 4. (**A**) Scheme of a generic f-SPME device and image of a MOF-based f-SPME. Adapted from [78], with permission from Elsevier, 2019. (**B**) Scheme of a generic multiple f-SPME device and image of the MOF-based monolithic f-SPME. Adapted from [70], with permission from Springer, 2019.

Given the solid nature of MOFs, different strategies arise for their immobilization on the f-SPME device. The most common approach is the in-situ growth of the MOF on the surface of the substrate used as core [61–63,79,84,94,99–104]. In this method, the support is immersed in a solution containing the reagents required to synthesize the MOF by the solvothermal method. The surface of the support offers nucleation sites in which the MOF starts growing to form the coating. Among the studies using this coating method, it is worth mentioning the f-SPME based on HKUST-1(Cu) prepared by Sun et al. [79]. In this case, the reaction solution contains the organic ligand and an oxidizing agent since the copper wire used as f-SPME core acts as source of copper ions itself to synthesize the MOF. In other cases, once the MOF attaches to the support (by the in-situ growth), there is an incorporation of additional materials to improve the efficiency of the final coating. Thus, it is interesting to mention the layer-by-layer deposition method of an ionic liquid (IL) and coating with PDMS after the in-situ growth of the MOF IRMOF-3(Zn) reported by Zheng et al. [100]. The PDMS layer helps to protect the coating, while the IL plays an important role on the extraction efficiency of the resulting f-SPME device. The in-situ growth approach has also been reported for the preparation of f-SPME devices coated with composites containing MOFs and carbon-based materials [92,105]. In these cases, the carbon-based material requires dispersion in the reaction solution together with the starting materials for the synthesis of the MOF. In the study reported by Wu et al. [92], an IL is also included in the resulting coating by the functionalization of graphene prior to its addition to the reaction solution. The incorporation of the IL leads to a better bonding between the graphene and the MOF-5(Zn) used for the preparation of the extracting phase, which also improves the uniformity and stability of the f-SPME device.

Other supporting methods base on the electrodeposition of the MOF [64,91]. In this strategy, the working electrode is also the core of the f-SPME device, and cyclic voltammetry ensures that the MOF coats its surface. In the examples reported, the electrodeposition step ensures that triethylamine-modified MOF-5 coats the stainless-steel rod by including triethylamine hydrochloride in the electrolyte solution together with the metal salt and the organic acid used as ligand.

A simpler coating method involves the immersion of the support in a dispersion of the MOF or directly in the MOF powder [93,106], using always the as-synthetized MOF by any of the usual routes (usually the solvothermal method). This procedure needs repetition several times with heating steps between the dipping cycles until reaching the desired thickness. Despite its simplicity, it is hardly used to include neat MOFs in the fibers but to prepare f-SPME devices with hybrid phases composed of MOFs together with carbonaceous materials [65,77,87,90]. For their preparation, the initial powder contains a mixture of the MOF with the carbon-based additive at a specific proportion and the fiber dips in the suspension or powder. MOF-based sorbents benefit from the incorporation of graphene derivatives and carbon nanotubes to improve the extraction performance of the device towards aromatic compounds.

Taking into account that all MOFs (including the abovementioned composites) appear as solid particles in contrast to the high viscous liquid-like polymers used in the preparation of commercial f-SPME devices, the fiber core for MOFs (and MOFs composites) must comply several requirements to avoid detachment of the solid coating from the support [32]. Thus, most reported MOF-based SPME fibers use stainless steel wires as core, with the same diameter as commercial fibers [61,63,64,84,87,90–93,99,100,102–104,106]. To increase the contact area between the core and the solid during the coating process there is a cleaning step of the metallic rod with different solvents and/or treating steps with acid solutions to obtain a rough surface. With the aim of amending the link of the stationary phase to the core while using a robust metallic support, the functionalization of the stainless-steel wires with silanization agents results are also quite interesting [63,87,90]. In this case, a microstructured silver layer on the surface of the wire solves the non-reactive character of the stainless steel.

Fused silica and quartz have also been used for the development of MOF-based coatings for this SPME configuration [62,65,77,94,101,105]. Despite the fragility exhibited by these supports, their composition allows an easy functionalization of the surface with amino or carboxylic groups by dipping the fibers in a solution containing the silanization agent, after pretreating them with acids and bases to expose the silanol groups. This step may ensure a chemical link between the support and the MOF-based extracting phase, and consequently upgrade the stability of the coating, since these groups can react with the organic ligands used for the synthesis of the MOF [32].

Table 1. Representative examples of MOF-based coatings prepared within all the different SPME configurations.

MOF	Support	Additive*	Size (Length/Diameter/Thickness)	Preparation Method	Sample/Analyte* (Number)	Analytical Method*	Extraction Time (min)	RSD$_{max}$/RSD$_{batch}$ a	Ref.
On-fiber solid-phase microextraction (f-SPME)									
HKUST-1(Cu)	stainless steel wire	–	–/–/40 μm	in-situ growth	indoor air/benzene derivatives (7)	HS mode and GC-FID	20	7.7/9.4	[61]
UiO-66(Zr)	fused silica fiber	–	–/–/25 μm	in-situ growth	water and soil/PAHs (10)	DI mode and GC-MS	20	8.2/8.9	[62]
ZIF-90(Zn)	stainless steel wire	–	–/–/30.5 μm	in-situ growth	water, soil, and vegetables/PCBs (6)	DI mode and GC-MS	40	5.5/9.1	[63]
E-MOF-5(Zn)	stainless steel wire	–	–/–/12.5 μm	electro-deposition	milk/hormones (4)	DI mode and LC-DAD	30	9.4/6.1	[64]
HKUST-1(Cu)	fused silica fiber	graphite oxide	–/–/40 μm	immersion in the composite	water and soil/OCPs (8)	HS mode and GC-ECD	40	8.8/12.8	[65]
MIL-53(Al)	stainless steel wire	epoxy glue as adhesive	–/–/50 μm	attachment with adhesive	water/PAHs (16)	HS mode and GC-MS/MS	50	12.5/13.9	[66]
UiO-66(Zr)	stainless steel wire	epoxy glue as-adhesive	–/–/150 μm	attachment with adhesive	water/phenols (6)	HS mode and GC-FID	50	6.2/10.1	[67]
MIL-101-NH$_2$(Cr)	quartz	PAN as adhesive	–/–/120 μm	attachment with adhesive	fish/antibiotics (6)	In-vivo and LC-MS/MS	10	6.8/9.5	[68]
MIL-101(Cr)	stainless steel wire	PDMS	–/–/70 μm	sol–gel	water/PAHs (5)	HS mode and GC-MS	20	9.3/13.8	[69]
ZIF-8(Zn)	fiber bundle with 4 monoliths	graphene oxide and MIP	3 cm/0.35 cm/–	mold polymerization	food/hormones (5)	DI mode and LC-MS	30	4.1/5.2	[70]
On-arrow-fiber solid-phase microextraction (af-SPME)									
ZIF-8(Zn)	arrow steel rod	PVC as adhesive	2 cm/–/70 μm	attachment with adhesive	wastewater, fish and mushroom/amines (2)	HS mode and GC-MS	5	10.3/15.6	[51]
Fe-BDC(Fe)	arrow steel rod	–	2 cm/–/2 μm	atomic layer deposition and conversion	wastewater/chloro-phenols (8)	HS mode and GC-MS	30	23.1/–	[71]

MOF	Support	Additive*	Size (Length/Diameter/Thickness)	Preparation Method	Sample/Analyte* (Number)	Analytical Method*	Extraction Time (min)	RSD$_{max}$/RSD$_{batch}$ [a]	Ref.
In-tube solid-phase microextraction (it-SPME)									
MIL-101(Cr)	capillary tube	BMA-EDMA and IL [C$_6$mim][BF$_4$]	10 cm/0.8 mm/–	microwave assisted polymerization	water/drugs (6)	CEC-UV-Vis	34	5.2/–	[72]
MIL-53(Al)	capillary tube	BMA-EDMA and IL [C$_6$mim][BF$_4$]	10 cm/0.8 mm/–	microwave assisted polymerization	water/sulfonamides (7)	CE-UV-Vis	36	6.4/5.3	[49]
MOF	Support	Additive*	Size (Length/Diameter/Thickness)	Preparation Method	Sample/Analyte* (Number)	Analytical Method*	Extraction Time (min)	RSD$_{max}$/RSD$_{batch}$ [a]	Ref.
Thin film solid-phase microextraction (tf-SPME)									
MIL-53(Al)	–	PVDF	2 cm/–/–	spreading	urine/estrogens (4)	LC-FD	45	11.4/–	[50]
Stir-bar solid-phase microextraction (sb-SPME)									
IRMOF-3(Zn)	capillary glass bar	PDMS	2 cm/–/100 μm	sol-gel	water/estrogens (7)	LC-UV	55	10.2/16.1	[73]
MIL-53-NH$_2$(Al)	capillary glass bar	PDMS	2 cm/–/125 μm	sol-gel	water/PAHs (15)	LC-FD	30	11.7/16.9	[74]
MOF-5(Fe)	Nd-Fe-B rod	MNP Fe$_3$O$_4$@NH$_2$	1 cm/–/–	magnetic interaction	fish/PCBs (6)	GC-MS	33	4.3/–	[75]
MIL-101-NH$_2$(Cr)	capillary glass bar	PDMS	2 cm/–/100 μm	sol-gel	water/OPPs (6)	GC-FPD	35	10.7/9.2	[48]
UiO-66-NH$_2$(Zr)	–	Nd-Fe-B powder, 4-VP	2 cm/30 mm/–	thermal polymerization	soil and water/herbicides (5)	LC-UV	60	13.8/9.5	[76]

[a] RSD$_{max}$ for maximum intra-fiber relative standard deviation; RSD$_{batch}$ for inter-fiber relative standard deviation. * for the definition of the abbreviations, refer to the list of abbreviations at the end of the article.

As mentioned in Section 3.1, commercial f-SPME devices with solid materials require a liquid polymer to attach the stationary phase to the core. This justifies the use of glues to attach the MOF coatings to the stainless-steel wires in a high number of studies [47,66,67,81,82,85,86,88,89,107–113], or even to fused silica [68]. The sealant is used in an amount that it does not block the pores of the solid sorbent and it does not participate in the extraction process [32,55]. In general, the support is first dipped in the sealant and then in the MOF powder to obtain the coating. The immersion of the fiber in the glue has also been accomplished as the final step of the coating procedure [82], with the glue acting as a protective layer; or even the glue is previously added to the MOF powder and the fiber is immersed in the mixture to obtain the f-SPME device [109,112]. In some cases, the procedure requires repetitions to control the thickness and obtain thicker coatings. Silicone and epoxy sealants are commonly used, but other adhesives consisting of different polymers have also been proposed, such as polyimide [47,109], polydopamine [86], polyethersulfone [112], and polyacrylonitrile [68].

More sophisticated methods have been described for the preparation of polymeric coatings containing MOFs, such as the sol–gel approach [69,78,83,95,96,114,115]. In these studies, the MOF particles need dispersion in the sol–gel solution, where the stainless-steel support is dipped to obtain the coating after letting it dry at room or high temperatures. This preparation method provides stationary phases that easily bond to the core, also ensuring a homogenous distribution of the MOF through the coating. In the study reported by Bagheri et al. [116], a MOF-polyaniline composite is electro-polymerized on the fiber core by applying a constant potential to the monomer solution, which contains the MOF particles dispersed.

Despite the widely use of f-SPME configurations, the enhancement of the extraction rate to reduce the time to reach the equilibrium in f-SPME applications can be accomplished by using a SPME device composed of multiple fibers, as recently proposed. These fibers have low diameters and are spaced in a way that the gap between the fibers is bigger than the boundary layer formed around the coatings, as shown in Figure 4B [41,117]. Mirzajani et al. reported MOFs in this approach [70]. The SPME device involves a fiber bundle prepared by combining four polymeric monoliths with a diameter of 0.35 cm. The composite consists of a molecularly imprinted polymer doped with graphene oxide and the MOF ZIF-8(Zn), which helps generating a highly selective material due to its pore topology. The use of monoliths yields a highly stable and flexible device that can be easily prepared using molds, which also provide high inter-batch reproducibility.

3.3. Analytical Performance of MOF-Based f-SPME Devices

Most of the MOF-based coatings reported have lengths of 1 cm, while their thicknesses, estimated by obtaining scanning electron microscopy micrographs of the resulting f-SPME device, ranged from 2 μm to 150 μm regardless of the composition of the stationary phase and the coating method. The as-prepared MOFs coatings in f-SPME are commonly incorporated into a 5 μL GC syringe [47,61,62,65–67,69,70,77,81,83–85,87,88,90,93–96,101–104,106,108,114,115], are mounted in a commercial f-SPME assembly [82,89,100,109,112], or into a lab-made device [68,78,116]. The average lifetime of the MOF f-SPME devices is around 100–120 extractions, with the exception of the fiber prepared with the MOF MAF-66 (Zn as metal center and 3-amino-1,2,4-triazole as organic ligand) for which the extraction performance was still the same after 270 extractions [106]. Regarding the inter-fiber precision, which provides information of the reproducibility of the preparation method despite evaluating the fibers for a specific application, it was always lower than 14%, being even lower than 5.2% for the multiple fiber device [70].

As expected, taking into account the characteristics of the SPME technique and the high thermal stability of MOFs, practically all the f-SPME devices combine with GC analysis. The desorption temperatures used are in general close to the maximum temperature at which MOFs keep their crystallinity, thus being always higher than 200 °C, with an average value of 250 °C. The highest desorption temperature reported was 300 °C for the f-SPME coatings prepared with MIL-88B(Fe) [84], MOF-5(Zn) [92], UiO-66(Zr) [81], and HKUST-1(Cu) [79].

MOFs fibers have been evaluated in HS mode in combination with GC for the extraction of an enormous variety of compounds: from PAHs [66,69,79,82,100,102,103,106,108,111], and benzene derivatives [47,82,99,101,110,114,116], to phenols [67,89,92,94]. Water is the most common matrix analyzed, but for example amines have been extracted from urine samples [115] and latex gloves [80], thus proving the validity of MOF f-SPME fibers when dealing with complex samples. MOF f-SPME devices are also useful for the determination of benzene homologues in indoor air [61] and aldehydes in exhaled breath [95].

The DI-SPME-GC methods with these fibers has been used for the analysis of water samples coming from different sources [62,81,85,88,96,104,105,107,109,113], aqueous extracts of foods [85,87,90], and aqueous extracts of soils [62,104,105]. PAHs [62,81,85,96,104,105,107,109] and pesticides [90,107,113] have been the most common analytes determined with the developed methods using the DI mode.

Only four studies reported liquid chromatography (LC) applications with MOFs fibers in the DI mode [68,70,78,107], and using a small amount of an organic solvent in the desorption step [64,68,78], or an aqueous solution at a fixed pH value in the case of the multiple fiber device [70]. It is important to highlight the stability of the triethylamine-modified MOF-5(Zn) coating prepared by electrodeposition [64,91], since it is stable in polar, non-polar, and even halogenated organic solvents, in contrast to commercial coatings, which tend to swell in organic solvents. These DI-SPME-LC methods were intended to the determination of hormones [64,70], and drugs [68,78], in biological and food samples, respectively. It is important to highlight the application of the MIL-101-NH$_2$ f-SPME device (Cr as metal center and 2-amino-1,4-benzenedicarboxylate as ligand, prepared using polyacrylonitrile as adhesive) for in-vivo analysis, exhibiting better results than commercial fibers for the extraction of antibiotics from living fishes [68].

4. MOFs in On-Arrow-Fiber Solid-Phase Microextraction (af-SPME)

SPME arrow fibers (af-SPME) appears as a variation of the f-SPME device to improve the robustness of the design [43]. In this geometry, a large volume of the sorbent (compared to conventional f-SPME devices) coats the sharp closed tip of a steel rod, as shown in Figure 5A. As the amount of extracting phase is quite big in this configuration, higher sensitivity is possible in certain applications, while protecting perfectly the coating from matrix components thanks to its design.

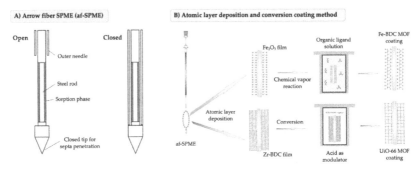

Figure 5. (**A**) Scheme of the af-SPME configuration. Adapted from [43], with permission from Elsevier, 2015. (**B**) Atomic layer deposition and conversion method proposed for the preparation of MOF-based af-SPME devices. Adapted from [71], with permission from Elsevier, 2018.

These af-SPME devices are already commercially available, manufactured by CTC Analytics [118]. The available stationary phases are the same as those for f-SPME: polymer-based coatings with different polarities depending on their composition. The length of the coating is 2 cm, the rods have outer diameters of 1.1 or 1.5 mm, and the thicknesses range from 100 μm to 250 μm for the PDMS phase. Despite the novelty of this configuration, MOFs have also been explored as potential sorbent materials for the development of af-SPME devices, which were used in combination with GC analysis [51,119].

The MOFs ZIF-8(Zn) [51] and UiO-66(Zr) [119] in af-SPME have been attached to stainless steel rods using adhesives. In the case of ZIF-8 af-SPME [51], a suspension containing the previously synthesized MOF and polyvinylchloride is prepared, and the fiber support (2 cm) is dipped several times in the mixture and subjected to high temperatures to obtain a thickness of 70 μm. These fibers were tested in the HS extraction of alkylamines from wastewater samples and from aqueous extracts of fish and mushrooms. For the UiO-66-based device [119], the coating method consisted of dipping the arrow fiber first in diluted silicone sealant and then in the suspension of the solid material several times to obtain a thickness of 25 μm. In order to increase the extraction capability of the sorbent towards PAHs, there is a combination of UiO-66 MOF with molybdenum disulfide. The device was evaluated in HS mode and in combination with GC for the analysis of aqueous extracts of fish samples.

Lan et al. [71] proposed a new coating strategy based on atomic layer deposition (ALD) and conversion methods. The entire approach permits the preparation of more selective af-SPME devices coated with different MOFs: the MOF Fe-BDC (composed of Fe metal centers and 1,4-benzenedicarboxylate ligands) was the best for the extraction of benzene-containing polar compounds, while the UiO-66(Zr) coating exhibited better results for polar and aromatic analytes. Figure 5B includes a scheme of the experimental procedure followed in this coating method. In the case of Fe-BDC MOF, ALD permitted the support of Fe_2O_3 films on the surface of the steel rod. This oxide layer acted then as a source of Fe ions for the synthesis of the MOF. In the conversion step, the af-SPME assembly was immersed in a solution containing the organic ligand to perform a simple vapor–solid reaction, thus obtaining the MOF structure. This method was also used for the preparation of Al-containing MOFs and using similar organic ligands, but the analytical characteristics of the coating were not satisfactory. For the UiO-66 af-SPME, a thin film of the MOF precursor (Zr-BDC) was supported directly on the steel wire instead of an oxide layer. This layer then easily transforms into UiO-66 using the modulator vapor. Despite the small thicknesses obtained for these coatings (~2 and 7.5 μm), comparative and even better results were achieved when extracting polar compounds from wastewaters compared with polymeric commercial coatings.

5. MOFs in In-Tube Solid-Phase Microextraction (it-SPME)

The in-tube solid-phase microextraction configuration (it-SPME) was developed practically after the development of the conventional f-SPME, mainly to improve the drawbacks related with the coupling of the technique with LC. Although the high success of f-SPME devices in many analytical applications, the extraction of non-volatile, semi-volatile, and/or thermo-labile compounds (not adequate for GC) was a significant hurdle to overcome.

The introduction of it-SPME devices facilitates the online and direct injection in a LC system, and even more important, its automation [120]. The first it-SPME devices consisted on 60 cm sections of a GC capillary column, with an internal diameter of 0.25 mm and an internal thin film of the stationary phase coating the capillary. Depending on the nature of the stationary phase, the film thickness varies, exhibiting slightly different internal volumes among the devices. Nevertheless, the nature of the film is the main factor responsible of the difference in the behavior [120]. Nowadays, most developed it-SPME devices use open tubular fused-silica capillaries, with a thin film of the extractant material on the inner walls. The development of other capillary modes shifts to the incorporation of novel materials and the improvement of the technique. Other capillary modes include sorbent-packed, fiber-packed, and monolithic phases [44,121,122]. Figure 6A compiles a representation of the main four it-SPME capillary configurations.

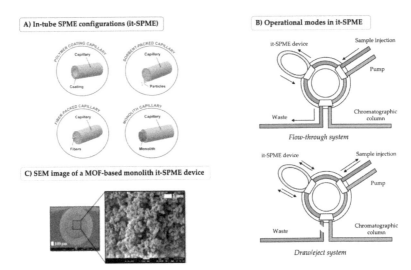

Figure 6. (**A**) Scheme of generic it-SPME devices reported in the literature. Adapted from [44], with permission from Elsevier, 2019. (**B**) Scheme of the two general operation modes of it-SPME devices. (**C**) Image of a MOF-based monolithic it-SPME device. Adapted from [123], with permission from Elsevier, 2016.

There are several operational modes for it-SPME depending on the number of pumps and valves. Nevertheless, they can be divided mainly into two configurations attending to the introduction of the sample: the flow-through system and the draw/eject system. In the first one, the injection of the sample can be performed manually or automated, and the sample is continuously injected into the device following a unique direction way. In the draw/eject mode, it requires an automatic sample introduction system (programmable). The sample is injected, flows through the device, and goes back to the sample vial through the device again completing a cycle. In this modality, it is important not only to optimize the sample flow, but also the number of required cycles to obtain the maximum extraction efficiency [44,122]. Figure 6B shows a schematic representation of both configurations.

Up to date, the use of MOFs as sorbent material in it-SPME is not extended, and only few studies have been reported so far using MIL-101(Cr) [72], MIL-53(Al) [49,123], and ZIF-8(Zn) [124], in all cases for the determination of environmental pollutants in water.

In the cases of MIL-101(Cr) and MIL-53(Al), the devices consist of a glass capillary filled with a monolith composed of a polymer and the MOF. Thus, the glass capillary was cut in sections of 4–10 cm length, followed by washing with concentrated NaOH to activate the silanol groups. Then, the inner walls of the capillary were vinylated to guarantee the attachment of the monolith. [49,72,123]. Afterwards, the mixture suspension containing the necessary amount of MOF (as prepared and already activated), butyl methacrylate as monomer, ethylene dimethacrylate as cross-linker agent, azo-bis-isobutyronitrile as radical initiator, and a porogenic solvent fills the capillary. Once the sides of the capillary are sealed, a microwave-assisted polymerization takes place. It is important to ensure the correct dispersion and homogenization of the mixture suspension before filling the capillary to get a homogenous it-SPME device. Finally, there is a clean-up step to remove the unreacted chemicals from the device [49,72,123]. Figure 6C shows an electronic scanning microscopy image of the MIL-53(Al) monolith-based capillary it-SPME device [123]. One of the most important factors to optimize in this kind of devices is the amount of MOF in the monolith. If large amounts of MOF are used, the monolith structure would be more compact, thus making the diffusion of the sample and solvents difficult (and in turns resulting in a decreasing of the extraction efficiency of the final device) [123].

Regarding the ZIF-8-based it-SPME device proposed by Ling and Chen [124], it consisted of a fiber-packed capillary. In this case, the incorporation of the MOF requires an electrodeposition step followed by an in-situ crystal growth. The general procedure starts by using a strong acid and a base in order to activate the surface of carbon fibers (bundle of 13 cm). Then, the electrodeposition of ZnO takes places by immersing the carbon fibers (as the working electrode on a three-electrodes system) in a solution of zinc nitrate. The deposition of the oxide takes places by cyclic voltammetry. Once the ZnO is formed all over the surface of the fibers, the cyclic voltammetry is stopped, and the fibers bundle is washed and heated at 100 °C to ensure the immobilization of the oxide. This strategy renders supported ZnO crystals of 30–80 nm. Consecutively, the solvothermal synthesis ensures the growth of the MOF ZIF-8 by immersing the ZnO-based carbon fibers bundle into a solution of the organic linker under adequate growing conditions, followed by packing it in a polyetheretherketone (PEEK) tube. The analytical applications involved the determination of Sudan dyes in environmental waters [124].

6. MOFs in Thin-Film Solid-Phase Microextraction (tf-SPME)

While it is clear that the enlargement of the thickness of the sorbent material in f-SPME devices implies an increase on the amount of extracted analyte, it also comes with long extraction times to reach the equilibrium due to the radial diffusion of the analytes [41]. Thin film solid-phase microextraction (tf-SPME) appears as a solution to increase the sensitivity (using larger sorbent amounts) without increasing the extraction time. Wilcockson and Gobas were the first to propose the tf-SPME configuration [125]. This first device consisted of a glass coverslip coated with a 0.33 μm thin film of ethylene vinyl acetate (acting as sorbent coating). The device was tested in the analysis of toxic organic chemicals in aqueous extracts of fish samples.

In tf-SPME, the sorbent material covers the surface of a flat material or forms a free membrane with a reduced thickness, with the increasing amount of sorbent being related to the extension of the surface, thus maintaining a high surface area to volume ratio. In this mode, higher sensitivities can be reached given the increased amount of sorbent but requiring shorter times (similar to those of f-SPME) because there are no extra difficulties in diffusion (same as those in f-SPME) [126,127].

The main challenge for the different sampling formats of tf-SPME is to avoid film folding. Among formats, it is possible to cite free-membrane, stainless steel rods, cotter pin, and mess holder configurations. Furthermore, it is possible to automate this extraction technique using 96-blades, which is a variety of the commercial 96-well plates system [128]. Figure 7A shows the main tf-SPME devices configurations.

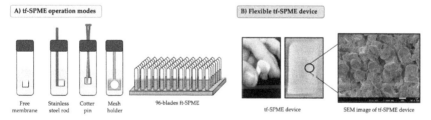

Figure 7. (**A**) Different tf-SPME sampling formats reported. (**B**) An example of MOFs incorporated in a flexible tf-SPME device. Adapted from [50], with permission from Elsevier, 2018.

It is possible to distinguish two different kind of tf-SPME devices attending to their thermal stability: thermostable and non-thermostable films. Thermostable films can be coupled to a temperature desorption unit and directly injected in the GC. As disadvantage, there is a limited number of thermostable films reported in the literature and most of them are the same as the polymeric coatings used in conventional f-SPME. Regarding thermo-labile films, they are used in solvent-assisted desorption applications (implying longer sample preparation times due to the slower diffusion of the analytes in the liquid phase). In addition, the increased size of the device requires the use of higher amounts of eluent solvent (in turn requiring a final step of solvent removal and reconstitution) [45].

The tf-SPME modality recently benefited from the introduction of MOFs. The preparation of MOF-based tf-SPME is easier than other SPME configurations because the increased surface facilitates the MOF growing.

MOFs reported in tf-SPME devices include MIL-53(Al) [50] and ZIF-67(Co) [129]. Other MOFs studied as sorbent material in tf-SPME are UiO-66(Zr), MIL-53(Fe), MIL-100(Fe), MIL-101(Cr), and ZIF-8(Zn) but presented worse analytical performance when compared with the abovementioned MOFs [50]. There are other thin films incorporating MOFs reported in the literature, but they are used as sorbent material in μ-SPE applications instead of tf-SPME strictly [130–133]. Figure 7B shows an example of a MOF-based tf-SPME device.

In the case of MIL-53(Al), it is incorporated in the thin-films by embedding the MOF (previously synthetized) in a polymer. This method involves the dispersion of the MOF in a volatile solvent (i.e., acetone), and addition of such suspension to a polyvinylidene difluoride (PVDF) solution in dimethylformamide under sonication to ensure homogeneity. Then, the volatile solvent is evaporated, and a dense ink is obtained [50]. The bar coating technique forms the thin film by spreading the ink over a surface. It requires an applicator with an adjustable gap to control the thickness of the film [45], followed by the aging of the film and solvent removal to ensure solidification of the film. The final shape of the tf-SPME device can be easily modulated by proper cutting of the solid membrane obtained. These composites combine the flexibility of the polymers and the high porosity offered by MOFs. The amount of MOF powder cannot be extremely high into the film because it becomes more fragile and flakier. The highest charge reported for a MOF into a membrane for tf-SPME application is 67% (w/w) [50].

Recently, Mohammadi et al. have proposed a method that combines electrospinning and the in-situ solvothermal growth to prepare a ZIF-67(Co)-based tf-SPME device [129]. The electrospinning implies forming a composite of polyacrylonitrile and Co_3O_4 nanofibers. By heating, the polyacrylonitrile suffers calcination and the polymer is removed from the film structure. Afterwards, this film gets in contact with the organic linker required for the preparation of the ZIF-67(Co) (2-methylimidazole) at adequate conditions to ensure formation of the nanofibers. The main advantage of this method is that the MOF is self-supported without the use of a mesh or a polymer, but still being a flexible membrane.

Regarding the applicability of the MOF-based tf-SPME devices, just the self-supported ZIF-67(Co) film permitted a thermal desorption. In this last case, the application was the determination of pesticides [129]. In terms of analytical performance, they present adequate intra- and inter-device precision, with reported relative standard deviation values lower than 11.4%. Samples analyzed include water [129] and biological fluids [50], for the determination of estrogens [50] and pesticides [129]. Table ?? recaps a representative study of tf-SPME using MOFs as sorbents.

7. MOFs in Stir-Bar (sb-SPME) and Stir-Cake Solid-Phase Microextraction (sc-SPME)

Baltussen et al. introduced the stir-bar solid-phase microextraction (sb-SPME) configuration as an alternative to conventional f-SPME, particularly useful for compounds with low octanol/water partitioning coefficient (non-polar compounds) [134]. The device consisted of a magnetic stir bar coated with PDMS. The sample is stirred with the bar at an adequate agitation rate. The bar is removed after proper extraction time, and a direct thermal desorption step takes place in a specific GC injection port called thermal desorption unit. In this configuration, part of the sorbent is in contact with the bottom of the sample container thus blocking possible interactions between the analytes and a portion of the extractant material. Stir-cake solid-phase microextraction (sc-SPME) emerged as a solution to this problem. The sorbent (in general a monolith) is located in a cylindrical device avoiding the contact between the sorbent and the bottom of the vessels thus improving the entire extraction efficiency [135,136].

Both configurations follow the same extraction fundamentals as conventional SPME. However, the amount of the sorbent material in both modes sb-SPME and sc-SPME are ~50–200 times bigger than the amount used in conventional f-SPME, thus permitting increasing the extraction capacity towards target analytes [137], but also increasing the extraction time.

Currently, there are only two commercially available sb-SPME devices distributed by Gerstel: one coated with PDMS and the other with a PDMS/ethylene glycol copolymer [138]. Although these coatings possess many merits such as high sensitivity and good reproducibility, they also have low selectivity and require long extraction times to reach the equilibrium conditions. In addition, recoveries for polar compounds are poor due to the non-polar nature of the sorbent, being necessary a derivatization step for their extraction. Given these drawbacks, recent developments of sb-SPME devices focus on the development of more selective coatings with faster extraction kinetics, with MOFs not being an exception [46].

MOFs used as sorbents in sb-SPME include IRMOF-3(Zn) [73], MIL-53(Al)-NH$_2$ [74], MOF-5(Zn and Fe) [75,139], ZIF-8 [140], MIL-101(Cr) and its amino functionalized version [48,141], MIL-68(Al) [142], ZIF-67(Co) [143], and UiO-66-NH$_2$ [76].

The main procedure followed to incorporate MOFs in sb-SPME devices is the sol–gel approach. The devices prepared by this procedure have three components: an iron wire or metallic rod of ~1–3 cm length, a glass jacket, and the sorbent. The iron wire or metallic rod is the responsible of the agitation under the magnetic field while the glass jacket isolates the metallic wire form the water sample, avoiding its corrosion. The glass jacket also offers a homogeneous tunable surface for the immobilization of the coating when immersing the bar into the sol–gel solution containing the MOF dispersed into a polymeric solution. Then, the device is removed from the sol–gel solution and the self-assembly of the coating finishes by heating [48,73,74].

An alternative to sol–gel is the synthesis of monoliths by polymerization. The general procedure implies filling a template with a pre-polymeric solution (containing the MOF powder dispersed or its precursors), polymerization, removal of the template, and a final wash to clean the monolith [76,140,141]. Thus, the shape and dimension of the devices depends on the template and not on the support. Even the use a support is not required if magnetic nanoparticles are dispersed in the pre-polymeric suspension [76]. Recently, Du et al. took advantage of this strategy for the preparation of the first MOF-based sc-SPME device by dispersing Fe$_3$O$_4$@HKUST-1 core–shell particles in a pre-polymeric solution of 2-ethylhexylacrylate/divinylbenzene/methyl methacrylate [52]. Although the MOF composite monolith does not utilize a classical sc-SPME support, its visual geometry and shape resembles that of the classical sc-SPME device.

Another option is the in-situ solvothermal growth of the crystals onto other type of supports. Hu et al. used this strategy with a porous copper foam as support. The foam immersed in the solution containing the precursors of MOF-5(Zn) and, after impregnation, the support and the solution are set on the Teflon-lined autoclave, which is heated to form the MOF [139]. In this case, the sb-SPME device is used in the HS mode and using a lab-made rotor to stir the device. As the direct growth of crystals over the support surface is not easy in terms of ensuring homogeneity, a similar approach to ALD strategy has been used, promoting the crystal growth out of the metal nanoparticles previously electrodeposited all over the surface of the support [143]. The main disadvantage of these devices is the weak union MOF-support. The friction between the stir bar and the sample container causes a progressive loose of the MOFs, thus reducing the lifetime of the device. Wang et al. developed the use of a dumbbell-shaped PEEK jacket to improve the mechanical strength. However, PEEK material is a highly inert material, requiring several aggressive pretreatment steps to obtain an activate surface before the in-situ growth [142].

Paradoxically, although the main attractive property of MOFs in this configuration is their thermal stability to perform direct thermal desorption, most of the studies published used a solvent desorption followed by LC [73,74,76,141–143].

8. Comparison with Other MOF-Based Extraction Methods

The number of studies that report the use of MOFs as extraction sorbents in µ-dSPE, m-µ-dSPE, and SPME (in all their variations), is similar. The reason behind the selection of any of these solid-phase strategies over others relies on the specific requirements for a certain application. Therefore, it is difficult to compare the analytical performance and features of the different solid-based extraction methods using MOFs from a generic point of view.

Trying to establish certain parallelism, specific analytical applications have been targeted with the intended comparison purpose. Thus, Table 2 includes some operational characteristics and analytical parameters of different solid-based extraction methods using MOFs for two representative applications: the determination of pesticides (including organochlorine and organophosphorus pesticides) and drugs (covering antibiotics and anti-inflammatory drugs) in waters [48,65,72,78,129,141,144–147]. These specific applications were selected for being those most commonly reported in the literature using the different SPME devices discussed in the present review article. It is important to highlight that the MOF used in each study is different (with MIL-101(Cr) and HKUST-1 the most used) and, therefore, the comparison of analytical performance must be taken into account only in a qualitative manner. In the same manner, the limit of detection (LOD) is not a reliable parameter to compare the proposed methods due to the variety of detection systems used in the selected applications, which present different selectivity and sensitivity towards the target analytes (not the same MS versus UV in terms of LOD). To sum up, LODs are not always calculated in the same manner by the different authors.

In any case, an important (if not main) advantage of the SPME approach over the remaining solid-based extraction methods lies in the extremely low amount of MOF used for the preparation of the SPME devices, which also provides impressive enrichment factors. MOFs amounts between 0.5 [145] and 40 mg [144,146] have been reported for µ-SPE, µ-dSPE, and m-µ-dSPE methods, while in the case of SPME, depending on the size of the device (length and thickness of the coatings), the maximum volume of sorbent used is around 2 µL. As for the volume of sample required, small volumes (10 mL as average) are required in all cases except for µ-SPE, for which a volume of 60 mL of water sample is needed to reach low LODs for the determination of drugs in waters, and this is despite the use of LC-MS/MS [146].

Regarding the operational features of each extraction method, it is worth mentioning the simplicity of the SPME approaches. The extraction procedure in these cases is accomplished in two steps: the extraction and the desorption. µ-SPE, µ-dSPE, and m-µ-dSPE strategies require more tedious and laborious steps during the process, such as washings, decantation, or centrifugation and filtration. Moreover, practically in all of the studies using non-SPME strategies, the desorption of the analytes from the MOF is accomplished using a solvent, which is then evaporated followed by reconstitution to ensure preconcentration and compatibility with the analytical system. The increasing number of steps is a potential source of errors, and the use of organic solvents is still required in the analysis, leading to environmental issues. SPME devices easily couple to GC systems (thermal desorption), thus permitting the development of greener methods [65,129].

As it can be also observed in Table 2, the extraction methods dealing with SPME devices require longer extraction times to reach similar results than those obtained with the other approaches. However, as it was mentioned before, the SPME extraction process involves only two steps, which is still simpler than µ-SPE or µ-dSPE methods despite their possibly being faster. Given this simplicity, the automation of SPME regardless of the configuration of the device has been already reported for many applications. In any case, the greatest appeal of SPME is the reusability of the extraction device, which is never recommended for µ-SPE [146] and has been barely proven for µ-dSPE applications [144]. All these facts contribute to reduce the costs of the analysis per sample in the case of SPME.

Table 2. Analytical performance of MOF-based SPME devices compared with other MOF-based solid-phase extraction methods for two representative applications.

Extraction Method*	MOF	Amount of Sorbent ^{a}	Volume of Sample	Desorption	Additional Steps	Extraction Time	Reuse of the Sorbent/Device	Analytical Technique*	LOD (ng·L^{-1})	Ref.
Analytical application 1: determination of pesticides in waters										
μ-dSPE	UiO-66(Zr)	40 mg	5 mL	liquid (1 mL acetone)	centrifugation, evaporation and reconstitution	~20 min	10 times	LC-MS/MS	20–400	[144]
m-μ-dSPE	ZIF-8(Zn)	0.5 mg	10 mL	liquid (1 mL methanol)	evaporation and reconstitution	~45 min	No	LC-MS/MS	0.19–1.20	[145]
f-SPME (HS mode)	HKUST-1(Cu)	– × ~0 μm	25 mL	thermal (280 °C)	–	~45 min	140 times	GC-ECD	2.8–6.9	[65]
tf-SPME	ZIF-67(Zn)	1 cm × 80 μm	15 mL	thermal (220 °C)	–	~22 min	No	SESI/MS	100	[129]
sb-SPME	MIL-101-NH$_2$(Cr)	2 cm × 100 μm	10 mL	liquid (50 μL acetone)	–	~35 min	50 times	GC-FPD	43–85	[48]
Analytical application 2: determination of drugs in waters										
μ-SPE	MIL-101(Cr)	40 mg	60 mL	liquid (4 mL methanol)	evaporation and reconstitution	~60 min	No	LC-MS/MS	30–80	[146]
m-μ-dSPE	MIL-101(Cr)	30 mg	50 mL	liquid (200 μL acetonitrile)	evaporation and reconstitution	~30 min	No	LC-MS/MS	3–60	[147]
f-SPME (HS mode)	HKUST-1(Cu)	1 cm × 30 μm	5 mL	liquid (2 mL acetonitrile:H$_2$O 1:1)	evaporation and reconstitution	~60 min	110 times	LC-UV-Vis	30–50	[78]
it-SPME	MIL-101(Cr)	3 cm × –	2 mL	liquid (200 μL methanol)	–	~35 min	45 times	CEC-UV-Vis	1200–4500	[72]
sb-SPME	MIL-101(Cr)	1 cm × –	10 mL	liquid (1 mL acetonitrile)	evaporation and reconstitution	~80 min	4 times	LC-MS/MS	11–35	[141]

^{a} amount of MOF in mg in the case of miniaturized solid-based extraction methods, and size of the device in the case of SPME methods. * for the definition of the abbreviations, refer to the list of abbreviations at the end of the article.

In summary, SPME (in all configurations) with MOF-based coatings is a promising alternative among reported solid-based extraction methods for routine analysis given the following advantages: high enrichment factors, the possibility of tuning the MOF for a certain application, the reduced number of steps in the process, and the possibility of reusing the device (up to more than 100 times in some cases) together with the ease of automation for the entire procedure (from the introduction of the device in the sample to the desorption or injection in the analytical system).

9. Concluding Remarks

The success of SPME methods within analytical laboratories is evident nowadays, given advantages such as the simplicity of its operation and the high sensitivity and preconcentration achieved due to the design of the different SPME devices. Considering the outstanding properties of MOFs—such as synthetic tunability, versatility, high chemical and thermal stability of MOFs, and impressive surface area—together with the advances on the different synthetic and deposition routes to prepare MOFs and MOF-coated surfaces, the increasing number of applications of MOFs in the SPME field is not surprising. Indeed, we foresee a rise in their applicability in a variety of SPME devices in the years to come. In any case, more efforts are still required within the MOFs-analytical community to have MOFs as any common extraction sorbent in analytical chemistry laboratories. Among them: scalable processes to ensure the production of high amounts of MOFs, the need of increasing research on green MOFs and greener ways to prepare MOFs, together with increasing studies with comparison of performance with other sorbents and with conventional (micro) extraction methods.

Funding: This research was funded by the Spanish Ministry of Economy, Industry and Competitiveness grant number MAT2017-89207-R.

Acknowledgments: A.G.-S. and I.P.-F. thank Agencia Canaria de Investigación, Innovación y Sociedad de la Información (ACIISI), co-funded by the European Social Fund, for their FPI PhD fellowships. J.P. thanks the "Agustín de Betancourt" Canary Program for his research associate position at ULL.

Conflicts of Interest: The authors declare no conflict of interest.

Abbreviations

af-SPME	arrow fiber solid-phase microextraction
ALD	atomic layer deposition
BMA-EDMA	butyl methacrylate-ethylene dimethacrylate
CE	capillary electrophoresis
CEC	capillary electrochromatography
d-μ-SPE	dispersive solid-phase microextraction
DAD	diode array detection
DI	direct immersion
ECD	electron capture detection
f-SPME	on-fiber solid-phase microextraction
FID	flame ionization detection
GC	gas chromatography
FPD	flame photometric detection
HS	headspace
IL	ionic liquid
IRMOF	isoreticular metal–organic framework
it-SPME	in-tube solid-phase microextraction
LC	liquid chromatography
LOD	limit of detection
m-d-μ-SPE	magnetic-assisted miniaturized solid-phase extraction
MIP	molecularly imprinted polymer
MNP	magnetic nanoparticle

MOF	metal–organic framework
MS	mass spectrometry
MS/MS	tandem mass spectrometry
OCP	organochlorine pesticide
OPP	organophosphorus pesticide
PAH	polycyclic aromatic hydrocarbon
PAN	polyacrylonitrile
PCB	polychlorinated biphenyl
PDMS	polydimethylsiloxane
PEEK	polyetheretherketone
PS	polystyrene
PVC	polyvinylchloride
PVDF	polyvinylidene difluoride
sb-SPME	stir-bar solid-phase microextraction
SBU	secondary building unit
sc-SPME	stir-cake solid-phase microextraction
SESI	secondary electrospray ionization
SPME	solid-phase microextraction
tf-SPME	thin-film solid-phase microextraction
μ-SPE	miniaturized solid-phase extraction

References

1. Rowsell, J.L.C.; Yaghi, O.M. Metal-Organic Frameworks: A New Class of Porous Materials. *Microporous Mesoporous Mater.* **2004**, *73*, 3–14. [CrossRef]
2. Schneemann, A.; Bon, V.; Schwedler, I.; Senkovska, I.; Kaskel, S.; Fischer, R.A. Flexible Metal-Organic Frameworks. *Chem. Soc. Rev.* **2014**, *43*, 6062–6096. [CrossRef] [PubMed]
3. Safaei, M.; Foroughi, M.M.; Ebrahimpoor, N.; Jahani, S.; Omidi, A.; Khatami, M. A Review on Metal-Organic Frameworks: Synthesis and Applications. *Trends Anal. Chem.* **2019**, *118*, 401–425. [CrossRef]
4. Kalmutzki, M.J.; Hanikel, N.; Yaghi, O.M. Secondary Building Units as the Turning Point in the Development of the Reticular Chemistry of MOFs. *Sci. Adv.* **2018**, *4*, 1–16. [CrossRef] [PubMed]
5. Yaghi, O.M. Reticular Chemistry—Construction, Properties, and Precision Reactions of Frameworks. *J. Am. Chem. Soc.* **2016**, *138*, 15507–15509. [CrossRef]
6. Eddaoudi, M.; Kim, J.; Rosi, N.; Vodak, D.; Wachter, J.; O'Keeffe, M.; Yaghi, O.M. Systematic Design of Pore Size and Functionality in Isoreticular MOFs and Their Application in Methane Storage. *Science* **2002**, *295*, 469–472. [CrossRef]
7. The Cambridge Crystallographic Data Center (CCDC). Available online: https://www.ccdc.cam.ac.uk/ (accessed on 25 July 2019).
8. Millange, F.; Serre, C. Synthesis, Structure Determination and Properties of MIL-53as and MIL-53ht: The First Cr^{III} Hybrid Inorganic—Organic Microporous Solids: $Cr^{III}(OH)\cdot\{O_2C–C_6H_4–CO_2\}\cdot\{HO_2C–C_6H_4–CO_2H\}_x$. *Chem. Commun.* **2002**, *8*, 822–823. [CrossRef]
9. Chui, S.S.Y.; Lo, S.M.F.; Charmant, J.P.H.; Orpen, A.G.; Williams, I.D. A Chemically Functionalizable Nanoporous Material $[Cu_3(TMA)_2 (H_2O)_3](N)$. *Science* **1999**, *283*, 1148–1150. [CrossRef]
10. Akporiayer, D.E.; Fjellvag, H.; Halvorsen, E.N.; Hustveit, J.; Karlsson, A.; Lillerud, K.P. The synthesis and structure solution of UiO-7, a new molecular sieve. *Chem. Commun.* **1996**, *5*, 601–602. [CrossRef]
11. Rocío-Bautista, P.; Pino, V.; Ayala, J.H.; Ruiz-Pérez, C.; Vallcorba, O.; Afonso, A.M.; Pasán, J. A Green Metal-Organic Framework to Monitor Water Contaminants. *RSC Adv.* **2018**, *8*, 31304–31310. [CrossRef]
12. Küsgens, P.; Rose, M.; Senkovska, I.; Fröde, H.; Henschel, A.; Siegle, S.; Kaskel, S. Characterization of Metal-Organic Frameworks by Water Adsorption. *Microporous Mesoporous Mater.* **2009**, *120*, 325–330. [CrossRef]
13. Tian, Y.; Cai, C.; Ji, Y.; You, X.; Peng, S.; Lee, G. $[Co_5(im)_{10}\cdot2MB]_\infty$: A Metal-Organic Open.Framework with Zeolite-Like Topology. *Angew. Chem.* **2002**, *114*, 1442–1444. [CrossRef]

14. Feng, D.; Gu, Z.Y.; Li, J.R.; Jiang, H.L.; Wei, Z.; Zhou, H.C. Zirconium-Metalloporphyrin PCN-222: Mesoporous Metal-Organic Frameworks with Ultrahigh Stability as Biomimetic Catalysts. *Angew. Chem. Int. Ed.* **2012**, *51*, 10307–10310. [CrossRef] [PubMed]

15. Julien, P.A.; Mottillo, C.; Friščić, T. Metal-Organic Frameworks Meet Scalable and Sustainable Synthesis. *Green Chem.* **2017**, *19*, 2729–2747. [CrossRef]

16. Ding, L.; Yazaydin, A.O. Hydrogen and Methane Storage in Ultrahigh Surface Area Metal-Organic Frameworks. *Microporous Mesoporous Mater.* **2013**, *182*, 185–190. [CrossRef]

17. Hönicke, I.M.; Senkovska, I.; Bon, V.; Baburin, I.A.; Bönisch, N.; Raschke, S.; Evans, J.D.; Kaskel, S. Balancing Mechanical Stability and Ultrahigh Porosity in Crystalline Framework Materials. *Angew. Chem. Int. Ed.* **2018**, *57*, 13780–13783. [CrossRef]

18. Howarth, A.J.; Peters, A.W.; Vermeulen, N.A.; Wang, T.C.; Hupp, J.T.; Farha, O.K. Best Practices for the Synthesis, Activation, and Characterization of Metal–organic Frameworks. *Chem. Mater.* **2017**, *29*, 26–39. [CrossRef]

19. Xue, D.X.; Wang, Q.; Bai, J. Amide-Functionalized Metal–Organic Frameworks: Syntheses, Structures and Improved Gas Storage and Separation Properties. *Coord. Chem. Rev.* **2019**, *378*, 2–16. [CrossRef]

20. Xu, C.; Fang, R.; Luque, R.; Chen, L.; Li, Y. Functional Metal–Organic Frameworks for Catalytic Applications. *Coord. Chem. Rev.* **2019**, *388*, 268–292. [CrossRef]

21. Anik, Ü.; Timur, S.; Dursun, Z. Metal Organic Frameworks in Electrochemical and Optical Sensing Platforms: A Review. *Microchim. Acta* **2019**, *186*, 18–24. [CrossRef]

22. He, L.; Liu, Y.; Lau, J.; Fan, W.; Li, Q.; Zhang, C.; Huang, P.; Chen, X. Recent Progress in Nanoscale Metal-Organic Frameworks for Drug Release and Cancer Therapy. *Nanomedicine* **2019**, *14*, 1343–1365. [CrossRef] [PubMed]

23. Mehtab, T.; Yasin, G.; Arif, M.; Shakeel, M.; Korai, R.M.; Nadeem, M.; Muhammad, N.; Lu, X. Metal-Organic Frameworks for Energy Storage Devices: Batteries and Supercapacitors. *J. Energy Storage* **2019**, *21*, 632–646. [CrossRef]

24. Rocío-Bautista, P.; Termopoli, V. Metal–Organic Frameworks in Solid-Phase Extraction Procedures for Environmental and Food Analyses. *Chromatographia* **2019**, *82*, 1191–1205. [CrossRef]

25. Rocío-Bautista, P.; González-Hernández, P.; Pino, V.; Pasán, J.; Afonso, A.M. Metal-Organic Frameworks as Novel Sorbents in Dispersive-Based Microextraction Approaches. *Trends Anal. Chem.* **2017**, *90*, 114–134. [CrossRef]

26. González-Hernández, P.; Gutiérrez-Serpa, A.; Rocío-Bautista, P.; Pasán, J.; Ayala, J.H.; Pino, V. Micro-solid Phase Extraction using MOFs. In *Metal Organic Frameworks*; Mittal, V., Ed.; Central West Publishing: Orange, Australia, 2019; pp. 99–136.

27. Pacheco-Fernández, I.; González-Hernández, P.; Pasán, J.; Ayala, J.H.; Pino, V. The Rise of Metal–Organic Frameworks in Analytical Chemistry. In *Handbook of Smart Materials in Analytical Chemistry*; De la Guardia, M., Esteve-Turrillas, F.A., Eds.; John Wiley & Sons Inc.: Hoboken, NJ, USA, 2019; pp. 463–502.

28. Maya, F.; Palomino Cabello, C.; Figuerola, A.; Turnes Palomino, G.; Cerdà, V. (Eds.) Immobilization of Metal–Organic Frameworks on Supports for Sample Preparation and Chromatographic Separation. *Chromatographia* **2019**, *82*, 361–375.

29. Liang, Y.; Zhang, L.; Zhang, Y. Well-Defined Materials for Chromatographic Separation. *Annu. Rev. Anal. Chem.* **2019**, *12*, 451–473. [CrossRef]

30. Faraji, M.; Yamini, Y.; Gholami, M. Recent Advances and Trends in Applications of Solid-Phase Extraction Techniques in Food and Environmental Analysis. *Chromatographia* **2019**, *82*, 1207–1249. [CrossRef]

31. Maya, F.; Palomino Cabello, C.; Frizzarin, R.M.; Estela, J.M.; Turnes Palomino, G.; Cerdà, V. Magnetic Solid-Phase Extraction Using Metal-Organic Frameworks (MOFs) and Their Derived Carbons. *Trends Anal. Chem.* **2017**, *90*, 142–152. [CrossRef]

32. Rocío-Bautista, P.; Pacheco-Fernández, I.; Pasán, J.; Pino, V. Are Metal-Organic Frameworks Able to Provide a New Generation of Solid-Phase Microextraction Coatings?—A Review. *Anal. Chim. Acta* **2016**, *939*, 26–41. [CrossRef]

33. Li, X.; Ma, W.; Li, H.; Bai, Y.; Liu, H. Metal-Organic Frameworks as Advanced Sorbents in Sample Preparation for Small Organic Analytes. *Coord. Chem. Rev.* **2019**, *397*, 1–13. [CrossRef]

34. Rocío-Bautista, P.; Taima-Mancera, I.; Pasán, J.; Pino, V. Metal-Organic Frameworks in Green Analytical Chemistry. *Separations* **2019**, *6*, 33. [CrossRef]

35. Zhou, Y.Y.; Yan, X.P.; Kim, K.N.; Wang, S.W.; Liu, M.G. Exploration of Coordination Polymer as Sorbent for Flow Injection Solid-Phase Extraction on-Line Coupled with High-Performance Liquid Chromatography for Determination of Polycyclic Aromatic Hydrocarbons in Environmental Materials. *J. Chromatogr. A* **2006**, *1116*, 172–178. [CrossRef] [PubMed]

36. Yang, X.Q.; Yang, C.X.; Yan, X.P. Zeolite Imidazolate Framework-8 as Sorbent for on-Line Solid-Phase Extraction Coupled with High-Performance Liquid Chromatography for the Determination of Tetracyclines in Water and Milk Samples. *J. Chromatogr. A* **2013**, *1304*, 28–33. [CrossRef] [PubMed]

37. Yang, S.; Chen, C.; Yan, Z.; Cai, Q.; Yao, S. Evaluation of metal-organic framework 5 as a new SPE material for the determination of polycyclic aromatic hydrocarbons in environmental waters. *J. Sep. Sci.* **2013**, *36*, 1283–1290. [CrossRef]

38. Ge, D.; Lee, H.K. Sonication-Assisted Emulsification Microextraction Combined with Vortex-Assisted Porous Membrane-Protected Micro-Solid-Phase Extraction Using Mixed Zeolitic Imidazolate Frameworks 8 as Sorbent. *J. Chromatogr. A* **2012**, *1263*, 1–6. [CrossRef]

39. Hashemi, B.; Zohrabi, P.; Raza, N.; Kim, K.H. Metal-Organic Frameworks as Advanced Sorbents for the Extraction and Determination of Pollutants from Environmental, Biological, and Food Media. *Trends Anal. Chem.* **2017**, *97*, 65–82. [CrossRef]

40. Arthur, C.L.; Pawliszyn, J. Solid Phase Microextraction with Thermal Desorption Using Fused Silica Optical Fibers. *Anal. Chem.* **1990**, *62*, 2145–2148. [CrossRef]

41. Piri-Moghadam, H.; Alam, M.N.; Pawliszyn, J. Review of Geometries and Coating Materials in Solid Phase Microextraction: Opportunities, Limitations, and Future Perspectives. *Anal. Chim. Acta* **2017**, *984*, 42–65. [CrossRef]

42. Lashgari, M.; Yamini, Y. An Overview of the Most Common Lab-Made Coating Materials in Solid Phase Microextraction. *Talanta* **2019**, *191*, 283–306. [CrossRef]

43. Helin, A.; Rönkkö, T.; Parshintsev, J.; Hartonen, K.; Schilling, B.; Läubli, T.; Riekkola, M.L. Solid Phase Microextraction Arrow for the Sampling of Volatile Amines in Wastewater and Atmosphere. *J. Chromatogr. A* **2015**, *1426*, 56–63. [CrossRef]

44. Costa Queiroz, M.E.; Donizeti de Souza, I.; Marchioni, C. Current Advances and Applications of In-Tube Solid-Phase Microextraction. *Trends Anal. Chem.* **2019**, *111*, 261–278. [CrossRef]

45. Olcer, Y.A.; Tascon, M.; Eroglu, A.E.; Boyacı, E. Thin Film Microextraction: Towards Faster and More Sensitive Microextraction. *Trends Anal. Chem.* **2019**, *113*, 93–101. [CrossRef]

46. David, F.; Ochiai, N.; Sandra, P. Two Decades of Stir Bar Sorptive Extraction: A Retrospective and Future Outlook. *Trends Anal. Chem.* **2019**, *112*, 102–111. [CrossRef]

47. Niu, J.; Li, Z.; Yang, H.; Ye, C.; Chen, C.; Li, D.; Xu, J.; Fan, L. A Water Resistant Solid-Phase Microextraction Fiber with High Selectivity Prepared by a Metal Organic Framework with Perfluorinated Pores. *J. Chromatogr. A* **2016**, *1441*, 16–23. [CrossRef]

48. Xiao, Z.; He, M.; Chen, B.; Hu, B. Polydimethylsiloxane/Metal-Organic Frameworks Coated Stir Bar Sorptive Extraction Coupled to Gas Chromatography-Flame Photometric Detection for the Determination of Organophosphorus Pesticides in Environmental Water Samples. *Talanta* **2016**, *156–157*, 126–133. [CrossRef]

49. Shih, Y.H.; Wang, K.Y.; Singco, B.; Lin, C.H.; Huang, H.Y. Metal-Organic Framework-Polymer Composite as a Highly Efficient Sorbent for Sulfonamide Adsorption and Desorption: Effect of Coordinatively Unsaturated Metal Site and Topology. *Langmuir* **2016**, *32*, 11465–11473. [CrossRef]

50. Gao, G.; Li, S.; Li, S.; Zhao, L.; Wang, T.; Hou, X. Development and application of vortex-assisted membrane extraction based on metal-organic framework mixed-matrix membrane for the analysis of estrogens in human urine. *Anal. Chim. Acta* **2018**, *1023*, 35–43. [CrossRef]

51. Lan, H.; Rönkkö, T.; Parshintsev, J.; Hartonen, K.; Gan, N.; Sakeye, M.; Sarfraz, J.; Riekkola, M.L. Modified Zeolitic Imidazolate Framework-8 as Solid-Phase Microextraction Arrow Coating for Sampling of Amines in Wastewater and Food Samples Followed by Gas Chromatography-Mass Spectrometry. *J. Chromatogr. A* **2017**, *1486*, 76–85. [CrossRef]

52. Du, F.; Sun, L.; Tan, W.; Wei, Z.; Nie, H.; Huang, Z.; Ruan, G.; Li, J. Magnetic Stir Cake Sorptive Extraction of Trace Tetracycline Antibiotics in Food Samples: Preparation of Metal–Organic Framework-Embedded PolyHIPE Monolithic Composites, Validation and Application. *Anal. Bioanal. Chem.* **2019**, *411*, 2239–2248. [CrossRef]

53. Merck Group SPME Fiber Assemblies. Available online: https://www.sigmaaldrich.com/analytical-chromatography/analytical-products.html?TablePage=9645337 (accessed on 25 July 2019).

54. Restek PAL SPME Fibers. Product Details. Available online: https://www.restek.com/catalog/view/47352 (accessed on 25 July 2019).

55. Shirey, R.E. SPME Commercial Devices and Fibre Coatings. In *Handbook of Solid Phase Microextraction*; Pawliszyn, J., Ed.; Elsevier Inc.: Amsterdam, The Netherlands, 2012; pp. 99–133.

56. Souza-Silva, É.A.; Gionfriddo, E.; Pawliszyn, J. A Critical Review of the State of the Art of Solid-Phase Microextraction of Complex Matrices I. Environmental Analysis. *Trends Anal. Chem.* **2015**, *71*, 224–235. [CrossRef]

57. Souza-Silva, É.A.; Gionfriddo, E.; Pawliszyn, J. A Critical Review of the State of the Art of Solid-Phase Microextraction of Complex Matrices II. Food Analysis. *Trends Anal. Chem.* **2015**, *71*, 236–248. [CrossRef]

58. Souza-Silva, É.A.; Reyes-Garcés, N.; Gómez-Ríos, G.A.; Boyaci, E.; Bojko, B.; Pawliszyn, J. A Critical Review of the State of the Art of Solid-Phase Microextraction of Complex Matrices III. Bioanalytical and Clinical Applications. *Trends Anal. Chem.* **2015**, *71*, 249–264. [CrossRef]

59. USEPA (U.S. Environmental Protection Agency). *Method 8272, 2007*; EPA: Washington, DC, USA, 2007.

60. American Society for Testing and Materials. *D 6438, 2005*; EPA: Washington, DC, USA, 2005.

61. Cui, X.Y.; Gu, Z.Y.; Jiang, D.Q.; Li, Y.; Wang, H.F.; Yan, X.P. In Situ Hydrothermal Growth of Metal-Organic Framework 199 Films on Stainless Steel Fibers for Solid-Phase Microextraction of Gaseous Benzene Homologues. *Anal. Chem.* **2009**, *81*, 9771–9777. [CrossRef] [PubMed]

62. Gao, J.; Huang, C.; Lin, Y.; Tong, P.; Zhang, L. In Situ Solvothermal Synthesis of Metal-Organic Framework Coated Fiber for Highly Sensitive Solid-Phase Microextraction of Polycyclic Aromatic Hydrocarbons. *J. Chromatogr. A* **2016**, *1436*, 1–8. [CrossRef] [PubMed]

63. Zhang, N.; Huang, C.; Feng, Z.; Chen, H.; Tong, P.; Wu, X.; Zhang, L. Metal-Organic Framework-Coated Stainless Steel Fiber for Solid-Phase Microextraction of Polychlorinated Biphenyls. *J. Chromatogr. A* **2018**, *1570*, 10–18. [CrossRef] [PubMed]

64. Lan, H.; Pan, D.; Sun, Y.; Guo, Y.; Wu, Z. Thin Metal Organic Frameworks Coatings by Cathodic Electrodeposition for Solid-Phase Microextraction and Analysis of Trace Exogenous Estrogens in Milk. *Anal. Chim. Acta* **2016**, *937*, 53–60. [CrossRef]

65. Zhang, S.; Du, Z.; Li, G. Metal-Organic Framework-199/Graphite Oxide Hybrid Composites Coated Solid-Phase Microextraction Fibers Coupled with Gas Chromatography for Determination of Organochlorine Pesticides from Complicated Samples. *Talanta* **2013**, *115*, 32–39. [CrossRef]

66. Chen, X.F.; Zang, H.; Wang, X.; Cheng, J.G.; Zhao, R.S.; Cheng, C.G.; Lu, X.Q. Metal-Organic Framework MIL-53(Al) as a Solid-Phase Microextraction Adsorbent for the Determination of 16 Polycyclic Aromatic Hydrocarbons in Water Samples by Gas Chromatography-Tandem Mass Spectrometry. *Analyst* **2012**, *137*, 5411–5419. [CrossRef]

67. Shang, H.B.; Yang, C.X.; Yan, X.P. Metal-Organic Framework UiO-66 Coated Stainless Steel Fiber for Solid-Phase Microextraction of Phenols in Water Samples. *J. Chromatogr. A* **2014**, *1357*, 165–171. [CrossRef]

68. Mondal, S.; Xu, J.; Chen, G.; Huang, S.; Huang, C.; Yin, L.; Ouyang, G. Solid-Phase Microextraction of Antibiotics from Fish Muscle by Using MIL-101(Cr)NH 2 -Polyacrylonitrile Fiber and Their Identification by Liquid Chromatography-Tandem Mass Spectrometry. *Anal. Chim. Acta* **2019**, *1047*, 62–70. [CrossRef]

69. Zhang, G.; Zang, X.; Li, Z.; Wang, C.; Wang, Z. Polydimethylsiloxane/Metal-Organic Frameworks Coated Fiber for Solid-Phase Microextraction of Polycyclic Aromatic Hydrocarbons in River and Lake Water Samples. *Talanta* **2014**, *129*, 600–605. [CrossRef] [PubMed]

70. Mirzajani, R.; Kardani, F.; Ramezani, Z. A Nanocomposite Consisting of Graphene Oxide, Zeolite Imidazolate Framework 8, and a Molecularly Imprinted Polymer for (Multiple) Fiber Solid Phase Microextraction of Sterol and Steroid Hormones Prior to Their Quantitation by HPLC. *Microchim. Acta* **2019**, *186*, 129. [CrossRef] [PubMed]

71. Lan, H.; Salmi, L.D.; Rönkkö, T.; Parshintsev, J.; Jussila, M.; Hartonen, K.; Kemell, M.; Riekkola, M.L. Integrated Atomic Layer Deposition and Chemical Vapor Reaction for the Preparation of Metal Organic Framework Coatings for Solid-Phase Microextraction Arrow. *Anal. Chim. Acta* **2018**, *1024*, 93–100. [CrossRef] [PubMed]

72. Lin, C.L.; Lirio, S.; Chen, Y.T.; Lin, C.H.; Huang, H.Y. A Novel Hybrid Metal-Organic Framework-Polymeric Monolith for Solid-Phase Microextraction. *Chem. A Eur. J.* **2014**, *20*, 3317–3321. [CrossRef]

73. Hu, C.; He, M.; Chen, B.; Zhong, C.; Hu, B. Polydimethylsiloxane/Metal-Organic Frameworks Coated Stir Bar Sorptive Extraction Coupled to High Performance Liquid Chromatography-Ultraviolet Detector for the Determination of Estrogens in Environmental Water Samples. *J. Chromatogr. A* **2013**, *1310*, 21–30. [CrossRef] [PubMed]

74. Hu, C.; He, M.; Chen, B.; Zhong, C.; Hu, B. Sorptive Extraction Using Polydimethylsiloxane/Metal-Organic Framework Coated Stir Bars Coupled with High Performance Liquid Chromatography-Fluorescence Detection for the Determination of Polycyclic Aromatic Hydrocarbons in Environmental Water Samples. *J. Chromatogr. A* **2014**, *1356*, 45–53. [CrossRef]

75. Lin, S.; Gan, N.; Qiao, L.; Zhang, J.; Cao, Y.; Chen, Y. Magnetic Metal-Organic Frameworks Coated Stir Bar Sorptive Extraction Coupled with GC-MS for Determination of Polychlorinated Biphenyls in Fish Samples. *Talanta* **2015**, *144*, 1139–1145. [CrossRef]

76. Yang, J.H.; Cui, C.X.; Qu, L.B.; Chen, J.; Zhou, X.M.; Zhang, Y.P. Preparation of a Monolithic Magnetic Stir Bar for the Determination of Sulfonylurea Herbicides Coupled with HPLC. *Microchem. J.* **2018**, *141*, 369–376. [CrossRef]

77. Zhang, Z.; Huang, Y.; Ding, W.; Li, G. Multilayer Interparticle Linking Hybrid MOF-199 for Noninvasive Enrichment and Analysis of Plant Hormone Ethylene. *Anal. Chem.* **2014**, *86*, 3533–3540. [CrossRef]

78. Mirzajani, R.; Kardani, F.; Ramezani, Z. Preparation and Characterization of Magnetic Metal–Organic Framework Nanocomposite as Solid-Phase Microextraction Fibers Coupled with High-Performance Liquid Chromatography for Determination of Non-Steroidal Anti-Inflammatory Drugs in Biological Fluids and Tablet Formulation Samples. *Microchem. J.* **2019**, *144*, 270–284.

79. Sun, S.; Huang, L.; Xiao, H.; Shuai, Q.; Hu, S. In Situ Self-Transformation Metal into Metal-Organic Framework Membrane for Solid-Phase Microextraction of Polycyclic Aromatic Hydrocarbons. *Talanta* **2019**, *202*, 145–151. [CrossRef] [PubMed]

80. Huang, Z.; Liu, S.; Xu, J.; Yin, L.; Sun, F.; Zhou, N.; Ouyang, G. Fabrication of 8-Aminocaprylic Acid Doped UIO-66 as Sensitive Solid-Phase Microextraction Fiber for Nitrosamines. *Talanta* **2018**, *178*, 629–635. [CrossRef]

81. Tian, Y.; Sun, M.; Wang, X.; Luo, C.; Feng, J. A Nanospherical Metal–Organic Framework UiO-66 for Solid-Phase Microextraction of Polycyclic Aromatic Hydrocarbons. *Chromatographia* **2018**, *81*, 1053–1061. [CrossRef]

82. Xie, L.; Liu, S.; Han, Z.; Jiang, R.; Liu, H.; Zhu, F.; Zeng, F.; Su, C.; Ouyang, G. Preparation and Characterization of Metal-Organic Framework MIL-101(Cr)-Coated Solid-Phase Microextraction Fiber. *Anal. Chim. Acta* **2015**, *853*, 303–310. [CrossRef] [PubMed]

83. Zang, X.; Zhang, G.; Chang, Q.; Zhang, X.; Wang, C.; Wang, Z. Metal Organic Framework MIL-101 Coated Fiber for Headspace Solid Phase Microextraction of Volatile Aromatic Compounds. *Anal. Methods* **2015**, *7*, 918–923. [CrossRef]

84. Wu, Y.Y.; Yang, C.X.; Yan, X.P. Fabrication of Metal-Organic Framework MIL-88B Films on Stainless Steel Fibers for Solid-Phase Microextraction of Polychlorinated Biphenyls. *J. Chromatogr. A* **2014**, *1334*, 1–8. [CrossRef]

85. Jia, Y.; Su, H.; Wang, Z.; Wong, Y.L.E.; Chen, X.; Wang, M.; Chan, T.W.D. Metal-Organic Framework@Microporous Organic Network as Adsorbent for Solid-Phase Microextraction. *Anal. Chem.* **2016**, *88*, 9364–9367. [CrossRef]

86. Lv, F.; Gan, N.; Huang, J.; Hu, F.; Cao, Y.; Zhou, Y.; Dong, Y.; Zhang, L.; Jiang, S. A Poly-Dopamine Based Metal-Organic Framework Coating of the Type PDA-MIL-53(Fe) for Ultrasound-Assisted Solid-Phase Microextraction of Polychlorinated Biphenyls Prior to Their Determination by GC-MS. *Microchim. Acta* **2017**, *184*, 2561–2568. [CrossRef]

87. Zhang, S.; Yang, Q.; Li, Z.; Wang, W.; Zang, X.; Wang, C.; Wang, Z. Solid Phase Microextraction of Phthalic Acid Esters from Vegetable Oils Using Iron (III)-Based Metal-Organic Framework/Graphene Oxide Coating. *Food Chem.* **2018**, *263*, 258–264. [CrossRef]

88. Zhang, B.; Xu, G.; Li, L.; Wang, X.; Li, N.; Zhao, R.S.; Lin, J. Facile Fabrication of MIL-96 as Coating Fiber for Solid-Phase Microextraction of Trihalomethanes and Halonitromethanes in Water Samples. *Chem. Eng. J.* **2018**, *350*, 240–247. [CrossRef]

89. Abolghasemi, M.M.; Yousefi, V.; Piryaei, M. Synthesis of a Metal-Organic Framework Confined in Periodic Mesoporous Silica with Enhanced Hydrostability as a Novel Fiber Coating for Solid-Phase Microextraction. *J. Sep. Sci.* **2015**, *38*, 1187–1193. [CrossRef] [PubMed]

90. Zhang, S.; Yang, Q.; Wang, W.; Wang, C.; Wang, Z. Covalent Bonding of Metal-Organic Framework-5/Graphene Oxide Hybrid Composite to Stainless Steel Fiber for Solid-Phase Microextraction of Triazole Fungicides from Fruit and Vegetable Samples. *J. Agric. Food Chem.* **2016**, *64*, 2792–2801. [CrossRef] [PubMed]

91. Lin, S.; Gan, N.; Zhang, J.; Qiao, L.; Chen, Y.; Cao, Y. Aptamer-Functionalized Stir Bar Sorptive Extraction Coupled with Gas Chromatography-Mass Spectrometry for Selective Enrichment and Determination of Polychlorinated Biphenyls in Fish Samples. *Talanta* **2016**, *149*, 266–274. [CrossRef] [PubMed]

92. Wu, M.; Ai, Y.; Zeng, B.; Zhao, F. In Situ Solvothermal Growth of Metal-Organic Framework-Ionic Liquid Functionalized Graphene Nanocomposite for Highly Efficient Enrichment of Chloramphenicol and Thiamphenicol. *J. Chromatogr. A* **2016**, *1427*, 1–7. [CrossRef] [PubMed]

93. Chang, N.; Gu, Z.Y.; Wang, H.F.; Yan, X.P. Metal-Organic-Framework-Based Tandem Molecular Sieves as a Dual Platform for Selective Microextraction and High-Resolution Gas Chromatographic Separation of n-Alkanes in Complex Matrixes. *Anal. Chem.* **2011**, *83*, 7094–7101. [CrossRef] [PubMed]

94. Yu, L.Q.; Yan, X.P. Covalent Bonding of Zeolitic Imidazolate Framework-90 to Functionalized Silica Fibers for Solid-Phase Microextraction. *Chem. Commun.* **2013**, *49*, 2142–2144. [CrossRef]

95. Yu, L.Q.; Wang, L.Y.; Su, F.H.; Hao, P.Y.; Wang, H.; Lv, Y.K. A Gate-Opening Controlled Metal-Organic Framework for Selective Solid-Phase Microextraction of Aldehydes from Exhaled Breath of Lung Cancer Patients. *Microchim. Acta* **2018**, *185*. [CrossRef]

96. Kong, J.; Zhu, F.; Huang, W.; He, H.; Hu, J.; Sun, C.; Xian, Q.; Yang, S. Sol–Gel Based Metal-Organic Framework Zeolite Imidazolate Framework-8 Fibers for Solid-Phase Microextraction of Nitro Polycyclic Aromatic Hydrocarbons and Polycyclic Aromatic Hydrocarbons in Water Samples. *J. Chromatogr. A* **2019**. [CrossRef]

97. Burtch, N.C.; Jasuja, H.; Walton, K.S. Water Stability and Adsorption in Metal-Organic Frameworks. *Chem. Rev.* **2014**, *114*, 10575–10612. [CrossRef]

98. Howarth, A.J.; Liu, Y.; Li, P.; Li, Z.; Wang, T.C.; Hupp, J.T.; Farha, O.K. Chemical, Thermal and Mechanical Stabilities of Metal-Organic Frameworks. *Nat. Rev. Mater.* **2016**, *1*, 1–15. [CrossRef]

99. He, C.T.; Tian, J.Y.; Liu, S.Y.; Ouyang, G.; Zhang, J.P.; Chen, X.M. A Porous Coordination Framework for Highly Sensitive and Selective Solid-Phase Microextraction of Non-Polar Volatile Organic Compounds. *Chem. Sci.* **2013**, *4*, 351–356. [CrossRef]

100. Zheng, J.; Li, S.; Wang, Y.; Li, L.; Su, C.; Liu, H.; Zhu, F.; Jiang, R.; Ouyang, G. In Situ Growth of IRMOF-3 Combined with Ionic Liquids to Prepare Solid-Phase Microextraction Fibers. *Anal. Chim. Acta* **2014**, *829*, 22–27. [CrossRef] [PubMed]

101. Li, Y.A.; Yang, F.; Liu, Z.C.; Liu, Q.K.; Dong, Y. Bin. A Porous Cd(Ii)-MOF-Coated Quartz Fiber for Solid-Phase Microextraction of BTEX. *J. Mater. Chem. A* **2014**, *2*, 13868–13872. [CrossRef]

102. Li, Q.L.; Wang, X.; Chen, X.F.; Wang, M.L.; Zhao, R.S. In Situ Hydrothermal Growth of Ytterbium-Based Metal-Organic Framework on Stainless Steel Wire for Solid-Phase Microextraction of Polycyclic Aromatic Hydrocarbons from Environmental Samples. *J. Chromatogr. A* **2015**, *1415*, 11–19. [CrossRef] [PubMed]

103. Huo, S.H.; Yu, J.; Fu, Y.Y.; Zhou, P.X. In Situ Hydrothermal Growth of a Dual-Ligand Metal-Organic Framework Film on a Stainless Steel Fiber for Solid-Phase Microextraction of Polycyclic Aromatic Hydrocarbons in Environmental Water Samples. *RSC Adv.* **2016**, *6*, 14042–14048. [CrossRef]

104. Li, J.; Liu, Y.; Su, H.; Elaine Wong, Y.L.; Chen, X.; Dominic Chan, T.W.; Chen, Q. In Situ Hydrothermal Growth of a Zirconium-Based Porphyrinic Metal-Organic Framework on Stainless Steel Fibers for Solid-Phase Microextraction of Nitrated Polycyclic Aromatic Hydrocarbons. *Microchim. Acta* **2017**, *184*, 3809–3815. [CrossRef]

105. Zhang, N.; Huang, C.; Tong, P.; Feng, Z.; Wu, X.; Zhang, L. Moisture Stable Ni-Zn MOF/g-C 3 N 4 Nanoflowers: A Highly Efficient Adsorbent for Solid-Phase Microextraction of PAHs. *J. Chromatogr. A* **2018**, *1556*, 37–46. [CrossRef]

106. Liu, M.; Liu, J.; Guo, C.; Li, Y. Metal Azolate Framework-66-Coated Fiber for Headspace Solid-Phase Microextraction of Polycyclic Aromatic Hydrocarbons. *J. Chromatogr. A* **2019**, *1584*, 57–63. [CrossRef]

107. Liu, S.; Zhou, Y.; Zheng, J.; Xu, J.; Jiang, R.; Shen, Y.; Jiang, J.; Zhu, F.; Su, C.; Ouyang, G. Isoreticular Bio-MOF 100–102 Coated Solid-Phase Microextraction Fibers for Fast and Sensitive Determination of Organic Pollutants by the Pore Structure Dominated Mechanism. *Analyst* **2015**, *140*, 4384–4387. [CrossRef]

108. Wang, G.; Lei, Y.; Song, H. Exploration of Metal-Organic Framework MOF-177 Coated Fibers for Headspace Solid-Phase Microextraction of Polychlorinated Biphenyls and Polycyclic Aromatic Hydrocarbons. *Talanta* **2015**, *144*, 369–374. [CrossRef]

109. Wei, S.; Lin, W.; Xu, J.; Wang, Y.; Liu, S.; Zhu, F.; Liu, Y.; Ouyang, G. Fabrication of a Polymeric Composite Incorporating Metal-Organic Framework Nanosheets for Solid-Phase Microextraction of Polycyclic Aromatic Hydrocarbons from Water Samples. *Anal. Chim. Acta* **2017**, *971*, 48–54. [CrossRef] [PubMed]

110. Liu, S.; Xie, L.; Hu, Q.; Yang, H.; Pan, G.; Zhu, F.; Yang, S.; Ouyang, G. A Tri-Metal Centered Metal-Organic Framework for Solid-Phase Microextraction of Environmental Contaminants with Enhanced Extraction Efficiency. *Anal. Chim. Acta* **2017**, *987*, 38–46. [CrossRef] [PubMed]

111. Amanzadeh, H.; Yamini, Y.; Masoomi, M.Y.; Morsali, A. Nanostructured Metal-Organic Frameworks, TMU-4, TMU-5, and TMU-6, as Novel Adsorbents for Solid Phase Microextraction of Polycyclic Aromatic Hydrocarbons. *New J. Chem.* **2017**, *41*, 12035–12043. [CrossRef]

112. Bagheri, H.; Amanzadeh, H.; Yamini, Y.; Masoomi, M.Y.; Morsali, A.; Salar-Amoli, J.; Hassan, J. A Nanocomposite Prepared from a Zinc-Based Metal-Organic Framework and Polyethersulfone as a Novel Coating for the Headspace Solid-Phase Microextraction of Organophosphorous Pesticides. *Microchim. Acta* **2018**, *185*, 62. [CrossRef]

113. Wang, J.; Du, Q.; You, X.; Lv, Y.; Bi, W.; Li, H.; Chen, D.D.Y. Solvent-Free High-Throughput Analysis of Herbicides in Environmental Water. *Anal. Chim. Acta* **2019**, *1071*, 8–16. [CrossRef]

114. Zang, X.; Zhang, X.; Chang, Q.; Li, S.; Wang, C.; Wang, Z. Metal–Organic Framework UiO-67-Coated Fiber for the Solid-Phase Microextraction of Nitrobenzene Compounds from Water. *J. Sep. Sci.* **2016**, *39*, 2770–2776. [CrossRef]

115. Niu, J.; Zhao, X.; Jin, Y.; Yang, G.; Li, Z.; Wang, J.; Zhao, R.; Li, Z. Determination of Aromatic Amines in the Urine of Smokers Using a Porous Organic Framework (JUC-Z2)-Coated Solid-Phase Microextraction Fiber. *J. Chromatogr. A* **2018**, *1555*, 37–44. [CrossRef]

116. Bagheri, H.; Javanmardi, H.; Abbasi, A.; Banihashemi, S. A Metal Organic Framework-Polyaniline Nanocomposite as a Fiber Coating for Solid Phase Microextraction. *J. Chromatogr. A* **2016**, *1431*, 27–35. [CrossRef]

117. Mei, M.; Huang, X.; Yuan, D. Multiple Monolithic Fiber Solid-Phase Microextraction: A New Extraction Approach for Aqueous Samples. *J. Chromatogr. A* **2014**, *1345*, 29–36. [CrossRef]

118. PAL SYSTEM: PAL Smart SPME Arrows. Available online: https://www.palsystem.com/index.php?id=822 (accessed on 25 July 2019).

119. Yuan, Y.; Lin, X.; Li, T.; Pang, T.; Dong, Y.; Zhuo, R.; Wang, Q.; Cao, Y.; Gan, N. A Solid Phase Microextraction Arrow with Zirconium Metal–Organic Framework/Molybdenum Disulfide Coating Coupled with Gas Chromatography–Mass Spectrometer for the Determination of Polycyclic Aromatic Hydrocarbons in Fish Samples. *J. Chromatogr. A* **2019**, *1592*, 9–18. [CrossRef]

120. Eisert, R.; Pawliszyn, J. Automated In-Tube Solid-Phase Microextraction Coupled to High-Performance Liquid Chromatography. *Anal. Chem.* **1997**, *69*, 3140–3147. [CrossRef]

121. Mullner-Martinez, Y.; Herraez-Hernández, R.; Verdú-Andrés, J.; Molins-Legua, C.; Campíns-Falcó, P. Recent Advances of In-Tube Solid-Phase Microextraction. *Trends Anal. Chem.* **2015**, *71*, 205–213. [CrossRef]

122. Fernández-Amado, M.; Prieto-Blanco, M.C.; López-Mahía, P.; Muniategui-Lorenzo, S.; Prada-Rodríguez, D. Strengths and Weaknesses of In-Tube Solid-Phase Microextraction: A Scoping Review. *Anal. Chim. Acta* **2016**, *906*, 41–57. [CrossRef] [PubMed]

123. Lirio, S.; Liu, W.L.; Lin, C.L.; Lin, C.H.; Huang, H.Y. Aluminum Based Metal-Organic Framework-Polymer Monolith in Solid-Phase Microextraction of Penicillins in River Water and Milk Samples. *J. Chromatogr. A* **2016**, *1428*, 236–245. [CrossRef]

124. Ling, X.; Chen, Z. Immobilization of Zeolitic Imidazolate Frameworks with Assist of Electrodeposited Zinc Oxide Layer and Application in Online Solid-Phase Microextraction of Sudan Dyes. *Talanta* **2019**, *192*, 142–146. [CrossRef]

125. Wilcockson, J.B.; Gobas, F.A.P.C. Thin-Film Solid-Phase Extraction to Measure Fugacities of Organic Chemicals with Low Volatility in Biological Samples. *Environ. Sci. Technol.* **2001**, *35*, 1425–1431. [CrossRef]

126. Jiang, R.; Pawliszyn, J. Thin-Film Microextraction Offers Another Geometry for Solid-Phase Microextraction. *Trends Anal. Chem.* **2012**, *39*, 245–253. [CrossRef]

127. Carasek, E.; Merib, J. Membrane-Based Microextraction Techniques in Analytical Chemistry: A Review. *Anal. Chim. Acta* **2015**, *880*, 8–25. [CrossRef]

128. Tascon, M.; Gómez-Ríos, G.A.; Reyes-Garcés, N.; Poole, J.; Boyacl, E.; Pawliszyn, J. High-Throughput Screening and Quantitation of Target Compounds in Biofluids by Coated Blade Spray-Mass Spectrometry. *Anal. Chem.* **2017**, *89*, 8421–8428. [CrossRef]

129. Mohammadi, V.; Jafari, M.T.; Saraji, M. Flexible/Self-Supported Zeolitic Imidazolate Framework-67 Film as an Adsorbent for Thin-Film Microextraction. *Microchem. J.* **2019**, *146*, 98–105. [CrossRef]

130. Ghani, M.; Font Picó, M.F.; Salehinia, S.; Palomino Cabello, C.; Maya, F.; Berlier, G.; Saraji, M.; Cerdà, V.; Turnes Palomino, G. Metal-Organic Framework Mixed-Matrix Disks: Versatile Supports for Automated Solid-Phase Extraction Prior to Chromatographic Separation. *J. Chromatogr. A* **2017**, *1488*, 1–9. [CrossRef] [PubMed]

131. Liu, F.; Xu, H. Development of a Novel Polystyrene/Metal-Organic Framework-199 Electrospun Nanofiber Adsorbent for Thin Film Microextraction of Aldehydes in Human Urine. *Talanta* **2017**, *162*, 261–267. [CrossRef] [PubMed]

132. Denny, M.S.; Cohen, S.M. In Situ Modification of Metal-Organic Frameworks in Mixed-Matrix Membranes. *Angew. Chem. Int. Ed.* **2015**, *54*, 9029–9032. [CrossRef]

133. Wang, S.; Wang, X.; Ren, Y.; Xu, H. Metal–Organic Framework 199 Film as a Novel Adsorbent of Thin-Film Extraction. *Chromatographia* **2015**, *78*, 621–629. [CrossRef]

134. Baltussen, E.; Sandra, P.; David, F.; Cramers, C. Stir Bar Sorptive Extraction (SBSE), a Novel Extraction Technique for Aqueous Samples: Theory and Principles. *J. Microcol. Sep.* **1999**, *11*, 737–747. [CrossRef]

135. Huang, X.; Chen, L.; Lin, F.; Yuan, D. Novel Extraction Approach for Liquid Samples: Stir Cake Sorptive Extraction Using Monolith. *J. Sep. Sci.* **2011**, *34*, 2145–2151. [CrossRef]

136. Płotka-Wasylka, J.; Szczepańska, N.; de la Guardia, M.; Namieśnik, J. Miniaturized Solid-Phase Extraction Techniques. *Trends Anal. Chem.* **2015**, *73*, 19–38. [CrossRef]

137. Prieto, A.; Basauri, O.; Rodil, R.; Usobiaga, A.; Fernández, L.A.; Etxebarria, N.; Zuloaga, O. Stir-Bar Sorptive Extraction: A View on Method Optimisation, Novel Applications, Limitations and Potential Solutions. *J. Chromatogr. A* **2010**, *1217*, 2642–2666. [CrossRef]

138. Automated Sample Preparation, GC/MS & LC/MS Solutions by GERSTEL. Available online: http://www.gerstel.com/ (accessed on 25 July 2019).

139. Hu, Y.; Lian, H.; Zhou, L.; Li, G. In Situ Solvothermal Growth of Metal-Organic Framework-5 Supported on Porous Copper Foam for Noninvasive Sampling of Plant Volatile Sulfides. *Anal. Chem.* **2015**, *87*, 406–412. [CrossRef]

140. You, L.; He, M.; Chen, B.; Hu, B. One-pot synthesis of zeolitic imidazolate framework-8/poly(methyl methacrylate-ethyleneglycol dimethacrylate) monolith coating for stir bat sorptive extraction of phytohormones from fruit samples followed by high performance liquid chromatography-ultraviolet detection. *J. Chromatogr. A* **2017**, *1524*, 57–65.

141. Wang, Y.; Jia, M.; Wu, X.; Wang, T.; Wang, J.; Hou, X. PEG Modified Column MIL-101(Cr)/PVA Cryogel as a Sorbent in Stir Bar Solid Phase Extraction for Determination of Non-Steroidal Anti-Inflammatory Drugs in Water Samples. *Microchem. J.* **2019**, *146*, 214–219. [CrossRef]

142. Wang, C.; Zhou, W.; Liao, X.; Wang, X.; Chen, Z. Covalent Immobilization of Metal Organic Frameworks onto Chemical Resistant Poly(Ether Ether Ketone) Jacket for Stir Bar Extraction. *Anal. Chim. Acta* **2018**, *1025*, 124–133. [CrossRef] [PubMed]

143. Ghani, M.; Ghoreishi, S.M.; Azamati, M. In-Situ Growth of Zeolitic Imidazole Framework-67 on Nanoporous Anodized Aluminum Bar as Stir-Bar Sorptive Extraction Sorbent for Determining Caffeine. *J. Chromatogr. A* **2018**, *1577*, 15–23. [CrossRef] [PubMed]

144. Cao, X.; Jiang, Z.; Wang, S.; Hong, S.; Li, H.; Zhang, C.; Shao, Y.; She, Y.; Jin, F.; Jin, M.; et al. Metal-organic framework UiO-66 for rapid dispersive solid phase extraction of neonicotinoid insecticides in water samples. *J. Chromatogr. B* **2018**, *1077*, 92–97. [CrossRef] [PubMed]

145. Su, H.; Lin, Y.; Wang, Z.; Wong, Y.-L.E.; Chen, X.; Chan, T.-W.D. Magnetic metal–organic framework–titanium dioxide nanocomposite as adsorbent in the magnetic solid-phase extraction of fungicides from environmental water samples. *J. Chromatogr. A* **2016**, *1466*, 21–28. [CrossRef]

146. Dai, X.; Jia, X.; Zhao, P.; Wang, T.; Wang, J.; Huang, P.; He, L.; Hou, X. A combined experimental/computational study on metal-organic framework MIL-101(Cr) as a SPE for the determination of sulphonamides in environmental water samples coupling with UPLC-MS/MS. *Talanta* **2016**, *154*, 581–588. [CrossRef]

147. Wang, T.; Liu, S.; Gao, G.; Zhao, P.; Lu, N.; Lun, X.; Hou, X. Magnetic solid phase extraction of non-steroidal anti-inflammatory drugs from water samples using a metal organic framework of type Fe3O4/MIL-101(Cr), and their quantitation by UPLC-MS/MS. *Microchim. Acta* **2017**, *184*, 2981–2990. [CrossRef]

Article

Low-Cost Quantitation of Multiple Volatile Organic Compounds in Air Using Solid-Phase Microextraction

Olga P. Ibragimova, Nassiba Baimatova and Bulat Kenessov *

Center of Physical Chemical Methods of Research and Analysis, Al-Farabi Kazakh National University, Almaty 050012, Kazakhstan; ibragimova@cfhma.kz (O.P.I.); baimatova@cfhma.kz (N.B.)
* Correspondence: bkenesov@cfhma.kz; Tel.: +7-727-2390624

Received: 7 September 2019; Accepted: 25 October 2019; Published: 1 November 2019

Abstract: Current standard approaches for quantitation of volatile organic compounds (VOCs) in outdoor air are labor-intensive and/or require additional equipment. Solid-phase microextraction (SPME) is a simpler alternative; however, its application is often limited by complex calibration, the need for highly pure gases and the lack of automation. Earlier, we proposed the simple, automated and accurate method for quantitation of benzene, toluene, ethylbenzene and xylenes (BTEX) in air using 20 mL headspace vials and standard addition calibration. The aim of present study was to expand this method for quantitation of >20 VOCs in air. Twenty-five VOCs were chosen for the method development. Polydimethylsiloxane/divinylbenzene (PDMS/DVB) fiber provided better combination of detection limits and relative standard deviations of calibration slopes than other studied fibers. Optimal extraction time was 10 min. For quantification of all analytes except *n*-undecane, crimp top vials with samples should not stand on the autosampler tray for >8 h, while 22 most stable analytes can be quantified during 24 h. The developed method was successfully tested for automated quantification of VOCs in outdoor air samples collected in Almaty, Kazakhstan. Relative standard deviations (RSDs) of the responses of 23 VOCs were below 15.6%. Toluene-to-benzene concentration ratios were below 1.0 in colder days, indicating that most BTEX originated from non-transport-related sources.

Keywords: SPME; gas chromatography; air monitoring; volatile organic compounds; fiber selection

---

1. Introduction

The pollution of ambient and indoor air are the main sources of risk to human health in the world [1]. Air pollution leads to destruction of ecosystems and creates huge economic and social damages to society. There is a direct relationship between a level of air pollution and risk in the development of cancer, cardiovascular, respiratory and other diseases [1]. The most difficult and important process in quantification of chemical pollutants in ambient air is sampling. Sampling must be representative taking into account physicochemical properties of analytes and their concentrations in air [2].

Current standard sampling approaches for quantification of VOCs in air [2–4] are mainly based on collecting air samples into evacuated canisters [2,5] or trapping analytes onto sorbent tubes [3,6] followed by the analysis on a gas chromatograph (GC) with a chosen detector, mostly being flame-ionization (FID) or mass spectrometry (MS). Despite good reliability, these sampling techniques [4] are quite complex, labor- and time-consuming, as well as requiring additional equipment. Air sampling by standard methods based, e.g., on sorbent tubes [2,3], requires additional equipment such as an air sampling pump and a thermal desorption system connected to a gas chromatograph. Before air sampling, it is necessary to thoroughly clean sorbent tubes from possible contaminants and residues from previous sampling by highly pure helium. In order to solve these problems, it is necessary to reduce the volume of organic solvents used for extraction, or completely exclude them; fully or partially automate the sampling process; integrate the sampling and measurement stages; and reduce laboratory work and time costs. Additional problems may include carryover of analytes and clogging of the cryogenic focusing system [7], which considerably limit the application of standard methods. Therefore, low-cost, simple and solvent-free methods for quantification of VOCs in the air combining sampling and sample preparation in one step are needed. Solid-phase microextraction (SPME) that is based on extraction of VOCs by a micro coating, followed by desorption in a GC injection port, meets these requirements [8]. SPME is widely used for the determination of VOCs in ambient air (Table 1), indoor air and different emissions [9–18]. Methods based on SPME do not need a pump and a thermal desorption system. Desorption of analytes is fast resulting in narrow peaks of analytes without a cryogenic focusing.

Table 1. Methods for quantification of organic compounds in ambient air by exposed solid-phase microextraction (SPME) fibers.

Sampling Principle	SPME Fiber, Extraction Time	Instrument	Analytes	LOD (µg m⁻³) Car/PDMS	PDMS	Ref.
SPME from open air	75-µm Car/PDMS, 100-µm PDMS, 20 min	GC–AED	Methanethiol Dimethyl sulfide Isopropanethiol Isobutanethiol	0.04–0.06 0.003–0.004 0.005–0.007 0.003–0.004	4 2 2 0.7	[9]
SPME from static or moving air	75-µm Car/PDMS, 1 min	GC–FID	Methanol Acetone Dichloromethane Methyl ethyl ketone Ethyl acetate Dichloroethane Methyl isobutyl ketone Toluene Butyl acetate Ethylbenzene *p*-Xylene	2–5		[10]
SFME from fan-blown air	65-µm PDMS/DVB, 2 h	GC–MS	Δ^3-Carene α-Pinene Limonene Pinonaldehyde Pinonic acid Dimethylamine + ethylamine	n/a		[19]
Air purging via bubbler imping- with KOH solution, HS SPME	75-µm Car/PDMS, 5 min	GC–MS	HCN	0.16		[20]

Table 1. *Cont.*

Sampling Principle	SPME Fiber, Extraction Time	Instrument	Analytes	LOD (µg m^{-3})	Ref.
Sampling on XAD-2 resin, accelerated solvent extraction with ACN, dilution with water, DI SPME	100-µm PDMS, 40 min	GC-Dual ECD	22 PCBs 19 OCPs	2×10^{-5}–4.9×10^{-3}	[21]
Sampling of PM10 on quartz fiber filter, microwave extraction with ethanol-water mixture, dilution with water and DI SPME	50/30-µm DVB/Car/PDMS, 5 min	GC-MS/MS	Tripropyl phosphate Tri-n-butyl phosphate Tris(2-chloroethyl) phosphate Tris(1-chloro-2-propyl) phosphate Tris(1,3-dichloro-2-propyl) phosphate Triphenyl phosphate Tricresyl phosphate	20 40 70 42 138 51 60	[22]
SPME from open air	100-µm PDMS, 30-45 min	GC-MS	BTEX propylbenzene 1,3,5-trimethylbenzene butyl benzene alkanes (C$_5$, C$_{10}$-C$_{27}$)	1–100	[23]
Sampling to Tedlar bags, SPME	75-µm Car/PDMS, 15 min	GC-MS	36 VOCs	0.01–0.93	[24]
Sampling into 20-mL vials, SPME	100-µm PDMS, 3 min	GC-MS	Benzene Toluene Ethylbenzene o-Xylene	5 2 2 2	[25]
Sampling into 20-mL vials, SPME	65-µm PDMS/DVB, 10 min	GC-MS	25 VOCs	0.01–6.9	This study

Notes: n/a—not available; ACN—acetonitrile; AED—atomic emission detector; BTEX—benzene, toluene, ethylbenzene, xylenes; Car—Carboxen; DI—direct immersion; DVB—divinylbenzene; ECD—electron capture detector; FID—flame ionization detector; GC—gas chromatography; HS—headspace; LOD—limit of detection; MS—mass spectrometry; MS/MS—tandem mass spectrometry; OCPs—organochlorine pesticides PCBs—polychlorinated biphenyls; PDMS—polydimethylsiloxane; SPME—solid-phase microextraction; VOCs—volatile organic compounds.

Despite the high efficiency of the described methods for determination of VOCs in air by SPME (Table 1), there are still challenges limiting their application in routine and research environmental laboratories. Some authors report limitations due to labor-intensive calibration, i.e., requirements for construction of gas generation system with a known concentration of analytes [19,21,24,26]. Most methods require using high-purity gases for preparation of calibration samples, which can be difficult to purchase and prepare. Baimatova et al. [25] developed a very simple, automated and accurate method for quantification of BTEX using SPME and successfully applied it for the analysis of ambient air in Almaty, Kazakhstan. Sampling was conducted with 20 mL crimp top vials, which were transported to the laboratory, located on the Combi PAL (CTC Analytics, Switzerland) autosampler tray and automatically analyzed using GC-MS. To simplify the method, the authors used standard addition calibration, which did not require any additional equipment and pure gases. The only major drawback of this method was that it allowed quantification of only four analytes [25], while more than 100 organic compounds are present in outdoor air of Almaty [27]. Lee et al. [24] developed the method for determination of 36 VOCs. However, the sampling was done into Tedlar bags, which did not allow automation. In addition, the calibration was carried out with a standard gas mixture of VOCs in pure nitrogen.

The objective of this study was to improve the method developed by Baimatova et al. [25] for quantitation of >20 VOCs in 20 mL ambient air samples using SPME and GC-MS. During this study, SPME fiber, extraction, desorption and storage times were optimized. The developed method was applied for quantification of chosen VOCs in outdoor air of Almaty, Kazakhstan.

2. Materials and Methods

2.1. Chemicals

Analytes of interest were chosen according to the literature review of VOCs determination in ambient air in different cities [28–33] and previous studies of compounds detected in the exhausts of six arbitrarily chosen cars of different models and production years [27]. Chosen analytes belong to several classes of pollutants having various physicochemical properties (Table S1 in Supplementary Materials). All solutions were prepared in methanol (purity ≥ 99.9%) that was obtained from Sigma-Aldrich (St. Louis, MO, USA). Helium (purity > 99.995%) was obtained from "Orenburg-Tehgas" (Orenburg, Russia).

2.2. GC-MS Conditions

All analyses were conducted on a 7890A/5975C Triple-Axis Detector diffusion pump-based GC-MS (Agilent, Wilmington, DE, USA) equipped with a split/splitless inlet and MPS2 (Gerstel, Mülheim an der Ruhr, Germany) autosampler capable of automated SPME. The inlet was equipped with a 0.75 mm ID SPME liner (Supelco, Bellefonte, PA, USA) and operated in splitless mode. For separation, a 60 m × 0.25 mm DB-WAXetr (Agilent, Santa Clara, CA, USA) column with a film thickness of 0.50 μm was used at the constant flow of He (1.0 mL min^{-1}). Oven temperature was programmed from initial 35 °C (held for 5 min) to 150 °C (held for 5 min) at the heating rate of 10 °C min^{-1}, then to 250 °C (held for 7 min) at the heating rate of 10 °C min^{-1}. Total GC run time of the analysis was 38.5 min. The MS detector worked in selected ion monitoring (SIM) mode. All ions were divided into six consequently detected groups for better shape of peaks and lower limits of detection (Table 2). An example of a chromatogram is shown in Figure S1 in Supplementary Materials. Peaks were identified using retention times of each analyte, which were preliminarily determined by analyzing standard solutions of pure analytes and confirmed in full scan ($m\,z^{-1}$ 10–250 amu) mode of the MS detector. Optimal dwell time for each ion was 50–100 ms. The temperatures of MS interface, ion source and quadrupole were 250, 230 and 150 °C, respectively.

Table 2. MS detection program of analytes in SIM mode.

No.	Retention Time (min)	Group No.	Analyte	Quantification Ion $m\ z^{-1}$ (amu (dwell))	Confirmation Ions $m\ z^{-1}$ (amu (dwell))	Group Start Time (min)
1	5.1	1	2,2,4-Trimethylpentane	57 (100)	56, 41 (50)	0
2	5.5		n-Heptane	43 (50)	41 (50)	
3	9.9		Methyl ethyl ketone	43 (50)	72 (50)	
4	10.4	2	Methylene chloride	49 (100)	84 (50)	10.2
5	10.8		Benzene	78 (100)		
6	11.8		n-Decane	142 (100)		
7	12.6	3	1,1,2,2-Tetrachloroethylene	166 (50)	164 (50)	12.2
8	13.1		Toluene	91 (100)		
9	13.5		1,2-Dichloroethane	62 (100)	64 (50)	
10	13.8		n-Undecane	156 (100)		
11	14.9		Ethylbenzene			
12	15.0		m-Xylene	106 (100)		
13	15.1		p-Xylene			
14	15.7	4	Propylbenzene	105 (100)		15.5
15	15.9		o-Xylene	106 (50)		
16	16.5		Chlorobenzene	112 (100)	77 (50)	
17	17.0		1,3,5-Trimethylbenzene	105 (100)		
18	17.7		1,2,4-Trimethylbenzene			
19	18.1		3-Picoline	93 (100)	66 (50)	
20	23.4	5	Benzaldehyde	77 (100)		22.0
21	24.8		n-Hexadecane	57 (100)	43 (100)	
22	27.9		Naphthalene	128 (100)		
23	31.0	6	Phenol	94 (100)		30.0
24	33.7		Acenaphthene	153 (100)		
25	36.8		Fluorene	166 (100)		

2.3. Selection of the Optimal SPME Fiber

Standard addition calibration plots were obtained for all 25 analytes using the four most common commercially available SPME fibers: 85 μm Carboxen(Car)/polydimethylsiloxane(PDMS), 100 μm PDMS, 65 μm PDMS/divinylbenzene(DVB) and 50/30 μm DVB/Car/PDMS (all–from Supelco, Bellefonte, PA, USA). The calibration process was the same as described by Baimatova et al. [25]. Calibration samples were prepared by adding 1.00 μL of a standard solution of analytes (0.50, 1.00, 2.00 and 4.00 ng μL^{-1} for benzene, toluene and alkanes; and 0.050, 0.100, 0.200 and 0.400 ng μL^{-1} for other analytes) into the 20 mL crimp-top headspace vial (HTA, Brescia, Italy) filled with laboratory air. Ranges of concentrations of VOCs added to calibration samples were chosen in order to cover their real concentrations in ambient air (according to the preliminary screening results). Added concentrations of benzene, toluene, and alkanes in the calibration samples were 25, 50, 100 and 200 μg m^{-3}. Added concentrations of ethylbenzene, *m-, p-, o-*xylenes, polycyclic aromatic hydrocarbons and other analytes were 2.5, 5, 10 and 20 μg m^{-3}. Extraction was conducted at room temperature (22 °C) for 10 min; desorption time was 1 min.

From the calibration plots, relative standard deviations (RSDs) of slopes and limits of detection (LODs) were determined. RSDs of slopes were determined using the LINEST function of Microsoft Excel software (Microsoft® Excel for Office 365, Version 1909, Redmond, WA, USA). LODs were calculated using:

$$LOD = \frac{\left(\frac{b}{a} + C_{add}\right) \times 3}{S/N} \tag{1}$$

where b is the intercept of a calibration plot; a is the slope of a calibration plot; C_{add} is the standard addition concentration (μg m^{-3}); and S/N is the signal-to-noise ratio.

2.4. Effects of Extraction and Desorption Times

The experiment was conducted on air samples with standard additions of all analytes at 100 μg m^{-3}. The following extraction times were studied: 1, 3, 5, 7, 10, 20 and 30 min followed by a 5 min desorption. Desorption times 1, 3, 5, 7 and 10 min were studied after 10 min extraction of analytes.

2.5. Effect of Storage Time

Effects of storage time on the responses of analytes were studied in crimped 20 mL vials with concentrations of standard additions of analytes at 100 μg m^{-3}. Samples were stored at room temperature (22 °C) on the autosampler tray during 0, 2, 4, 8, 16, 24, 36 and 48 h, and extracted by 65 μm PDMS/DVB fiber for 10 min followed by a 1 min desorption. Two replicate samples were analyzed after each storage time. Significance of differences (*p*-value) between the initial response of analytes and its response after a certain storage time was estimated using a two-sample two-tailed Student's *t*-test with a preset relative standard deviation (10%).

2.6. Estimation of the Method Accuracy

Accuracy of the method was estimated using spike recoveries from laboratory air samples. Concentrations of analytes in laboratory air were determined using a standard addition calibration by dividing intercepts by slopes. Three replicate laboratory air samples, which were collected at the same time as samples used for preparing calibration standards, were spiked at C = 100 μg m^{-3} for benzene, toluene and alkanes, and at C = 10.0 μg m^{-3} for other analytes. After analysis, spike recoveries (R, %) were determined using

$$R = \frac{C_{meas} - C_{air}}{C_{sp}} \times 100\%, \tag{2}$$

where C_{meas} is the determined concentration of an analyte in a spiked sample (μg m^{-3}); C_{air} is the concentration of an analyte in the laboratory air (μg m^{-3}); and C_{sp} is the concentration of the standard addition of an analyte (μg m^{-3}).

2.7. Air Sampling and Analysis

The developed method was applied for monitoring of VOCs in ambient air in Almaty on 30 March, 2 April and 4 April 2019. The sampling process and coordinates of sampling locations (Table S2 in Supplementary Materials) were identical to those used by Baimatova et al. in 2015 [25].

Prior to sampling, all 20 mL vials and septa were washed using distilled water and conditioned at 160 °C for 4 h. Ambient air samples were collected into 20 mL crimp vials (i.e., by opening the vial to air and shaking for ~60 sec) and then sealed with aluminum caps and PTFE-silicone septa (Agilent, Santa Clara, CA, USA). Vials were transported to the laboratory in 1 L clean glass jars to prevent possible losses of analytes during the transportation. Vials with air samples were placed on the autosampler tray. Air samples were extracted from the vial using 65 μm PDMS/DVB fiber coating at optimized method parameters. Calibration plots were obtained before each sampling day. Weather conditions, such as temperature, humidity, wind velocity and pressure, were taken from the public database Gismeteo (Table S3 in Supplementary Materials).

3. Results

3.1. Selection of the Optimal SPME Fiber

Selection of the optimal SPME fiber for quantification of multiple analytes having different physicochemical properties is a difficult process. In most cases, the fibers are chosen based on an experimental or theoretical basis. Experimental fiber selection is straightforward only when one fiber provides greater responses for all analytes. In other cases, a theoretical approach can be involved based on known selectivity of the coatings to compounds having different molecular weights and polarities [34]. In our study, the selection of the optimal fiber was conducted based on the two most important indicators: limit of detection (LOD) and relative standard deviation (RSD) of a calibration slope. Lower LODs will allow greater applicability of the method, while lower RSDs would provide better accuracy and precision. We estimated how many analytes can be determined at different LODs and RSDs. After determining LOD and RSD for each analyte using the four most common commercial fibers (Car/PDMS, PDMS, DVB/Car/PDMS and PDMS/DVB), it was checked how many analytes have LODs below 1, 2, 5 and 10 $\mu g\ m^{-3}$, and RSDs below 1%, 2%, 5% and 10% using each fiber.

LODs ≤ 1 $\mu g\ m^{-3}$ for the greatest number of analytes (20 of 25) were achieved using the DVB/Car/PDMS fiber (Table 3). Car/PDMS and PDMS/DVB fibers provided such LODs only for 17 analytes. LODs ≤ 2 $\mu g\ m^{-3}$ were achieved for 23 analytes using DVB/Car/PDMS and PDMS/DVB fibers. Such LOD using these fibers was not achieved only for *n*-hexane and *n*-hexadecane. LODs ≤ 5 $\mu g\ m^{-3}$ were achieved for 24 analytes using PDMS/DVB fiber. LODs ≤ 10 $\mu g\ m^{-3}$ were achieved for all 25 analytes using PDMS, DVB/Car/PDMS and PDMS/DVB fibers. Overall, DVB/Car/PDMS and PDMS/DVB fibers provide greatest numbers of analytes at most target LODs. At the same time, PDMS/DVB provides lower LODs for three PAHs, which are considered more toxic compared to other analytes.

When comparing RSDs of calibration slopes (Table 4), PDMS/DVB fiber also provides better values. RSDs are below 5% for 17 analytes and below 10%—for 22 analytes, which is greater than for DVB/Car/PDMS fiber—11 and 20 analytes, respectively. When using PDMS/DVB fiber, RSDs of slopes above 10% were obtained only for methyl ethyl ketone (25%), 1,2-dichloroethane (20%) and *p*-xylene (15%). When using DVB/Car/PDMS fiber, RSDs of slopes for benzaldehyde and *n*-hexadecane were 79% and 32%, respectively. Thus, based on these results, PDMS/DVB fiber was chosen as most appropriate for simultaneous quantification of 25 VOCs.

Table 3. Limits of detection obtained using different SPME fibers.

Analyte	Limit of Detection ($\mu g\ m^{-3}$)			
	Car/PDMS	PDMS	DVB/Car/PDMS	PDMS/DVB
2,2,4-Trimethylpentane	3	8	0.7	1.8
n-Heptane	50	9	8	7
Methyl ethyl ketone	15	7	0.8	1.9
Methylene chloride	1.8	9	1.1	0.6
Benzene	0.6	6	0.5	1.2
n-Decane	3	3	1.2	1.5
1,1,2,2-Tetrachloroethylene	0.04	0.2	0.04	0.04
Toluene	0.5	4	1.6	1.2
1,2-Dichloroethane	0.2	1.2	0.8	1.7
n-Undecane	2	1.0	0.8	1.0
Ethylbenzene	0.010	0.10	0.2	0.03
m-Xylene	0.2	0.2	0.6	0.2
p-Xylene	0.10	0.2	0.2	0.2
Propylbenzene	0.3	0.3	0.2	0.10
o-Xylene	0.04	0.10	0.10	0.04
Chlorobenzene	0.04	0.10	0.05	0.04
1,3,5-Trimethylbenzene	0.3	0.10	0.10	0.10
1,2,4-Trimethylbenzene	0.2	0.04	0.04	0.10
3-Picoline	0.5	0.2	0.10	0.010
Benzaldehyde	0.10	0.10	0.4	0.10
n-Hexadecane	-	5	10	5
Naphthalene	0.2	0.10	0.10	0.04
Phenol	0.8	0.10	0.10	0.10
Acenaphthene	0.3	0.10	0.2	0.10
Fluorene	5	0.10	0.6	0.10
Number of analytes with a limit of detection $\leq$				
1 $\mu g\ m^{-3}$	17	16	20	17
2 $\mu g\ m^{-3}$	19	17	23	23
5 $\mu g\ m^{-3}$	22	20	23	24
10 $\mu g\ m^{-3}$	22	25	25	25

Table 4. Relative standard deviations of calibration slopes obtained using different SPME fibers.

Analyte	Relative Standard Deviation of a Slope (%)			
	Car/PDMS	PDMS	DVB/Car/PDMS	PDMS/DVB
2,2,4-Trimethylpentane	0.50	2.7	1.7	2.7
n-Heptane	44	11	4.5	5.2
Methyl ethyl ketone	42	14	7.8	25
Methylene chloride	95	200	5.3	4.2
Benzene	4.4	9.4	3.2	1.1
n-Decane	3.5	5.6	0.50	5.9
1,1,2,2-Tetrachloroethylene	2.6	1.2	0.40	3.1
Toluene	18	3.4	5.8	6.4
1,2-Dichloroethane	2.1	9.0	10	20
n-Undecane	5.9	5.7	1.8	4.7
Ethylbenzene	0.50	2.7	4.8	4.4
m-Xylene	3.8	1.7	9.6	4.6
p-Xylene	1.2	6.8	7.5	15
Propylbenzene	4.0	2.4	9.6	2.2

Table 4. *Cont.*

Analyte	Relative Standard Deviation of a Slope (%)			
	Car/PDMS	PDMS	DVB/Car/PDMS	PDMS/DVB
o-Xylene	0.60	1.3	7.5	3.4
Chlorobenzene	3.8	1.3	1.3	1.3
1,3,5-Trimethylbenzene	0.30	0.80	2.2	3.2
1,2,4-Trimethylbenzene	7.6	3.5	6.1	3.8
3-Picoline	5.1	6.5	15	6.2
Benzaldehyde	8.0	3.2	79	3.7
n-Hexadecane	-	4.5	32	8.3
Naphthalene	5.7	1.8	20	2.2
Phenol	15	1.4	24	2.5
Acenaphthene	4.2	5.3	4.3	2.5
Fluorene	5.5	1.5	4.0	3.5
Number of analytes with a relative standard deviation of a slope ≤				
1%	4	1	2	0
2%	5	8	5	2
5%	13	15	11	17
10%	19	22	20	22

3.2. Effects of Extraction and Desorption Times

Extraction and desorption times are important parameters of VOC quantification by SPME, which have an impact on intensity of analyte responses. Speed of equilibration during the extraction stage depends on a vessel volume, the diffusion coefficient of an analyte and its distribution constant between the coating and the air [35]. The equilibrium between the fiber and air for almost all analytes was reached after 5–10 min of extraction (Figure 1). Extraction time did not affect the responses of methylene chloride, methyl ethyl ketone and 1,2-dichloroethane—their responses varied by 1–13%. The responses for benzene were stabilized after 3 min of extraction. Based on the obtained results, an extraction time of 10 min was chosen as optimal.

The increase in desorption time above 1 min had no significant effects on responses of all studied VOCs (Figure S2 in Supplementary Materials). After this time, the responses varied by 0.43–15%. Therefore, the desorption time of 1 min was chosen as the optimal.

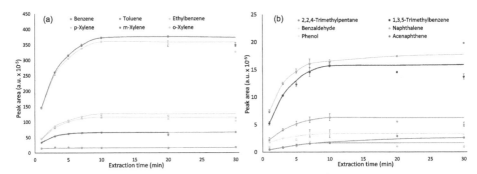

Figure 1. *Cont.*

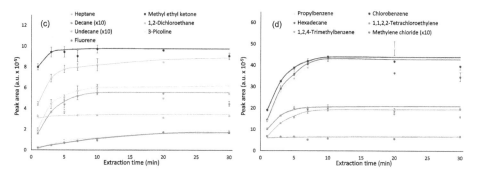

Figure 1. Effect of extraction time on responses of analytes: (**a**)—benzene, toluene, ethylbenzene, *m,p,o*-xylenes; (**b**)—2,2,4-trimethylpentane, benzaldehyde, phenol, 1,3,5-trimethylbenzene, naphthalene, acenaphthene; (**c**)—*n*-heptane, *n*-decane, *n*-undecane, fluorene, methyl ethyl ketone, 1,2-dichloroethane, 3-picoline, and (**d**)—propylbenzene, *n*-hexadecane, 1,2,4-trimethylbenzene, chlorobenzene, 1,1,2,2-tetrachloroethylene, methylene chloride.

3.3. Effect of Storage Time

During transportation and storage of air samples, concentrations of analytes can decrease due to their decomposition, losses via leaks and adsorption to internal walls of a vial and septum. The approach proposed by Baimatova et al. [25] was used to minimize the losses of analytes. The goal of this experiment was to estimate losses of analytes during their storage on the autosampler tray.

Figure 2 shows the effect of storage time on responses of analytes. Two-sample two-tailed *t*-tests indicated that the changes in responses of *n*-undecane, acenaphthene and fluorene in relation to initial values were significant ($p < 0.05$ at RSD = 10%) after 24 h of storage (Table S4 in Supplementary Materials), while responses of other 22 analytes were stable. After 48 h of storage, changes in responses of *n*-undecane, *n*-hexadecane, acenaphthene and fluorene were significant. Greater losses of more hydrophobic analytes could be explained by their adsorption to a hydrophobic surface of a PTFE-lined septum being in direct contact with air. Despite these septa being considered highly inert, adsorption of very hydrophobic compounds by PTFE was earlier reported in the literature [36]. For achieving the greatest accuracy for these analytes, samples should be analyzed as quickly as possible, e.g., during the first 8 h after sampling.

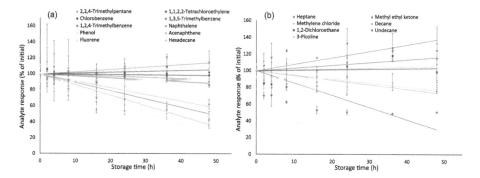

Figure 2. *Cont.*

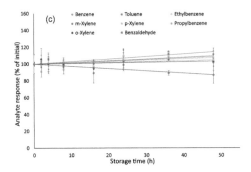

Figure 2. Effect of storage time on responses of analytes: (**a**)—2,2,4-trimethylpentane, chlorobenzene, 1,2,4-trimethylbenzene, phenol, fluorene, 1,1,2,2-tetrachloroethylene, 1,3,5-trimethylbenzene, naphthalene, acenaphthene, hexadecane; (**b**)—*n*-heptane, methylene chloride, 1,2-dichloroethane, 3-picoline, methyl ethyl ketone, *n*-decane, *n*-undecane, and (**c**)—benzene, toluene, ethylbenzene, *m,p,o*-xylenes, propylbenzene, benzaldehyde.

3.4. Estimation of the Method Accuracy

Spike recoveries of all analytes except methyl ethyl ketone, methylene chloride, 3-picoline and *n*-hexadecane were 90–105% (Table 5), which is consistent with the results of previous experiments. Lower recoveries of methyl ethyl ketone, methylene chloride, 3-picoline and *n*-hexadecane could be explained by high RSDs in their determined concentrations, which were 7.4%, 17%, 43% and 11%, respectively. RSDs of other analytes were 1.8–6.5%.

Table 5. Spike recoveries of analytes.

Analyte	C_{air} (μg m^{-3})	C_{sp} (μg m^{-3})	C_{meas} (μg m^{-3})	Recovery (%)
2,2,4-Trimethylpentane	22.3	100	124	102
n-Heptane	55.0	100	158	103
Methyl ethyl ketone	88.4	10	93.6	51
Methylene chloride	20.7	10	29.6	89
Benzene	80.2	100	183	103
n-Decane	17.7	100	117	100
1,1,2,2-Tetrachloroethylene	0.58	10	10.6	100
Toluene	25.7	100	128	102
1,2-Dichloroethane	n/d	10	9.3	93
n-Undecane	50.2	100	146	96
Ethylbenzene	1.36	10	11.4	101
m-Xylene	1.74	10	11.9	102
p-Xylene	1.92	10	12.0	100
Propylbenzene	1.17	10	11.2	100
o-Xylene	1.57	10	11.7	101
Chlorobenzene	0.60	10	10.6	100
1,3,5-Trimethylbenzene	1.82	10	11.6	97
1,2,4-Trimethylbenzene	4.33	10	14.2	98
3-Picoline	8.63	10	17.2	86
Benzaldehyde	0.83	10	10.4	96
n-Hexadecane	132	100	213	81
Naphthalene	3.80	10	13.6	98
Phenol	3.52	10	13.5	100
Acenaphthene	1.61	10	12.1	105
Fluorene	4.64	10	14.7	101

3.5. Air Sampling and Analysis

During the monitoring of the atmospheric air in Almaty using the optimized method, all analytes were detected except methyl ethyl ketone and 1,2-dichloroethane. Mean concentrations of analytes ranged from 0.2 to 83, from 0.1 to 70 and from 0.1 to 74 µg m^{-3} on 30 March, 2 April and 4 April, respectively. The highest concentrations (0.7–89 µg m^{-3}) for 16 of the 23 analytes were detected on the 3rd day of sampling (Table 6). It can be caused by higher temperatures (14–16 °C) than on previous sampling days (6–11 °C). The highest concentrations for the rest of the VOCs, such as benzene, propylbenzene, benzaldehyde and hexadecane, were detected on March 30, which made up 56, 0.3, 1.8 and 123 µg m^{-3}, respectively. The 2nd sampling day showed the highest concentrations of naphthalene, phenol and fluorene—2.4, 3.9 and 0.8 µg m^{-3}, respectively. The lowest concentrations of the greatest number of analytes (16) were detected in sampling point P2 (Table S5 in Supplementary Materials) located in the upper part of the city close to mountains. The highest concentrations of the greatest number of analytes (12) were detected in sampling point P3 located in the central part of the city.

The relative standard deviations of three replicate analyses of the air samples did not exceed 15.6%. From 108 measurements, the greatest numbers of outliers (one out of three replicate measurements according to Grubbs' test) were identified for *n*-hexadecane (19), methylene chloride (14), *n*-undecane (13) and acenaphthene (12). No outliers were identified for ethylbenzene and *m*-xylene.

Toluene-to-benzene (T/B) concentration ratios during the sampling period varied from 0.46 to 1.69. During the first two days of sampling, T/B ratios were below 1 indicating that the main source of BTEX was not transport. During these two days, the temperatures were 3–7 °C lower than during the third day of sampling, and the central and domestic heating systems were more active. During the third day of sampling, T/B ratios were 1.69 and 1.06, and the main BTEX emissions originated from transport. The same trend was reported for the similar period in 2015 [25]. However, T/B were lower than 1 mostly in days with negative temperatures. In 2019, such ratios were observed at temperatures between 6 and 11 °C, which could mean that the fraction of BTEX emissions from transport-related sources decreased since 2015.

Table 6. Measured VOC concentrations in air.

| | Concentration ± Standard Deviation (µg m⁻³) | | | | | | | | | Outliers | |
| Sampling Date >> | Saturday, 30 March | | | Tuesday, 2 April | | | Thursday, 4 April | | | | |
Analyte	8 AM	8 PM	Mean	8 AM	8 PM	Mean	8 AM	8 PM	Mean	Number	%
2,2,4-Trimethylpentane	18 ± 2	20 ± 2	19 ± 2	19 ± 3	15 ± 2	17 ± 2	34 ± 6	22 ± 2	28 ± 4	6	5.7
n-Heptane	46 ± 5	53 ± 5	50 ± 5	46 ± 3	38 ± 5	42 ± 4	89 ± 9	60 ± 6	74 ± 8	5	4.6
Methyl ethyl ketone	n/d	n/d	n/d	n/d	n/d	n/d	n/d	n/d	n/d	n/a	n/a
Methylene chloride	25 ± 7	25 ± 5	25 ± 6	10 ± 1	8 ± 2	9 ± 2	45 ± 7	53 ± 13	49 ± 10	14	13
Benzene	40 ± 5	56 ± 4	48 ± 4	37 ± 3	46 ± 9	41 ± 6	48 ± 4	56 ± 7	52 ± 6	6	5.6
n-Decane	11 ± 3	13 ± 2	12 ± 2	4.8 ± 1.2	8.4 ± 1.0	6.6 ± 1.1	30 ± 6	28 ± 4	29 ± 5	6	5.6
1,1,2,2-Tetrachloroethylene	0.14 ± 0.05	0.18 ± 0.03	0.16 ± 0.04	0.08 ± 0.01	0.12 ± 0.07	0.10 ± 0.04	1.3 ± 0.6	1.2 ± 0.2	1.2 ± 0.4	9	8.3
Toluene	34 ± 3	50 ± 3	42 ± 3	28 ± 1	21 ± 6	25 ± 3	81 ± 15	60 ± 6	70 ± 11	6	5.6
1,2-Dichloroethane	n/d	n/d	n/d	n/d	n/d	n/d	n/d	n/d	n/d	n/a	n/a
n-Undecane	22 ± 6	27 ± 3	25 ± 4	13 ± 2	14 ± 2	13 ± 2	36 ± 7	22 ± 4	29 ± 5	13	12
Ethylbenzene	0.49 ± 0.13	0.68 ± 0.05	0.58 ± 0.09	0.43 ± 0.02	0.35 ± 0.03	0.39 ± 0.03	0.94 ± 0.14	0.84 ± 0.08	0.89 ± 0.11	n/d	n/d
m-Xylene	0.55 ± 0.14	0.90 ± 0.05	0.73 ± 0.09	0.67 ± 0.03	0.47 ± 0.04	0.57 ± 0.04	1.3 ± 0.2	0.99 ± 0.09	1.1 ± 0.2	n/d	n/d
p-Xylene	0.81 ± 0.16	1.26 ± 0.09	1.04 ± 0.13	0.95 ± 0.04	0.72 ± 0.07	0.83 ± 0.05	1.9 ± 0.2	1.82 ± 0.12	1.9 ± 0.2	1	1.0
Propylbenzene	0.28 ± 0.12	0.11 ± 0.02	0.20 ± 0.07	0.18 ± 0.01	0.06 ± 0.02	0.12 ± 0.02	0.22 ± 0.13	0.07 ± 0.02	0.14 ± 0.08	11	10
o-Xylene	0.55 ± 0.14	0.59 ± 0.04	0.57 ± 0.09	0.45 ± 0.13	0.30 ± 0.02	0.37 ± 0.08	0.70 ± 0.16	0.61 ± 0.04	0.65 ± 0.10	2	1.9
Chlorobenzene	1.1 ± 0.4	1.49 ± 0.09	1.3 ± 0.2	1.1 ± 0.3	0.76 ± 0.06	0.9 ± 0.2	1.5 ± 0.2	1.25 ± 0.07	1.38 ± 0.18	2	1.9
1,3,5-Trimethylbenzene	2.0 ± 0.6	1.22 ± 0.08	1.6 ± 0.4	2.1 ± 0.2	0.79 ± 0.05	1.45 ± 0.13	3.1 ± 1.0	1.09 ± 0.05	2.1 ± 0.5	3	2.8
1,2,4-Trimethylbenzene	1.3 ± 0.5	2.97 ± 0.14	2.2 ± 0.3	1.3 ± 0.4	1.57 ± 0.11	1.4 ± 0.3	2.0 ± 0.8	3.2 ± 0.7	2.6 ± 0.7	5	4.6
3-Picoline	8.1 ± 2.6	0.9 ± 0.2	4.5 ± 1.4	7.0 ± 1.9	0.39 ± 0.08	3.7 ± 1.0	12.5 ± 5.3	1.4 ± 1.1	7.0 ± 3.2	9	8.3
Benzaldehyde	1.3 ± 0.7	1.8 ± 0.3	1.5 ± 0.5	0.7 ± 0.4	1.4 ± 0.2	1.1 ± 0.3	0.6 ± 0.4	1.4 ± 0.5	1.0 ± 0.4	8	7.4
n-Hexadecane	123 ± 16	44 ± 6	84 ± 11	90 ± 10	50 ± 9	71 ± 10	85 ± 14	47 ± 4	66 ± 9	19	18
Naphthalene	1.8 ± 0.6	1.8 ± 0.2	1.8 ± 0.4	1.3 ± 0.4	2.4 ± 0.6	1.9 ± 0.5	1.5 ± 0.3	2.3 ± 0.4	1.9 ± 0.3	4	3.7
Phenol	2.1 ± 0.6	2.9 ± 0.5	2.5 ± 0.5	2.4 ± 0.6	3.9 ± 0.9	3.1 ± 0.8	3.3 ± 1.1	3.3 ± 1.2	3.3 ± 1.2	10	9.3
Acenaphthene	2.24 ± 0.13	0.13 ± 0.04	1.19 ± 0.09	2.6 ± 0.8	0.3 ± 0.03	1.4 ± 0.4	2.6 ± 0.8	0.29 ± 0.10	1.5 ± 0.5	12	12
Fluorene	0.4 ± 0.2	0.59 ± 0.01	0.48 ± 0.11	0.8 ± 0.2	0.57 ± 0.12	0.7 ± 0.2	0.6 ± 0.3	0.5 ± 0.3	0.5 ± 0.3	7	7.2

Note: n/d—not detected; n/a – not available.

4. Conclusions

A low-cost method for quantitation of multiple VOCs in ambient air using SPME-GC-MS was developed. It was proven that 65 μm PDMS/DVB fiber provides a better combination of detection limits, accuracy and precision compared to 85 μm Car/PDMS, 100 μm PDMS and 50/30 μm DVB/Car/PDMS. The increase in extraction time above 10 min did not have a significant impact on the responses of analytes. Optimal desorption time is 1 min. For quantification of all analytes, except undecane, vials with samples should not stand on the autosampler tray for more than 8 h. Quantification of 22 of the most stable analytes can be conducted during 24 h after sampling. Spike recoveries of 21 of the 25 chosen analytes were 90–105%. Recoveries of other analytes were 51–89% at RSDs of 7.4–43%.

The developed method was successfully applied for quantification of chosen analytes in atmospheric air of Almaty in Spring, 2019. On average, the completely automated analysis of one sample took 50–60 min, which was enough to analyze 24 (18 air + 6 calibration) air samples per day. All analytes were detected, except methyl ethyl ketone and 1,2-dichloroethane. RSDs of the responses of 23 VOCs varied from 0.1% to 15.6%. The use of three replicate samples allowed identifying outliers. For 18 detected analytes, the fraction of outliers was <18%. Results for the other five detected analytes contained 10–20% outliers. Mean concentrations of 23 VOCs during all sampling times ranged from 0.1 to 83 μg m^{-3}. Toluene-to-benzene concentrations ratios were below 1.0 in colder days of sampling, indicating that most BTEX in these days originated from non-transport-related sources. The obtained results prove that the method is very simple, automated, low-cost and provides sufficiently low detection limits, which allow recommending it for monitoring of a wide range of VOCs in atmospheric air of Almaty and other similar cities. The measured concentrations cannot be used to generalize the air pollution problem in Almaty because additional research is needed for this purpose. These data along with the developed method can be useful for improving the air pollution monitoring program in Almaty.

Supplementary Materials: The following are available online at http://www.mdpi.com/2297-8739/6/4/51/s1, Figure S1: Chromatogram obtained using the developed method based on SPME-GC-MS of air sample with C_{add} = 100 μg m^{-3}, Figure S2: Effect of desorption time on responses of analytes, Table S1: The list of chosen VOCs and its physical properties, Table S2: Coordinates of sampling locations, Table S3: Weather conditions on sampling days, Table S4: Probabilities of difference between initial responses of analytes and their responses after different storage times, Table S5: Sampling locations where lowest and highest concentrations of analytes were determined at different sampling times.

Author Contributions: Conceptualization, B.K. and N.B.; methodology, O.P.I. and N.B.; validation, O.P.I., N.B. and B.K.; formal analysis, O.P.I., N.B. and B.K.; investigation, O.P.I. and N.B.; writing—original draft preparation, O.P.I. and N.B.; writing—review and editing, B.K.; visualization, O.P.I., N.B. and B.K.; supervision, B.K.; project administration, N.B.; funding acquisition, B.K.

Funding: This research was funded by the Ministry of Education and Science of the Republic of Kazakhstan, grant number AP05133158.

Acknowledgments: The authors would like to thank Al-Farabi Kazakh National University for the postdoctoral scholarship of Nassiba Baimatova, and a Ph.D. student of Al-Farabi Kazakh National University, Bauyrzhan Bukenov, for technical support during this study.

Conflicts of Interest: The authors declare no conflict of interest.

References

1. World Health Organization. *Ambient Air Pollution: A Global Assessment of Exposure and Burden of Disease*; WHO: Geneva, Switzerland, 2016.
2. US EPA. *Compendium Method TO-14A Determination of Volatile Organic Compounds (VOCs) in Ambient Air Using Specially Prepared Canisters with Subsequent Analysis by Gas Chromatography*; United States Environmental Protection Agency: Cincinnati, OH, USA, 1999.
3. US EPA. *Compendium Method TO-17 Determination of Volatile Organic Compounds in Ambient Air Using Active Sampling Onto Sorbent Tubes*; United States Environmental Protection Agency: Cincinnati, OH, USA, 1999.

4. Król, S.; Zabiegała, B.; Namieśnik, J. Monitoring VOCs in atmospheric air II. Sample collection and preparation. *Trends Anal. Chem.* **2010**, *29*, 1101–1112. [CrossRef]

5. Miller, L.; Xu, X. Multi-season, multi-year concentrations and correlations amongst the BTEX group of VOCs in an urbanized industrial city. *Atmos. Environ.* **2012**, *61*, 305–315. [CrossRef]

6. Goodman, N.B.; Steinemann, A.; Wheeler, A.J.; Paevere, P.J.; Cheng, M.; Brown, S.K. Volatile organic compounds within indoor environments in Australia. *Build. Environ.* **2017**, *122*, 116–125. [CrossRef]

7. Woolfenden, E. Monitoring VOCs in air using sorbent tubes followed by thermal desorption-capillary GC analysis: Summary of data and practical guidelines. *J. Air Waste Manag. Assoc.* **1997**, *47*, 20–36. [CrossRef]

8. Pawliszyn, J. (Ed.) Applications of Solid Phase Microextraction. In *RSC Chromatography Monographs*; Royal Society of Chemistry: Cambridge, UK, 1999; ISBN 978-0-85404-525-9.

9. Haberhauer-Troyer, C.; Rosenberg, E.; Grasserbauer, M. Evaluation of solid-phase microextraction for sampling of volatile organic sulfur compounds in air for subsequent gas chromatographic analysis with atomic emission detection. *J. Chromatogr. A* **1999**, *848*, 305–315. [CrossRef]

10. Tuduri, L.; Desauziers, V.; Fanlo, J.L. Dynamic versus static sampling for the quantitative analysis of volatile organic compounds in air with polydimethylsiloxane-Carboxen solid-phase microextraction fibers. *J. Chromatogr. A* **2002**, *963*, 49–56. [CrossRef]

11. Ouyang, G. 8-SPME and Environmental Analysis. In *Handbook of Solid Phase Microextraction*; Elsevier Inc.: Amsterdam, The Netherlands, 2012; pp. 251–290. [CrossRef]

12. Tumbiolo, S.; Gal, J.-F.; Maria, P.-C.; Zerbinati, O. Determination of benzene, toluene, ethylbenzene and xylenes in air by solid phase micro-extraction/gas chromatography/mass spectrometry. *Anal. Bioanal. Chem.* **2004**, *380*, 824–830. [CrossRef] [PubMed]

13. Prikryl, P.; Sevcik, J.G.K. Characterization of sorption mechanisms of solid-phase microextraction with volatile organic compounds in air samples using a linear solvation energy relationship approach. *J. Chromatogr. A* **2008**, *1179*, 24–32. [CrossRef]

14. Yassaa, N.; Meklati, B.Y.; Cecinato, A. Analysis of volatile organic compounds in the ambient air of Algiers by gas chromatography with a b-cyclodextrin capillary column. *J. Chromatogr. A* **1999**, *846*, 287–293. [CrossRef]

15. Tumbiolo, S.; Gal, J.-F.; Maria, P.; Zerbinati, O. SPME sampling of BTEX before GC/MS analysis: Examples of outdoor and indoor air quality measurements in public and private sites. *Ann. Chim.* **2005**, *95*, 757–766. [CrossRef]

16. Koziel, J.A.; Pawliszyn, J. Air sampling and analysis of volatile organic compounds with solid phase microextraction. *J. Air Waste Manag. Assoc.* **2001**, *51*, 173–184. [CrossRef] [PubMed]

17. Curran, K.; Underhill, M.; Gibson, L.T.; Strlic, M. The development of a SPME-GC/MS method for the analysis of VOC emissions from historic plastic and rubber materials. *Microchem. J.* **2016**, *124*, 909–918. [CrossRef]

18. Luca, A.; Kjær, A.; Edelenbos, M. Volatile organic compounds as markers of quality changes during the storage of wild rocket. *Food Chem.* **2017**, *232*, 579–586. [CrossRef]

19. Parshintsev, J.; Niina, K.; Hartonen, K.; Miguel, L.; Jussila, M.; Kajos, M.; Kulmala, M.; Riekkola, M. Field measurements of biogenic volatile organic compounds in the atmosphere by dynamic solid-phase microextraction and portable gas chromatography-mass spectrometry. *Atmos. Environ.* **2015**, *115*, 214–222.

20. Zain, S.M.S.M.; Shaharudin, R.; Kamaluddin, M.A.; Daud, S.F. Determination of hydrogen cyanide in residential ambient air using SPME coupled with GC–MS. *Atmos. Pollut. Res.* **2017**, *8*, 678–685. [CrossRef]

21. Mokbel, H.; Al Dine, E.J.; Elmoll, A.; Liaud, C.; Millet, M. Simultaneous analysis of organochlorine pesticides and polychlorinated biphenyls in air samples by using accelerated solvent extraction (ASE) and solid-phase micro-extraction (SPME) coupled to gas chromatography dual electron capture detection. *Environ. Sci. Pollut. Res.* **2016**, *23*, 8053–8063. [CrossRef]

22. Naccarato, A.; Tassone, A.; Moretti, S.; Elliani, R.; Sprovieri, F.; Pirrone, N.; Tagarelli, A. A green approach for organophosphate ester determination in airborne particulate matter: Microwave-assisted extraction using hydroalcoholic mixture coupled with solid-phase microextraction gas chromatography-tandem mass spectrometry. *Talanta* **2018**, *189*, 657–665. [CrossRef]

23. Hussam, A.; Alauddin, M.; Khan, A.H.; Chowdhury, D.; Bibi, H.; Bhattacharjee, M.; Sultana, S. Solid phase microextraction: Measurement of volatile organic compounds (VOCs) in Dhaka city air pollution. *J. Environ. Sci. Health Part A* **2002**, *37*, 1223–1239. [CrossRef]

24. Lee, J.H.; Hwang, S.M.; Lee, D.W.; Heo, G.S. Determination of volatile organic compounds (VOCs) using tedlar bag/solid-phase microextraction/gas chromatography/mass spectrometry (SPME/GC/MS) in ambient and workplace air. *Bull. Korean Chem. Soc.* **2002**, *23*, 488–496.
25. Baimatova, N.; Kenessov, B.; Koziel, J.A.; Carlsen, L.; Bektassov, M.; Demyanenko, O.P. Simple and accurate quantification of BTEX in ambient air by SPME and GC-MS. *Talanta* **2016**, *154*, 46–52. [CrossRef]
26. Woolcock, P.J.; Koziel, J.A.; Johnston, P.A.; Brown, R.C.; Broer, K.M. Analysis of trace contaminants in hot gas streams using time-weighted average solid-phase microextraction: Pilot-scale validation. *Fuel* **2015**, *153*, 552–558. [CrossRef]
27. Carlsen, L.; Baimatova, N.; Kenessov, B.; Kenessova, O. Assessment of the air quality of Almaty. Focussing on the traffic component. *Int. J. Biol. Chem.* **2013**, *5*, 49–69.
28. Nicoara, S.; Tonidandel, L.; Traldi, P.; Watson, J.; Morgan, G.; Popa, O. Determining the levels of volatile organic pollutants in urban air using a gas chromatography-mass spectrometry method. *J. Environ. Public Health* **2009**, *2009*, 148527. [CrossRef] [PubMed]
29. Lee, S.C.; Chiu, M.Y. Volatile organic compounds (VOCs) in urban atmosphere of Hong Kong. *Chemosphere* **2002**, *48*, 375–382. [CrossRef]
30. Khan, A.; Szulejko, J.E.; Kim, K.H.; Brown, R.J.C. Airborne volatile aromatic hydrocarbons at an urban monitoring station in Korea from 2013 to 2015. *J. Environ. Manag.* **2018**, *209*, 525–538. [CrossRef] [PubMed]
31. Li, L.; Li, H.; Zhang, X.; Wang, L.; Xu, L.; Wang, X.; Yu, Y.; Zhang, Y.; Cao, G. Pollution characteristics and health risk assessment of benzene homologues in ambient air in the northeastern urban area of Beijing, China. *J. Environ. Sci.* **2014**, *26*, 214–223. [CrossRef]
32. Zhang, Y.; Mu, Y. Atmospheric BTEX and carbonyls during summer seasons of 2008–2010 in Beijing. *Atmos. Environ.* **2012**, *59*, 186–191. [CrossRef]
33. Bigazzi, A.Y.; Figliozzi, M.A.; Luo, W.; Pankow, J.F. Breath Biomarkers to Measure Uptake of Volatile Organic Compounds by Bicyclists. *Environ. Sci. Technol.* **2016**, *50*, 5357–5363. [CrossRef]
34. Pawliszyn, J. *Handbook of Solid Phase Microextraction*; Elsevier Inc.: Amsterdam, The Netherlands, 2012; ISBN 9780124160170.
35. Kenessov, B.; Derbissalin, M.; Koziel, J.A.; Kosyakov, D.S. Modeling solid-phase microextraction of volatile organic compounds by porous coatings using finite element analysis. *Anal. Chim. Acta* **2019**, *1076*, 73–81. [CrossRef]
36. Lion, L.W. *Sorption and Transport of Polynuclear Aromatic Hydrocarbons in Low-Carbon Aquifer Materials*; AFESC: Ithaca, NY, USA, 1988.

Review

Recent Applications and Newly Developed Strategies of Solid-Phase Microextraction in Contaminant Analysis: Through the Environment to Humans

Attilio Naccarato [1,*] **and Antonio Tagarelli** [2,*]

1   CNR-Institute of Atmospheric Pollution Research, Division of Rende, UNICAL-Polifunzionale,
     I-87036 Arcavacata di Rende, CS, Italy
2   Dipartimento di Chimica e Tecnologie Chimiche, Università della Calabria, Via P. Bucci Cubo 12/C,
     I-87036 Arcavacata di Rende, CS, Italy
*   Correspondence: attilio.naccarato@iia.cnr.it (A.N.); a.tagarelli@unical.it (A.T.)

Received: 10 October 2019; Accepted: 1 November 2019; Published: 6 November 2019

Abstract: The present review aims to describe the recent and most impactful applications in pollutant analysis using solid-phase microextraction (SPME) technology in environmental, food, and bio-clinical analysis. The covered papers were published in the last 5 years (2014–2019) thus providing the reader with information about the current state-of-the-art and the future potential directions of the research in pollutant monitoring using SPME. To this end, we revised the studies focused on the investigation of persistent organic pollutants (POPs), pesticides, and emerging pollutants (EPs) including personal care products (PPCPs), in different environmental, food, and bio-clinical matrices. We especially emphasized the role that SPME is having in contaminant surveys following the path that goes from the environment to humans passing through the food web. Besides, this review covers the last technological developments encompassing the use of novel extraction coatings (e.g., metal-organic frameworks, covalent organic frameworks, PDMS-overcoated fiber), geometries (e.g., Arrow-SPME, multiple monolithic fiber-SPME), approaches (e.g., vacuum and cold fiber SPME), and on-site devices. The applications of SPME hyphenated with ambient mass spectrometry have also been described.

Keywords: solid phase microextraction (SPME); air analysis; environmental waters analysis; soil analysis; food monitoring; on-site sampling; human biomonitoring (HBM); chromatography; ambient mass spectrometry; ultra-trace analysis

---

1. Introduction

The evolution of modern lifestyles due to the development of industrial civilization has influenced the relationship between humankind and his environment. If, on the one hand, the quality of life has generally changed considerably during the past decades, we may be facing a turnaround. Indeed, for many years, the impact that the current living habits have had on the environment has been underestimated and the receptiveness to topics such as sustainable development has only been recently established. The impact on the environment occurs in many ways, and with a different extent. Generally, less evident but equally important is the impact due to the inordinate use of chemical products. Although their daily use contributes to improving our quality of life, their uncontrollable dispersion in the environment associated with low biodegradability is undoubtedly the main mode of introduction of pollutants into the biological cycles, including those involving humans through nutrition and direct exposure. In this context, the identification and quantification of contaminants in environmental, food, and bio-clinical matrices find more and more space in both routine and research laboratories often driven by growing regulatory attention at the national and international level.

Solid-phase microextraction (SPME) is a well-established green technique for simultaneous extraction and pre-concentration of the compounds from a variety of matrices. Since its introduction in the early 1990s, this technique has been experiencing rapid development and growth in terms of coating materials, geometries and applications. Although SPME is only part of the broad panorama of microextraction analytical techniques, it plays an important role. Given the simplicity, versatility, and availability in different formats, SPME addresses several challenges associated with the traditional sample preparation procedures and we expect a noteworthy impact on the methods of analysis in the next coming years. The purpose of this review is to highlight the role that SPME is having in contaminant monitoring through the path that goes from the environment to humans. To this end, we revised the studies focused on the analysis of persistent organic pollutants (POPs), pesticides, and emerging pollutants (EPs) including personal care products (PPCPs). We wanted to cover solely the most impactful advancements published in the last 5 years (2014–2019) giving to the reader a picture of the aspects towards the research is directed and at the same time highlighting as the broadly available panorama of SPME strategies can effectively solve even highly complex analytical problems.

2. The Beginning Step: Environmental Matrices

The journey undertaken by contaminants starts from their release into the environment in at least one of its components, i.e., air, water, soil. As constitutive elements of the biosphere, they are factors in a continuous dynamic equilibrium characterized by exchanges between them and make up a complex system with the life forms they host. In the environmental field, the SPME is a technique that includes a high number of studies: in particular in the analysis of environmental waters, whereas to a less extent are the applications to air and soil associated matrices (Figure 1 and Table 1).

Figure 1. Main solid-phase microextraction—geometries and strategies used in the analysis of environmental matrices during the covered period (2014–2019).

2.1. Air

Although ambient air may seem a simple matrix for less experienced analysts, it presents important analytical challenges because of the difficulty in sampling and calibration procedures. The air comprises many components of both organic and inorganic nature present in the gaseous and particulate phase which are in continuous mixing. In air can occur complex reactions the may convert the pollutants into other chemical species. Unlike the other environmental components, in the air, the analytes can be quickly transported covering even long distances around the world. In addition, phenomena such as release, volatilization, deposition, and resuspension driven by weather conditions lead to cycles of reduction and increase of pollutants and contribute to introducing of new contaminants from soil or water. To further complicate the matrix, due to the presence of suspended particulate matter, the analytes can be present as gaseous compounds as well as bound to the particles, depending on their chemical–physical properties.

In air sampling, the SPME has been exploited in different geometries and strategies (Figure 1, Table 1). The areas in which the research has mainly been addressed during the last five years have regarded the use of commercially available coatings, as well as the development of new coatings and their application. Many studies have been conducted in indoor environments in order to monitor exposure to volatile organic compounds (VOCs) and semivolatile organic compounds (SVOCs) that are released into the air by many activities [1–3], but also by used furnishing [4,5].

Commercially available (divinylbenzene/carboxen/polydimethylsiloxane) DVB/CAR/PDMS fiber has been successfully employed in a method for the simultaneous analysis of trihalomethanes (THMs) such as trichloromethane, bromodichloromethane, dibromochloromethane, and tribromomethane, in ambient air [1]. This method was validated for swimming pool air, bearing improvements over previous methods such as a decrease in instrumental runtime, minimization of sample contamination, and elimination of the need for harsh chemicals. Similarly, other commercially available SPME fibers, such as a carboxen/polydimethylsiloxane (CAR/PDMS) and polydimethylsiloxane-divinylbenzene (PDMS/DVB) fiber, were used in the investigation of some VOCs present in a laboratory environment [2] and in the implementation of a method for the analysis of trace carbonyls based on on-fiber derivatization with (pentafluorobenzyl)hydroxylamine (PFBHA) and gas chromatographic (GC) analysis, which was then applied to the monitoring in dated office rooms [5].

As regards the application in an outdoor environment, among the most interesting applications there is the use of the SPME fibers in the arrow version (Figure 2). SPME Arrow consists of a steel rod coated with a larger amount of sorbent material than the traditional SPME fiber, while still being compatible with desorption in a standard GC liner due to its dimensions and sharp, closed tip. The sorbent-coated rod can be withdrawn in a steel tube when the device is not in use. Because of the steel rod, the device is less fragile than a conventional SPME fiber [6].

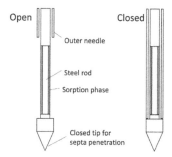

Figure 2. The Arrow SPME system with sorbent exposed (left) and with sorbent covered by a steel tube (right) [6].

The SPME Arrow device coated with commercial and self-made functionalized mesoporous silica materials was used on board an aerial drone, which was used for the simultaneous collection of air samples in two difficult access places such as boreal forest and wetland [7]. The sampled VOCs were detected by gas chromatography with a polar column and mass spectrometry. Established pollutants such as polycyclic aromatic hydrocarbons (PAHs), and other hazardous substances including phthalates, adipates, vulcanizing agents and antioxidants were successfully analyzed in the air generated above synthetic turf football fields following heating of the rubber material using a PDMS/DVB as fiber coating in headspace mode [8]. Benzene, toluene, ethylbenzene, and xylenes (BTEX) in ambient air have been the target of one research with the aim of developing a simpler, low-budget, and accurate method for their quantification based on SPME and gas chromatography coupled with mass spectrometry (GC–MS) [9]. This article shows how in urban areas with highly contaminated air, 20 mL vials can be used for the collection of air samples, and a 100 µm polydimethylsiloxane (PDMS) fiber can be used to sufficiently preconcentrate the analytes before the analysis with GC–MS. Exposure to ambient HCN concentration in a residential area close to a gold mine was assessed by SPME using 75 µm CAR/PDMS fiber [10]. Given the low detection limit, this method provides promising results for monitoring ambient HCN concentrations, and at the same time, minimizes the work for sample preparation, reducing the time and cost of the monitoring.

SPME is not only exploited for direct sampling in the air but it is also used as a convenient strategy for the introduction of the analytes into a gas chromatographic system after the sample preparation step.

This strategy was recently used to quantify a class of largely studied pollutants such as organophosphate esters (OPEs) [11,12] bound to airborne particulate matter by a green protocol based on the combination of microwave-assisted extraction (MAE) and SPME followed by gas chromatography coupled with tandem mass spectrometry (GC-MS/MS) analysis [13]. Similarly, aliphatic and aromatic amines (AA) in indoor air were investigated by SPME-GC-MS after the ultrasonic extraction of XAD-2 adsorbent without derivatization [3]. In this paper, the author reached detection limits lower from about a factor of five in comparison to direct injection. This result, consequence of the solvent-less nature of SPME injection, is consistent with the improvement in chromatographic performance reported in the literature, also in the analysis of polar compounds with SPME [14]. The use of commercial SPME fibers has also recently found space in the quantification of some pesticides in atmospheric samples. Thirty-one pesticides belonging to different chemical classes (urea, phenoxy acids, pyrethrenoïds, etc.) and commonly used in non-agricultural areas such as public or private gardens were investigated. After the sampling on glass fiber filters and on XAD-2 resin traps followed by the extraction using the accelerated solvent extraction (ASE) technique, an 85 µm polyacrylate (PA) fiber was immersed in the ASE extract to preconcentrate the analytes before GC-MS analysis with on-injector derivatization using N-methyl-N-(tert.-butyldimethylsilyl) trifluoroacetamide (MtBSTFA) [15].

Porous materials are attracting the attention of the scientific community in numerous scientific fields due to their properties and different possible uses. In this connection, also in the development of SPME coatings these so-called advanced porous materials and cavitands find space, and their use for the analysis of pollutants in the air constitutes a robust line of research still growing [16]. In particular, interesting articles have recently been published on the development of new coatings based on materials such as metal-organic frameworks (MOFs) and covalent organic frameworks (COFs), and their application in air analysis. These were followed by other papers focused on the use of microporous organic network (MON), or other hybrids materials with MON, which made it possible to improve the extraction efficiency by countering the tendency of some competitors such as water molecules to occupy the pores of MOF [17,18]. Most of the recent applications of these materials have focused on the analysis of established pollutants in particulate matter after a previous extraction of the analytes from the solid matrix [17–19], whereas a COFs coated fiber-based with gas chromatography-mass spectrometric detection was used in the investigation of some volatile and harmful benzene homologs by exploiting the favorable π-π and hydrophobic interactions between the π-conjugated aromatic groups of the coating and the aromatic rings of the analytes [20]. This material was followed by the use of functionalized cavitand that, given its molecular structure, allowed to obtain high enrichment factors, very low detection limits and increased selectivity toward the benzene. For this reason, this coating was proposed as a selective SPME coating for the determination of BTEX at trace levels even for the assessment of short-term exposure in workers [21].

Analytical approaches that are not yet fully explored are the needle-trap and cold-fiber SPME, partly because of the difficulty in commercially obtaining the necessary equipment for the analytic set-up [22,23]. Recently, some studies have been published on SPME fibers used as a passive sampling device to get the Time-Weighted Average (TWA) concentration of VOCs. These papers aim to improve the technique in terms of accuracy, particularly with longer sampling times [24,25]. Advances in this field could contribute in the coming years to the effective use of the SPME in the environmental monitoring programs targeted to the chronic exposure or background concentrations.

2.2. Water

The presence of organic and inorganic pollutants in the environmental waters is a serious problem for human health and the well-being of ecosystems. Protecting this important environmental sector involves national and international monitoring interventions along with regulatory legislative actions, which are necessarily based on the results of analytical studies in the environmental field. Using microextraction techniques, such as the SPME, have offered a significant contribution to the identification and quantification of established and emerging pollutants in environmental waters by offering reliable analysis tools with growing selectivity and sensitivity [26]. In the last 5 years, the number of published articles in which the SPME is employed to address analytical issues in environmental waters is remarkable (Table 1). Most of these investigations (over one hundred in the covered period) were directed on the development of new coating materials and their use in real case scenarios (Figure 1). These studies, in terms of numbers, are followed by works in which new strategies in using SPME are presented, e.g., new coupling with mass spectrometer equipment [27–29] or the development of a new mechanically robust SPME sampler for the on-site sampling [30]. The involved classes of molecules are various and include both pollutants traditionally investigated such as PAHs [19,31–41] and polychlorinated biphenyls (PCBs) [33,42–45], and new polluting molecules such as dyes [46], additives for materials [14], new pesticides [47–53], antibiotics [54–57], pollutants coming from a number of polluting processes including those in industries [58–60], and last but not least, ultraviolet filters, whose determination in natural water is one of the issues that is attracting greater interest [37,61–73].

The investigation of PAHs is still current, and despite the numerous studies already present in the literature, PAHs are the target in many studies because of their high relevance as pollutants, and for this reason, they are also used as reference compounds to test new SPME uses and coating materials [74,75]. Some noteworthy applications report the successful analysis in environmental waters using coating based on polymer materials [31], MOF [19,32–34], mesoporous carbon materials [35], polyhedral oligomeric silsesquioxanes (POSSs) [36], titanium dioxide-nanosheets [37], coatings based on nanoparticles [38,75], nanotubes (MONTs) [39,40], and material derived from low-cost waste such as biochar [41]. The latter analytical strategy seems particularly interesting as it opens new scenarios involving the recovery of waste materials and their exploitation in an analytical context. Similarly, BTEX were also taken as a reference for verifying the analytical performance of a new SPME coating in environmental waters. These studies were mainly carried out by prof. Ouyang's group, which has achieved satisfactory results for analysis of river, lake, pond and seawater by developing SPME coatings that exploit different materials such as tri-metal centered MOFs (tM-MOFs) [76], graphene–carbon nanotubes (G-CNTs) [77], Prussian blue nanoparticles-doped graphene oxide [75], knitting aromatic polymers (KAPs) [78] and porous organic polymers (POPs) [79] including Scholl-coupling microporous polymers [80].

Among the most impactful trends, there is the application of the newly developed geometries to real environmental case studies. Multiple monolithic fiber solid phase microextraction (MMF-SPME) was developed as a new extraction approach for aqueous samples; considering its peculiarities, it is proposed as an improved alternative to the traditional SPME in terms of extraction capacity, mass-transfer speed and flexibility [48,81–84]. MMF-SPME consists of four independent thin fibers bound together to form a fiber bunch (Figure 3).

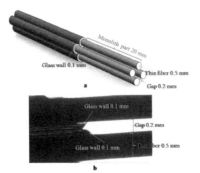

Figure 3. Schematic diagram of MMF-SPME (**a**) and the microscope image of the gap between thin fibers (**b**) [81].

Similarly, monolithic fiber has also found application in the in-tube SPME (IT-SPME) through the development of novel materials such as the MOF-monolithic adsorbent with enhanced surface area, which was successfully used to detect fluoroquinolones at ultra-trace level in river water [54], but also the development of new strategies such as magnetism-enhanced monolith-based in-tube solid-phase microextraction (ME-MB/IT-SPME). This technique used modified absorbent material with Fe_3O_4 nanoparticles and the exertion of a variable magnetic field to overcome the main drawbacks of the traditional monolith-based in-tube solid-phase microextraction (MB/IT-SPME), that is the low extraction efficiency; this method was used for the extraction of triazines from river and lake water [85].

Recently, Kabir and Furton proposed the fabric phase sorptive extraction (FPSE) [86] which is a new promising member of the sorbent-based sorptive microextraction group. This technique overcomes some of the major shortcomings of traditional SPME related to the sorbent coating technique and the geometry of the microextraction device such as the small primary contact surface area and the low amount (typically ~0.5 µL) of sorbent loading that often results in poor extraction sensitivity. Despite its recent development, FPSE has not only been used for the analysis of pollutants such as non-steroidal anti-inflammatory drugs [87], and cytostatic compounds in environmental water [88], but it has already been the topic of some studies focused on its own evolution that suggest interesting scenarios in the next years [89,90].

2.3. Soil

The monitoring of pollutants in the soil is very important to ensure environmental and food safety. The main pollutants that are being investigated are pesticides, petroleum hydrocarbons, PAHs, PCBs, pharmaceuticals, and industrial residuals. Although soil is one of the environmental compartments together with water and air, unlike them, the presence of pollutants in the soil presents different analytical challenges determined by the complexity of the matrix. Compared with the pollution of air and water, soil pollution is very nonhomogeneous and often local because of a slower diffusion of chemicals. Moreover, soil samples have different physicochemical properties and affinity to analytes [91]. In fact, the main issue in soil analysis using SPME is certainly related to the matrix effect, which can affect the reliability of the analysis and lead to the fouling of the fiber coating caused by irreversible adsorption of macromolecules on the extraction phase. This occurrence can result in the changes in fiber properties and the extraction performance of the fiber upon subsequent use. Currently, despite the recent technical developments, the use of SPME in soil analysis is still a challenge and requires, at least during method development, robust expertise in the field.

During the last five years, SPME has found a place in the analysis of soil pollutants in several respects. Similar to what we highlighted for the study in environmental waters, a significant part of the research is aimed at the development and use of new, better-performing coatings, above all in terms of sensitivity and specificity (Figure 1, Table 1). A cavitand-based SPME coating was synthesized and used for the selective determination of nitroaromatic explosives and explosive taggants at ultratrace levels [92]. Among the most used materials, the MOFs have a leading role. Their application as SPME coating for soil analysis has been extensively investigated in recent years, both as regards the use of new structural variants and their synthesis. After their preparation, these SPME fibers were successfully used in the analysis of trace levels of fungicides [93], PAHs [19,94–96], PCBs [97,98], polybrominated diphenyl ethers (PBDEs) [99].

As for commercial fibers, their use in soil analysis still has many potentials and they have been used not only in method development for new harmful contaminants [100–102] but rather as an analytical tool to carry out other studies, principally with ecological–environmental purposes. Indeed, given its analytical features, SPME allows for the determination of analyte free concentration and for this reason it has been used in bioavailability [103], bio-accessibility [104], and soil sorption studies involving the binding potential of dissolved organic matter (DOM) and the effects of bioremediation on contaminated industrial and agricultural soils [105,106].

Of particular interest is also the deployment of untraditional SPME approaches including the fabric-phase sorptive extraction used for alkyl phenols determination [107], MMF-SPME exploited for the sulfonylurea herbicides assay [47], ionic liquid-coated PTFE tube used for mercury extraction before cold vapor atomic absorption spectrometry (CV-AAS) determination [108], and vacuum-assisted headspace solid-phase microextraction (Vac-HSSPME). The latter was recently reviewed by Psillakis [109] and appears to be a promising route for the analysis of pollutants in solid matrices such as soil because increasing the volatility of the analytes, it allows the analysis in HS-SPME with the consequent reduction of the matrix effect and improvement of the fiber lifetime.

Table 1. Selected SPME applications in environmental matrices.

Analytes	Matrix	SPME Approach and Coating Material	Instrumentation	Calibration Range	[Ref] Publishing Year
THMs	Ambient air	Fiber—DVB/CAR/PDMS	GC-MS	2–5000 µg/m³	[1]—2019
VOCs	Indoor air	fiber—CAR/PDMS	GC-MS, GC-FID	-	[2]—2018
aliphatic and aromatic amines	Indoor air	Fiber—DVB/CAR/PDMS	GC-MS	10–50,000 ng/m³	[3]—2018
OPEs	Indoor air	fiber—PDMS	GC-MS	0.05–500 mg/m³	[4]—2017
Formaldehyde, acetaldehyde, acetone, hexanal	Indoor air	fiber—PDMS/DVB	GC-MS, GC-FID	-	[5]—2014
VOCs	Ambient air	SPME Arrow—Carbon WR, Carbon WR/PDMS, PDMS/DVB, lab-made functionalized mesoporous silica material	GC-MS	-	[7]—2019
PAHs, phthalates, adipates, vulcanisation additives and antioxidants	Ambient air	fiber—PDMS/DVB	GC-MS	0.01–2 µg/L	[8]—2018
BTEX	Ambient air	fiber—PDMS	GC-MS	2–200 mg/m³	[9]—2016
HCN	Ambient air	fiber—CAR/PDMS	GC-MS	5–500 µg/L	[10]—2017
OPEs	PM10	fiber—DVB/CAR/PDMS	GC-MS/MS	0.1–10 ng/mL	[13]—2018
pesticides of different chemical classes	Ambient air and PM	fiber—PA	GC-MS	2–2000 ng of each pesticide	[15]—2014
Short-chain chlorinated paraffin	water, sediment, organisms, and PM	fiber—hollow microporous organic network (H-MON)	GC-MS	0.05–10 ng/mL	[17]—2018
PAHs	environmental water, PM2.5, and smoked meat	fiber—MOF@microporous organic network (MON) hybrid materials	GC-MS/MS	0.1–500 ng/L	[18]—2016
nitrated polycyclic aromatic hydrocarbons	environmental water, PM2.5, and soil	fiber—porphyrinic zirconium MOF	GC-MS	0.4–400 ng/L	[19]—2017
benzene homologues	indoor air	fiber—Covalent organic frameworks (COF)	GC-MS	0.10–20 ng/L	[20]—2017
BTEX	ambient air	fiber—functionalized tetraquinoxaline cavitand	GC-MS	3.5–470 ng/m³	[21]—2016

Table 1. *Cont.*

Analytes	Matrix	SPME Approach and Coating Material	Instrumentation	Calibration Range	[Ref] Publishing Year
acrolein	ambient air	cold fiber—PDMS	GC-MS	-	[23]—2017
Acetic acid	indoor air	fiber—Car/PDMS	GC-MS	-	[25]—2019
pesticides	river water	SPME-TM	DART-MS/MS DART-orbitrap	0.10–100 ng/mL	[27]—2017
triazine herbicides obtained	lake water	IT-SPME	DART-MS/MS	0.02–0.46 ng/mL	[28]—2014
perfluorinated compounds (PFCs)	lake and river water	wooden-tip SPME ambient MS	LC-MS/MS orbitrap	0.5–100 ng/L	[29]—2014
PAHs	rain and river water	IT-SPME—PEEK tube was packed with polyester fibers	LC- diode array detector	0.03–80 µg/L	[31]—2016
PAHs	lake and river water	fiber—boron nitride nanotube	GC-MS/MS	1–1000 ng/L	[40]—2014
PAHs	river water	fiber—peanut shell-derived biochar materials	GC-MS	10–2000 ng/L	[41]—2019
PAHs	lake water	fiber—MOF	GC-MS	0.01–10 µg/L	[32]—2019
PCBs	lake and river water	fiber—MOF	GC-MS	1–50 ng/L	[33]—2015
PAHs	lake and river water	fiber—zeolite imidazolate MOF	GC-MS	10–20,000 ng/L	[34]—2019
PAHs	lake and river water	fiber—hollow mesoporous carbon spheres	GC-MS	5–2000 ng/L	[35]—2017
PAHs	river water	fiber—titanium dioxide-nanosheets	HPLC-UV	0.05–300 mg/L	[37]—2015
PAHs	volcanic area water	fiber—silver nanoparticles	GC-FID	5–300 µg/L	[38]—2018
nitro-polycyclic aromatic hydrocarbons (NPAHs)	lake and snow water	fiber—metal–organic nanotubes	GC-MS/MS	10–1000 ng/L	[39]—2018
PCBs	river water	fiber—bamboo charcoal	GC-MS/MS	0.2–1000 ng/L	[42]—2014
PCBs	seawater	fiber—metal–organic nanotubes	GC-MS/MS	10–5000 pg/L	[43]—2016
PCBs	pond and lake water	fiber—multimodal porous carbons (MPCs)	GC-ECD	10–1000 ng/L	[44]—2019
PCBs	pond, river, underground and lake water	fiber—metal–organic nanotubes	GC-MS/MS	0.1–500 ng/L	[45]—2014

Table 1. *Cont.*

Analytes	Matrix	SPME Approach and Coating Material	Instrumentation	Calibration Range	[Ref]—Publishing Year
Sudan dyes	lake water	PEEK tube—zeolitic imidazolate frameworks	HPLC-UV	0.02–20 ng/mL	[46]—2019
sulfonylurea herbicides (SUHs)	lake, river and well water	MMF-SPME—mixed functional monomers	HPLC-DAD	0.1–200 µg/L	[47]—2018
triazine herbicides	lake and river water	MMF-SPME—polydopamine-based monolith	HPLC-DAD	0.1–200 µg/L	[48]—2016
chlorinated herbicides	river water	Fiber—polyethersulfone	GC-MS	0.05–5 ng/mL	[49]—2014
organophosphorous pesticides	well water	fiber—metal-organic framework/polyethersulfone nanocomposite (TMU-4/PES)	GC-NPD	0.015–50 µg/L	[50]—2018
organochlorine pesticides	well and pond water	fiber—gold nanoparticles	GC-ECD	0.56–10 µg/L	[51]—2016
organochlorine pesticides	river and pond water	fiber—nitrogen-doped ordered mesoporous polymer (NOMP)	GC-MS	9–1500 ng/L	[52]—2016
carbamate pesticides	river water	MMF-SPME—boron-rich coating	HPLC-DAD	0.057–0.96 µg/L	[53]—2019
fluoroquinolones	river water	IT-SPME—MOF-monolith composite	HPLC-FLD	0.001–5.0 µg/L	[54]—2019
cefaclor and cefalexin	lake water	stir bar—molecular imprinted polymers and magnetic carbon nanotubes	HPLC-UV	15–320 ng/mL	[55]—2017
sulfadiazine	well water	stir bar—graphene oxide-silica composite reinforced	UV-vis	5–150 µg/L	[57]—2017
nitrophenols	lake and river water	MMF-SPME—AMED coating	HPLC-DAD	0.5–200 µg/L	[58]—2015
chlorophenol and nitrophenols	river and spring water	fiber—cobalt (II)-based metal-organic nanotubes (Co-MONTs)	GC-MS	0.5–1000 ng/L	[59]—2017
ultraviolet filters	river and rain water	fiber—phenyl functionalization of titania nanoparticles	HPLC-UV	0.005–25 µg/L	[61]—2015
ultraviolet filters	river and rain water	fiber—gold nanoparticles	HPLC-UV	0.10–400 µg/L	[70]—2014
ultraviolet filters	river and rain water	fiber—silica nanoparticle	HPLC-UV	0.05–300 µg/L	[71]—2017

Table 1. *Cont.*

Analytes	Matrix	SPME Approach and Coating Material	Instrumentation	Calibration Range	[Ref] Publishing Year
ultraviolet filters	river water	IT-SPME—polyaniline coating	HPLC-DAD	0.06–100 µg/L	[62]—2017
ultraviolet filters	river water	fiber—oriented ZnO nanosheets	HPLC-UV	0.05–500 ng/mL	[63]—2019
ultraviolet filters	river water	fiber—nitrogen-enriched carbonaceous material	HPLC-UV	0.2–200 µg/L	[65]—2017
ultraviolet filters	river water	fiber—in situ fabricated rod-like TiO_2 coating	HPLC-UV	0.05–200 µg/L	[68]—2014
BTEX, organochlorine pesticides	sea, pond and river water	fiber—Prussian blue nanoparticles-doped graphene oxide	GC-MS	1–1000 ng/L, 2–2000 ng/L	[75]—2019
BTEX	pond and river water	fiber—tri-metal centered metal-organic frameworks (tM-MOFs)	GC-MS	5–2000 ng/L	[76]—2017
BTEX	lake and river water	fiber—graphene-carbon nanotubes composite	GC-MS	5–5000 ng/L	[77]—2018
BTEX	river water	fiber—porous organic polymers	GC-MS	2–500 ng/L	[79]—2017
BTEX and PAHs	pond and river water	fiber—microporous polymer	GC-MS	1–20,000 ng/L	[80]—2018
benzoylurea insecticides	r ver water	MMF-SPME—poly(methacrylic acid-co-ethylene dimethacrylate)	HPLC-DAD	0.10–200 µg/L	[82]—2015
endocrine disrupting	lake and river water	MMF-SPME—polymeric ionic liquid-based adsorbent	HPLC-UV	0.10–200 µg/L	[83]—2017
perfluoroalkane sulfonamides	lake a nd river water	MMF-SPME—polymeric material with boron	HPLC-MS/MS	0.0025–30.0 µg/L	[84]—2019
estrogens	lake and river water	magnetism-enhanced monolith-based in-tube IT-SPME—polymeric monolith with modified Fe_3O_4 nanoparticles	HPLC-DAD	0.5–200 µg/L	[85]—2016
non-steroidal anti-inflammatory drugs	river water	fabric phase sorptive extraction—poly(dime-thyldiphenylsiloxane); poly(tetrahydrofuran);	GC-MS	3–20,000 ng/L	[87]—2015
triazine herbicides	river water	Stir fabric phase sorptive extraction	UPLC-DAD	0. 26–1.50 µg/L	[89]—2015

Table 1. *Cont.*

Analytes	Matrix	SPME Approach and Coating Material	Instrumentation	Calibration Range	[Ref] Publishing Year
nitroaromatic Explosives	soil	fiber—quinoxaline-bridged cavitand	GC-MS	120–1200 ng/Kg	[92]—2014
PAHs	soil	fiber—nanoporous carbon derived from an aluminum- based MOF	GC-MS	0.1–12 µg/L	[95]—2015
PCBs	soil	fiber—different MOF networks	GC-MS	0.01–600 ng/L	[97]—2018
PCBs	soil	fiber—MOF MIL-88B	GC-MS	5–200 ng/L	[98]—2014
polybrominated diphenyl ethers	soil	fiber—Ag(I)-organic frameworks	GC-µECD	0.1–500 ng/g	[99]—2015
dimethylhydrazine	soil	fiber—Car/PDMS	GC-MS	0.5–2.5 mg/Kg	[100]—2018
1-methyl-1H-1,2,4-triazole	soil	fiber—PDMS/DVB	GC-MS	-	[102]—2015
DDE	soil	fiber—PDMS	GC-MS	-	[103]—2017
PCBs	soil	fiber—PDMS	GC-MS	-	[104]—2019
PAHs	soil	fiber—PDMS	HPLC-UV	-	[106]—2016
mercury	soil	ionic liquid coated PTFE tube	CV AAS	0.5–60 ng/mL	[108]—2014

3. The Spread Step: Food Matrices and Drinking Water

Chemical pollution of food is perceived as a global safety issue. Most times, the source of contaminants is the environment where the food has been produced. This is the situation of several organic substances coming from industrial processes or, in general, from human activities that persist in the environment and become globally dispersed in air and water sources, and therefore concentrate on fruits, vegetables, and animals through the food chain. Because of the type of contamination, some food products may be more contaminated than others owing to factors such as the specific exposure to pollutants or the differences in plant uptake systems from the ecosystem.

Food samples are complex matrices which often consist of compounds such as proteins, fats, acids, bases, and salts that can largely interfere with the analysis. Moreover, for solid foods, SPME is usually forerun by other previous extraction procedures to get an analyzable liquid extract.

3.1. Drinking Water

Intensive industrialization of the world has resulted in an increased input of organic pollutants, which may significantly affect the quality of surface waters that are often sources of drinking water for a large part of the world's population. Since most water contaminants are toxic and dangerous, not only to humans but also to animals and plants, these pollutants should be monitored in tap and surface waters. As with environmental water samples, microextraction techniques and in particular SPME have been giving a significant contribution to the determination of several contaminants in drinking water. Given the presence of drawbacks in the use of a traditional commercial coating, such as limited variety of the fibers available, insufficient thermal or solvent instability and limited selectivity, the greatest efforts have been made in the development of new coating materials to offer reliable analysis tools with better selectivity and sensitivity (Figure 4, Table 2).

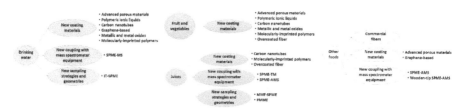

Figure 4. Main solid-phase microextraction geometries and strategies used in the analysis of food matrices during the covered period (2014–2019).

The use of carbon nanotubes (CNTs) has been exploited for the extraction of benzene derivatives [110,111], and phthalates [112] from drinking water samples. Owing to the carbon backbone provided by a two-dimensional structure with unique structural and chemical properties, CNTs are highly hydrophobic and mostly applied to extract hydrophobic analytes, through π-π stacking interactions. However, the surface of CNTs can be modified by chemical and physical functionalization to introduce different functional groups, resulting in enhanced dispersibility and accessible surface. In above-cited papers, CNTs have been combined with a polypyrrole/titanium oxide composite [111], multiwalled carbon nanotubes (MWCNT) functionalized with polyimidazolium ionic liquid was coated on an electrodeposited polyaniline film supported by a stainless-steel fiber [110], and MWCNTs on polystyrene (PS) microspheres have been designed and prepared by layer-by-layer assembly via electrostatic interaction [112]. In general, these coatings offered excellent thermal stability, high EFs and low LODs compared with other analytical methods. The MWCNTs composite microspheres could be of substantial scientific and technological interest with potential applications for the extraction of pollutants in environmental samples. Conductive polymers (CPs) have been also exploited as SPME coating for the extraction of contaminants from drinking water. In particular, thermal and mechanical stability of the polypyrrole-based SPME fibers have been evaluated for the analysis of haloanisoles in tap water [113] whereas polyaniline/silver (PANI/Ag) composites were prepared, and fabricated into SPME coatings for the extraction of bifenthrin from tap water and the following matrix-free laser desorption/ionization (LDI) of the target analyte [114].

Graphene, functional graphene materials or graphene composites have been successfully used as SPME coatings to detect various organic contaminants. In particular, several functionalized graphene coatings have been developed in order to enhance its extraction capacity and, above all, its selectivity for specific analytes. For example, hydroxy-terminated poly(ethylene glycol) (PEG) grafted onto graphene sheets was prepared via a covalent interaction and then PEG-g-graphene was coated on the etched stainless steel wire by a sol-gel process [115]. This coating was tested for the determination of volatile aromatic compounds (VACs) in tap and mineral waters. In another work, polyethylene glycol–graphene oxide (PEG–GO) sol-gel coating was successfully applied for the analysis of aromatic amines in aqueous samples as target compounds [116]. Due to the adsorptive and inherent advantages of GO nano-sheets as well as the performance of the sol-gel coating technology, this fiber exhibited a porous surface structure, good precision and accuracy, high selectivity and sensitivity, longer life span (over 200 uses) and high thermal stability. Similarly, graphene coatings have also found application in the IT-SPME for the determination of triazines [117,118]. In one case, a method was developed based on the use of a packed column containing graphene oxide supported on aminopropyl silica and following analysis by high performance liquid chromatography and tandem mass spectrometry (HPLC-MS/MS) [117], whereas in the other one a coated column was prepared by the covalent modification of monolayer graphene oxide sheets onto the inner wall of a fused-silica capillary [118]. Other porous carbons have been selected and developed as novel SPME coatings focusing on the two key factors for the choice of suitable porous carbons: surface area and pore structure. Li et al. proposed a C18 composite fiber, prepared with a new method and applied to the analysis of organochlorine pesticides (OCPs) in drinking water samples [119]. The prepared fiber showed excellent thermal stability, solvent resistance and extraction performance more than seven times higher than those of commercial fibers. Ordered mesoporous carbon film [120] and different activated carbon-polymer monoliths [120] were also used as a coating for the quantification of BTEX and phthalates in drinking waters, respectively.

MOFs are porous hybrid materials composed of metal ions at their center, and organic linkers. In the last years, they have become very popular as SPME coatings, due to the easy modification of their pore surfaces, which can lead to enhanced selectivity toward specific analytes. A wide variety of MOFs was proposed in the literature depending upon fiber format, the method used for assembling MOFs onto the fiber surface, the metal ion and ligand in the synthesis of MOFs. Metal-organic aerogel (MOA)/MIL-53(Fe) was fabricated by gluing them on a nichrome wire using silicone glue [121] and the resulting fiber was applied to the analysis of chlorobenzenes in tap water. In another application for the determination of chlorobenzene in HS mode, three types of MOFs with Zn and Cd as metal centers were synthesized with 4,4-biphenyldicarboxylate, terephthalic acid, and 2,6-naphthalene dicarboxylate as ligands [122]. MOF coatings were also prepared by using 2-aminoterephthalic acid and Al salts and termed MIL-53 (Al). These MOFs were employed for the extraction of organochlorine pesticides [123] and PAHs [95]. Experimental results showed that the NH_2-MIL-53(Al) SPME coating was solvent resistant and thermostable, and its efficiency for organochlorine pesticides was higher than that of commercially available SPME fiber coatings such as polydimethylsiloxane, polydimethylsiloxane-divinylbenzene, and polyacrylate. A sol-gel coating technique was applied for the preparation of a solid-phase microextraction fiber by coating the metal-organic framework UiO-67 onto a stainless-steel wire. The prepared fiber was explored for the HS-SPME of nitrobenzene compounds from tap water [124]. Again, the sol-gel technique was used for the preparation of fiber by coating MIL-101 onto stainless steel wires. The prepared fiber was explored for the HS-SPME of seven VACs [125]. Metal-organic nanotubes (MONTs) are a novel class of hybrid materials that bridge inorganic and organic nanotubes and possess the advantages of CNTs and MOFs. The study conducted by Li et al. investigates the feasibility of using $[Cu_3(\mu_3\text{-}O)(\mu\text{-}OH)(\text{triazolate})_2]^+$

MONTs (Cu-MONTs) as an SPME coating material to extract PCBs from water samples for GC-MS/MS detection [45]. The novel fibers achieved good thermal stability (~340 °C), high enhancement factors (396–1343), excellent repeatability (2.12–7.22%), wide linear ranges (0.1–500 ng/L) and low LODs (3.9–21.7 pg/L) for PCBs. A particular subfamily of MOFs, i.e., zeolitic imidazolate frameworks (ZIFs), was prepared in chemically resistant plastic microtubes for SPME on a polydopamine layer [126]. The extraction efficiency of ZIFs modified microtube was systematically investigated and more than 500-fold enrichment was obtained for analysis of PAHs in tap water.

Ionic liquids (ILs) seem to be an excellent alternative for the currently used SPME fiber sorptive materials, due to the change of their physical and chemical properties by the selection of appropriate ions. Several ILs-based SPME coatings have been prepared to achieve enhanced robustness and therefore a longer lifetime of fiber. A new stationary phase microextraction with physically fixed ionic ILs as sorptive coatings was proposed by Kang et al. for the determination of phosphorus flame retardants (PFR) in tap water [127]. Among the four ILs tested, the coating based on 1-octyl-3-methyloimidazole hexafluorophosphate demonstrated the best performances. Moreover, the prepared fiber has higher extraction capacity, better mechanical stability, lower cost, and comparable reproducibility compared with the commercially available SPME fibers. Several crosslinked polymeric ionic liquid (PIL)-based sorbent coatings of different natures were prepared for the determination of polar organic pollutants [128]. The PIL coatings contained either vinyl alkyl or vinyl benzyl imidazolium-based (ViCnIm⁻ orViBCnIm⁻) IL monomers with different anions, as well as different dicationic IL crosslinkers. In the work proposed by Pena-Pereira et al., three bis(trifluoromethanesulfonyl)imide anion-based ILs were used to prepare ionogel fibers for the quantification of chlorinated organic pollutants [129]. Ionogels were a family of hybrid materials in which ionic liquids are confined in a sol-gel network. The ionogel based on 1-butyl-1methylpyrrolidinium bis(trifluoromethanesulfonyl)imide [C$_4$C$_1$Pyrr][TFSI] exhibited the best performances in terms of extractability of target analytes. Cross-linked PIL bucky gels were proposed by free-radical polymerization of polymerizable ionic liquids gelled with MWCNT [130]. The PIL bucky gel sorbent coatings demonstrated higher efficiency for the extraction of PAHs from tap water respect to the neat PIL-based sorbent coating, due to a significant enhancement of the π–π interaction between the sorbent coatings and the aromatic analytes. Neat crosslinked PIL sorbent compatible with high-performance liquid chromatography was proposed by Yu et al. [131]. Six structurally different PILs were crosslinked to nitinol supports and applied for the determination of phenols, and multiclass insecticides. Superior extraction performance compared to the other studied PILs was achieved by the PIL-based sorbent coating polymerized from the IL monomer 1-vinyl-3-(10-hydroxydecyl) imidazolium chloride [VC$_{10}$OHIM][Cl] and IL crosslinker 1,12-di(3-vinylbenzylimidazolium) dodecane dichloride [(VBIM)$_2$C$_{12}$] 2[Cl]. ILs were used as coatings also for the particular design of the capillary for IT- SPME system, called fiber-in-tube SPME. In particular, to improve the durability and extraction efficiency of an ionic liquid coating, 1-dodecyl-3-vinylimidazolium bromide was polymerized and grafted onto basalt fibers [132]. The tube was connected to an HPLC instrument and the system was applied to the extraction of phthalates from bottled water

Another extensively exploited strategy in the development of new coating materials is the usage of metallic and metal oxides nanomaterials. For the analysis of drinking water, a palladium coating was fabricated on the SPME fiber by a simple in situ oxidation–reduction process to quantify PAHs and phthalates [133]. Moreover, new materials based on Co-Al bimetallic hydroxide nanocomposites [134] and gold nanoparticles [135] were proposed for fiber IT-SPME configuration in order to assay PAHs in tap water. Silica is another kind of inorganic material that has been widely used due to its features, such as the controllable morphology, excellent stability, and easy modification. VOCs were analyzed by ionogel fibers prepared by sol-gel processing using methyltrimethoxysilane as the silicon alkoxide precursor with the IL 1-methyl-3-butylimidazolium bis(trifluoromethylsulfonyl)imide ([C4MIM][TFSI]) confined within the hybrid network [136]. Enrichment factors in the range 275–7400 were obtained under optimum conditions. Remarkably, IL-rich SPME fibers yielded extractability up to 20-fold higher than that of the SPME fiber obtained after removal of the IL by solvent extraction. The very promising results obtained with ionogel fibers make us consider them as an excellent option for the preparation of advanced SPME coatings. Another silica-based material was used for the determination of chlorophenols [137]. In this work, the prepared continuous ordered mesoporous silica film supported on the anodized titanium wire demonstrated higher extraction efficiency toward the selected chlorophenols compared to the commercial PA fiber. Electrospinning is the most commonly used technique for the fabrication of SPME nanofibers from a wide range of materials. A polyetherimide (PEI) nanofibrous coating was prepared for the assay of PAHs, demonstrating a high filtration capacity and an increased extraction capacity for the analytes [138]. The applicability of inorganic oxide nanoparticles on the extraction efficiency of polyethylene terephthalate-based nanocomposites was evaluated by HS-SPME of BTEX [139]. Four types of nanoparticles including Fe_3O_4, SiO_2, CoO, and NiO were examined as the doping agents and, among them, the presence of SiO_2 in the prepared nanocomposite was prominent. BTEX were also analyzed by using sol-gel hybrid organic-inorganic materials prepared in the presence of polyethyleneoxide (PEO) non-ionic surfactants (Triton X-100) [140]. After the analytical procedure was optimized, the dynamic linear range obtained using PDMS-TX100 and PDMS-no TX100 fibers was 4–200,000 and 100–200,000 pg/mL and the limits of detection were 1–3 and 30–300 pg/mL, respectively. Molecularly imprinted polymers (MIPs) are typically synthesized from the copolymerization of a complex (the template and functional monomer), which can form recognition sites being able to rebind a target molecule. In recent years, MIPs have been prepared as monoliths by in situ polymerization directly within micro-columns or capillaries. Recently, several kinds of MIPs have been prepared and used as SPME coatings. For drinking water, a nanostructured molecularly imprinted fiber based on methyltriethoxysilane as the sol-gel precursor was prepared for the extraction of simazine [141]. Actually, SPME can also be coupled with MS directly without chromatographic separation, producing workflows that are not only more robust, sensitive, and selective, but also faster, cheaper, and cleaner. In 2016, Mirabelli et al. proposed a new strategy for the direct coupling of SPME with mass spectrometry, based on thermal desorption of analytes extracted on the fibers, followed by ionization with a dielectric barrier discharge ionization (DBDI) source [142]. The coupling of SPME with mass spectrometry reported in this study has several novel aspects. The work is the only one employing a thermal desorption of SPME fibers for a direct coupling with ambient ionization. This system has allowed to achieve LODs in the low-ng/L range for pesticides belong to various classes in tap water samples using the commercial PDMS/DVB fiber. The advantage over chromatographic approaches, in addition to the much shorter analytical procedure, is the absence of suppression effects from chromatography solvents. Finally, the small overall size of the setup could also allow one to perform in situ analyses with portable MS instruments.

3.2. Fruits and Vegetables

Fruits and vegetables, as a group of crops from the horticulture class, have very wide importance both as a source of food and health care. Fruits and vegetables are among the most studied food kind in terms of both nutritional principles and contaminants. Also for this food category, SPME has been contributing to the determination of several pollutants in various matrices. As for the water matrix, in the last five years, most of the studies have been focused on preparing new coating materials to be used instead of commercial fibers (Table 2).

A crosslinked PIL on a functionalized stainless steel wire through the oxidized MWCNT was fabricated by Feng et al. for the analysis of naphthol in pomelo and orange samples [143]. The following SPME extraction was carried out in multiple HS mode involving several consecutive extraction cycles of the same sample. The CNTs-based coating was also proposed for the determination of carbamate pesticides in apple and lettuce matrices [144]. In this work, a poly(3,4-ethylenedioxythiophene)-ionic liquid polymer functionalized multiwalled carbon nanotubes (PEDOT-PIL/MWCNTs) composite coating was fabricated which was successively dipped in Nafion solution. The outer layer Nafion enhances the durability and stability of the coating, being robust enough for replicated extraction for at least 150 times. Authors reported the direct GC analysis of carbamates without derivatization, in analogy to other studies [145,146]. Nanohybrids of CNTs/metal oxides have been applied to the determination of pollutants in vegetables. In particular, the synthesis of CNTs@SiO$_2$ nanohybrids with high surface area as an SPME coating was carried out and the obtained fiber was used for the assay of four organophosphorus pesticides in pear, grape, and eggplant [147]. The extracted compounds were detected using gas chromatography–corona discharge ion mobility spectrometry (GC-CD-IMS), demonstrating that the developed CNTs@SiO$_2$ fiber presented better extraction efficiency than the commercial SPME fibers (PA, PDMS, and PDMS/DVB). The same instrumental approach was employed for the analysis of organophosphorus pesticides in cucumber, lettuce, and apple by extracting the analytes with a polypyrrole/montmorillonite nanocomposites coating directly deposited on a Ni-Cr wire [148]. Polypyrrole/montmorillonite nanocomposites film provided a high specific surface due to non-smooth porous structure, resulting in the higher loading capacity and thermal stability. A comparison of the prepared fiber with commercial fibers revealed that the fabricated fiber has higher extraction efficiency for the extraction of OPPs relative to commercial PDMS and PDMS/DVB fibers and pure Ppy. Polypyrrole was also considered for the fabrication of polypyrrole nanowire (PPy NW) which was utilized for the quantification in headspace mode of bisphenol A in canned beans, corn, and peas [149]. The developed protocol involves the detection of the analyte by ion mobility spectrometry (IMS) without chromatographic separation. In a work based on MIP coating, an SPME fiber was developed on silica fiber via sol-gel using calixarene as a functional monomer for extraction of organophosphorus pesticides from apple and pineapple samples [150]. A comparison of MIP-SPME was made with liquid-liquid extraction coupled with gas chromatography demonstrating that much lower limits of detection and better recoveries were achieved by the SPME approach. The porous carbon can be directly obtained by the carbonization of different materials to achieve higher surface area and more abundant pores. In the work carried out by Liang et al., the carbon precursor was a barley husk biomaterial [151]. The obtained carbon was coated onto a stainless-steel wire through the sol-gel technique to prepare a solid-phase microextraction fiber for the extraction of trace levels of twelve multiclass pesticides from vegetable samples. COFs are analogs of metal-organic frameworks without metal in their structure. Wu et al. have designed a novel hydrazone COF and developed a polydopamine (PDA) based method to immobilize COF on a stainless steel fiber for carrying out the HS-SPME quantitative analysis of pyrethroids in apple and cucumber samples [152]. The authors ascribe the very satisfactory performances of this new coating firstly to hydrophobic nature of COFs and, secondly, to the fact of the hydrazone COF possesses abundant phenyl rings and –C=N groups, which provide strong π-π stacking interaction with pyrehroids. In another study reported by the same group, cross-linked hydrazone COFs were prepared via the thiol-ene "click" reaction and applied for the extraction of pesticides in cucumber [153]. The comparison of the cross-linked hydrazone COFs-based fiber with PDMS (7, 85, 100 μm), Car/PDMS, and PA fibers demonstrated that the extraction efficiency of the new coating is superior respect to commercial ones.

MOFs represent a suitable material as SPME coatings also in combination with graphene oxide. In particular, a hybrid material of the zinc-based metal-organic framework-5 and graphene oxide was prepared as a novel fiber coating material and the prepared fiber was used for the extraction of five triazole fungicides from grape, apple, cucumber, celery cabbage, pear, cabbage, and tomato samples [154]. This new fiber was stable enough for 120 extraction cycles without a significant loss of extraction efficiency. The same authors prepared a new coating material, a zeolitic imidazole framework-67 (ZIF-67) templated nanoporous carbon, Co-NPC, by one-step direct carbonization of ZIF-67 without using any other carbon precursors [155]. Successively, the SPME fiber prepared by coating the Co-NPC onto a functionalized stainless-steel wire was used for the determination of five organochlorine pesticides.

ILs, as stable coating compounds in SPME, were also employed together with other materials. For the analysis of vegetable samples, a new ionic liquid 1-vinyl-3-butylimidazolium ditrifluoro methyl sulfimide -calixarene coated fiber has been synthesized on the surface of quartz fiber by the sol-gel method [156]. The fiber was then applied to the assay of triazines in garlic sprout, cherry tomato, strawberry, cole, cabbage, cucumber, and tomato. Although potato is a common food in many countries and, as a consequence, is extensively studied [157], only one study is reported about the determination of contaminants in this matrix [158]. In this application, graphene oxide was firstly chemical-bonded on the support and then the novel 1-aminoethyl-3-methylimidazolium bromide ($C_2NH_2MIm^+Br^-$) or polymeric 1-vinyl-3-hexylimidazolium bromide (poly($VHIm^+Br^-$)) was assembled to the surface of GO by surface radical chain-transfer reaction, respectively. Afterward, $C_2NH_2MIm^+NTf_2^-$-GO-coated and poly($VHIm^+NTf_2^-$)-GO-coated fibers were obtained through on-fiber anion exchange. Extraction performance of ILs and PILs coatings with different anions were investigated with PAHs and PAEs as the model analytes. Finally, the proposed poly($VHIm^+NTf_2^-$)-GO-SPME fiber was used to determine several PAHs and phthalates in potatoes and food-wrap samples, respectively.

The metal oxides can be hybrid with organic/inorganic materials, leading to higher extraction efficiency and great convenience for the coating preparation. A biocompatible environmentally friendly SPME fiber coating (halloysite nanotubes-titanium dioxide (HNTs-TiO_2)) was prepared by Saraji et al. [159]. HNTs-TiO_2 was chemically coated on the surface of a fused-silica fiber using a sol-gel process and the fiber was evaluated in the determination of parathion in apple, strawberry, and celery. The HNTs-TiO_2 fiber was compared in terms of extraction efficiency with bare-silica (sol-gel based coating without HNTs-TiO_2), HNTs, carbon nanotubes and commercial SPME fibers (PA, PDMS, and PDMS-DVB). The HNTs-TiO_2 fiber showed the highest extraction efficiency among the studied fibers. In another application, zinc oxide hybridized with graphite-like C_3N_4 (ZnO/g-C_3N_4) nanoflowers based SPME coating was fabricated [160]. This fiber was successfully used for the simultaneous determination of nine pesticides in cucumber, pear, and green tea. The high extraction performance of ZnO/g-C_3N_4 nanoflowers fiber towards the pesticide residues may be due to its high dispersion in solution and to the pesticide hydrogen bonding interaction force and the π-π stacking interaction force between the analytes and the organic linker of the ZnO/g-C_3N_4.

Recently, a new matrix-compatible fiber was developed by Pawliszyn and coworkers by modification of the solid coating of a commercial SPME fiber with a thin layer of polydimethylsiloxane [161]. In particular, the outer PDMS layer was employed to protect the polydimethylsiloxane/divinylbenzene (PDMS/DVB), thereby merging the proven suitability of PDMS for sampling in complex matrixes and the extraction capability associated with the original solid porous coating. In the last five years, this fiber was tested for the determination of pesticides and contaminants in various fruits and vegetables in direct immersion mode [162–164]. In an application of DI-SPME for the extraction of multiclass pesticides and other contaminants in the avocado pulp, the polydimethylsiloxane-divinylbenzene-polydimethylsiloxane (PDMS/DVB/PDMS) compared to the DVB/PDMS coating, showed excellent robustness and matrix compatibility for oily matrices [162]. The optimized extraction conditions involving dilution of avocado puree with water and cleaning steps pre- and post-desorption extended the coating lifetime, with enhanced reproducibility for more than 100 consecutive extraction cycles. The robustness and endurance of this new coating were evaluated for analyses of vegetables (i.e., spinach, tomato, and carrot) that present different analytical challenges such as pigmentation, water content, interfering matrix compounds, and vegetable texture [163]. Multiclass pesticides and other contaminants were selected as target analytes to test PDMS/DVB/PDMS fiber in new challenging analytical scenarios. The PDMS/DVB/PDMS fiber was shown to be suitable for use for more than one hundred extractions in raw blended vegetable samples. Moreover, the overcoated fiber was revealed to provide advancements not only in terms of robustness and durability, but also in cleanability and sensitivity in respect to the commercial coating (Figure 5).

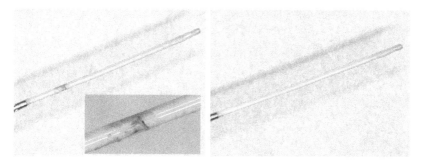

Figure 5. PDMS/DVB/PDMS fiber lifetime evaluation in spinach: stereomicroscope images of the fiber before (**left**) and after (**right**) manual cleaning of the coating [163].

In another application, a method for the determination of 40 pesticides, belonging to 21 different classes, was optimized for extractions from the grape pulp by means of Design of Experimental (DoE), using the matrix compatible PDMS/DVB/PDMS coating in direct immersion mode [164]. In the broad area of chemometrics, which plays an important role in many scientific disciplines [165–167] experimental design is a multivariate approach to achieve the optimization of a procedure by evaluating the factors simultaneously. The following instrumental analysis was carried out by GC-ToFMS. Commercial PDMS fiber was used by Abdulra'uf et al. for the assay of pesticides belong to various classes in apple, tomato, cucumber, and cabbage [168]. In this study, the authors proposed the sonication of samples for 5 min prior to HS-SPME extraction in order to improve the partition of the targeted analytes into the sample headspace.

3.3. Juices

Juices are also among the most analyzed food commodities by SPME for safety assessment. A CNTs-based coating was prepared for in-tube and glass capillary SPME configurations [28,169]. In the first work, IT-SPME directly coupled with DART-MS has been reported [28] and applied to the determination of triazine herbicides in orange juice samples. The extraction device consisted of a syringe barrel coupled to one end of the syringe pinhead. A capillary column replaced the other end of the pinhead. This method greatly improved the detection sensitivity, compared with the offline mode, because the majority of the desorption solvent was introduced into DART-MS for detection. The limits of detection (LODs) of the proposed method for the six triazine herbicides were only 0.02–0.14 ng/mL, and the negative matrix effect was minimized due to the IT-SPME procedures. In the study reported by Wang et al. a polymer monolith microextraction (PMME) procedure coupled to plasma-assisted laser desorption ionization mass spectrometry (PALDI-MS) was developed [169]. The extraction device used a "Dip-it" sampler coated with an MWNT incorporated monolith, and laser effectively desorbed the triazines adsorbed on monoliths. In another two works, the direct interface of microextraction technologies to mass spectrometry (SPME-transmission mode, SPME-TM) was proposed and applied to the analysis of multiclass pesticides in various matrices such as grape juice, orange juice, cow milk, and surface water [27,170]. These studies demonstrated the great potential of SPME-TM as a tool for fast concomitant screening and quantitation of agrochemicals in complex matrices. Limits of quantitation in the sub-nanogram-per-milliliter range were attained and the total analysis time did not exceed 2 min per sample [27]. Moreover, it was demonstrated the suitability of SPME-TM for on-site semi-quantitative analyses of target analytes in complex matrices via DART coupled to portable mass spectrometry [170].

In another application, a poly(methacrylic acid-co-ethylene dimethacrylate) monolith was prepared and used as the sorbent of multiple monolithic fiber solid-phase microextraction (MMF-SPME) [82]. The combination of MMF-SPME with high-performance liquid chromatography-diode array detection (MMF-SPME-HPLC-DAD) showed good analytical performance for the quantification of five benzoylurea insecticides in grape and orange juice samples. HPLC-UV was also used for the analysis of parabens in orange, lemon, and peach juices, milk, and waters after the extraction by an in-tube fiber with a nanostructured polyaniline-polypyrrole composite as a coating [171]. Under the optimized conditions, part-per-trillion (ppt) level detection limits were achieved for the analytes. Besides, shorter sample analysis time, more accurate quantification, and satisfactory reproducibility were achieved by in-tube SPME-HPLC, which are favorable for routine analysis of the parabens in various matrices.

Molecularly imprinted fibers were prepared by de Souza Freitas et al. to extract triazole fungicides from grape juice samples followed by gas chromatography-mass spectrometry analysis [172]. This coating, synthesized from methacrylic acid, ethylene glycol dimethacrylate, and triadimenol as a template, is able to renew its selective binding sites because of the gradual thermal decomposition of the polymeric network.

A novel hybrid material incorporating porous aromatic frameworks and an ionic liquid, 1-triethoxy silyl)-propyl-3-aminopropyl imidazole hexafluorophosphate, was developed and applied to the analysis of organochlorine pesticides in apple juice, peach juice, and milk [173]. These materials, prepared in general by combining gel and ionic liquids, are made up of highly conjugated repeating aromatic monomers that involve a strong enrichment ability for benzene homologs. The work reported by Pelit et al. describes the novel usage of polythiophene–ionic liquid modified clay surfaces for fiber production and the following application to the analysis of multiclass pesticides in grape juice samples [174]. Among the fibers developed, the polythiophene fiber co-deposited with C12mimBr modified clay has given the best results in terms of recoveries and sensitivities.

The metal-oxide coating was used also for fruit juice analysis. In the study published by Vinas et al. was described the use of magnetic nanoparticles of cobalt ferrite, with oleic acid as the surfactant ($CoFe_2O_4$/oleic acid) for the determination of alkylphenols in orange, pineapple, apple, peach, and grapefruit juices [175]. This demonstrated that appropriate modification of the magnetic core with oleic acid as a surfactant is useful for overcoming some limitations such as the chemical stability and oxidation of magnetic nanoparticles.

Forty pesticides pertaining to various classes were determined by a fast and sensitive direct immersion–solid-phase microextraction gas chromatography time-of-flight mass spectrometry (DI-SPME-GC-ToFMS) method in grapes employing a PDMS/DVB/PDMS fiber (i.e., PDMS-overcoated fiber) [164]. The validated method yielded good accuracy, precision, and sensitivity. With regard to the limitations of the proposed approach, the DI-SPME method did not provide a satisfactory performance toward more polar pesticides and highly hydrophobic pesticides, such as pyrethroids. The PDMS/DVB/PDMS coating was successfully used for the quantitative determination of multiclass pesticides in grape juice by direct coupling to mass spectrometry through dielectric barrier discharge ionization (DBDI) [176]. The use of a matrix compatible SPME coating is critical especially when a direct-MS analysis is carried out for complex food matrices since the occurrence of matrix effects is drastically minimized or avoided. Moreover, the throughput of the analytical procedure is extremely high, since no matrix pre-treatment is necessary due to the anti-fouling properties of the SPME coating used.

3.4. Other Foods

Various contaminants were determined by SPME technique in other food commodities (Table 2), such as milk [29,177–182], fish [183–187], honey [188–190], tea [191–193], coffee [194,195], oil [196,197], butter [198], rice [199], chili [166,200,201], and seaweeds [202]. In particular, in milk SPME has been exploited in different coatings. The MOF-based coating was prepared for the analysis of bisphenol A [177], commercial fibers were used to assay organochlorine pesticides [178] and PAHs [179], whereas graphene-based fiber was fabricated for the determination of PCBs [180]. A very interesting approach for the analysis of contaminants in complex matrices was developed by Deng et al. [29]. In this work, a surface coated wooden tip was proposed and realized for the first time to form a novel SPME probe that was used for a new SPME and ambient mass spectrometry hyphenated strategy. The proposed SPME-AMS method was applied to the direct ultra-trace analysis of perfluorinated compounds which has been recognized as one of the hot research topics in recent years [203,204].

Analysis of several pollutants (i.e., PAHs, anesthetics, trihalomethanes, furan, organophosphorus pesticides, personal care products, PCBs) in fish was carried out by the conventional ex vivo SPME extraction by using various coatings [185–187] and by the in vivo SPME approach. In vivo SPME is introduced as a low-invasive technique that utilizes biocompatible probes and has been used in a number of animal studies, and the results have shown that it is capable of extracting trace endogenous components from a living system [205,206]. In the last five years, in vivo SPME was applied to the analysis in living fish of benzo[a]pyrene in order to examine cellular responses to BaP exposure [183] and of anesthetics by using a biocompatible custom PDMS fiber [184].

One of the strategies of coupling SPME with ambient mass spectrometry is the surface desorption/ionization of analytes from SPME for AMS. One of the reported ambient ionization techniques coupled with SPME via this strategy is the desorption corona beam ionization (DCBI) [207]. SPME coupled with DCBI is performed by placing an SPME in the stream position of reactive species, and the analytes enriched on SPME was directly desorbed/ionized after the reactive species impacted on the surface of SPME. The reported SPME coupled with DCBI-MS methods were based on thin-film microextraction (TFME). This configuration was proposed by Chen et al. for the determination of Sudan dyes (I-IV) and Rhodamine B in chili oil and chili powder [200]. A small piece of commercial carbon nanotube film was used for the extraction of 1 mL of the sample solution. After extraction, the carbon nanotube film was attached to the front end of a glass capillary, and then transferred to the visible plasma beam of the DCBI source for surface desorption/ionization of the enriched analytes for MS analysis. In another application, the coupling of SPME with ambient mass spectrometry was again proposed for the analysis of Sudan dyes in chili powder [201]. In this case, a bifunctional monolith dip-it, prepared by in situ polymerization of poly(BMA–EDMA–MAA) monolith in the glass capillary of dip-it, was used as an SPME device for direct analysis in real-time mass spectrometry (DART-MS). This sample loading device showed a strong affinity to four Sudan dyes through hydrophilic interaction and hydrogen bond interaction and could be directly analyzed by DART-MS without organic solvent elution or laser desorption.

Table 2. Selected SPME applications in food matrices.

Analytes	Matrix	SPME Approach and Coating Material	Instrumentation	Calibration Range	[Ref] Publishing Year
benzene derivatives	tap water	fiber—PANI-PIL/MWCNTs	GC-FID	0.05–250 µg/L	[110]—2015
BTEX	tap water, mineral water	fiber—polypyrrole/CNT/TiO$_2$	GC-FID	0.03–500 µg/L	[111]—2015
aromatic amines	tap water	fiber—poly(ethylene glycol)–graphene oxide	GC-FID	1–2000 ng/L	[116]—2015
triazines	mineral water	IT-SPME—graphene oxide	HPLC-MS/MS	0.2–4 µg/L	[117]—2018
triazines	tap water	IT-SPME—GO	LC-MS/MS	5–500 ng/L	[118]—2015
PAHs	tap water	IT-SPME—zeolitic imidazolate framework (ZIF)—ZIF-8	HPLC-FLD	0.01–5 µg/L	[126]—2015
phenols, multiclass insecticides	tap water	fiber—PIL-1-vinyl-3-(10-hydroxydecyl) imidazolium chloride [VC$_{10}$OHIM][Cl]	HPLC-UV	1–500 µg/L	[131]—2016
phthalates	bottle water	IT-SPME—1-dodecyl-3-vinylimidazolium bromide	HPLC-DAD	0.03–12 µg/L	[132]—2018
PAHs	tap water	IT-SPME—Co-Al bimetallic hydroxide nanocomposites	HPLC-DAD	0.003–15 µg/L	[134]—2018
PAHs	tap water	IT-SPME—gold nanoparticles	HPLC-DAD	0.01–20 µg/L	[135]—2018
VOCs	tap water, mineral water	fiber—hybrid silica-based material with IL 1-methyl-3-butylimidazolium bis(trifluoromethylsulfonyl)imide ([C4MIM][TFSI])	GC—barrier ionization discharge (GC-BID)	0.025–75 µg/L	[136]—2014
chlorophenols	tap water	fiber—Ordered mesoporous silica (OMS)	GC-FID	0.2–200 µg/L	[137]—2017
PAHs	tap water	fiber—polyetherimide	GC-MS	0.005–1.2 µg/L	[138]—2014
BTEX	tap water	fiber—polyethylene terephthalate nanocomposites	GC-MS	0.01–1 µg/L	[139]—2015
BTEX	tap water, mineral water	fiber—PDMS-TX100	GC-FID	0.004–200 µg/L	[140]—2014
multiclass pesticides	tap water	fiber—PDMS/DVB	MS—dielectric barrier discharge ionization (DBDI)	0.01–30 µg/L	[142]—2016

Table 2. *Cont.*

Analytes	Matrix	SPME Approach and Coating Material	Instrumentation	Calibration Range	[Ref] Publishing Year
parabens	tap water, milk, juice	in-tube—polyaniline–polypyrrole composite	HPLC-UV	0.07–50 µg/L	[171]—2015
furan	tap water, canned tuna	fiber—MIP with pyrrole as template	GC-MS	0.5–100 µg/L	[186]—2016
benzoylurea insecticides	orange juice, grape juice	fiber—poly(methacrylic acid -co-ethylene dimethacrylate)	HPLC-DAD	0.5–200 µg/L	[82]—2015
multiclass pesticides	fruit juices	fiber—polythiophene–ionic liquid-Montmorillonite (PTh–IL–Mmt)	GC-ECD	0.5–10 µg/L	[174]—2015
multiclass pesticides	grape juice	fiber—PDMS/DVB/PDMS	DBDI-MS	0.5–100 µg/L	[176]—2018
alkylphenols	fruit juices	magnetic dispersive—CoFe$_2$O$_4$/oleic acid	LC-DAD-MS/MS	16–200 µg/L	[175]—2016
triazine herbicides	orange juice	in tube—poly(MAA-EDMA-SWNT)	DART-MS	0.1–50 µg/L	[28]—2014
triazoles	grape juice	fiber—MIP	GC-MS	100–2000 µg/L	[172]—2014
multiclass pesticides	grape juice, orange juice, cow milk	mesh—HLB/PAN	DART/MS	0.1–100 µg/L	[27]—2017
multiclass pesticides	grape juice, milk	mesh—HLB/PAN	DART/MS	5–500 µg/L	[170]—2017
organochlorine pesticides	juice, milk	fiber—PAF/IL	GC-ECD	1–500 µg/L	[173]—2016
bisphenol A	milk	fiber—(Et$_3$NH)$_2$Zn$_3$(BDC)$_4$ (E-MOF-5)	HPLC-SPD	1–200 µg/L	[177]—2016
PAHs	milk	home-made PDMS fiber	GC-MS	0.1–5 µg/L	[179]—2016
PCBs	milk	fiber—MoS$_2$/RGO	GC-MS	0.25–100 µg/L	[180]—2017
PCBs	milk	fiber—PIL 1-vinylbenzyl-3-hexadecylimidazolium bis[(trifluoromethyl)sulfonyl]imide [VBHDIM] [NTf$_2$]	GC-MS	2.5–100 ng/L	[181]—2014
perfluorinated compounds (PFCs)	milk	surface coated wooden-tip probe—n-octadecyldimethyl [3-(trimethoxysilyl)propyl]ammonium chloride	Orbitrap MS	0.5–100 ng/L	[29]—2014

Table 2. *Cont.*

Analytes	Matrix	SPME Approach and Coating Material	Instrumentation	Calibration Range	[Ref] Publishing Year
2-naphthol	pomelo and orange	fiber—MWCNTs-PILs	GC-FID	0.5–5000 µg/Kg	[143]—2014
carbamate pesticides	apple, lettuce	fiber—IL/CNT	GC-FID	0.05–250 µg/Kg	[144]—2016
organophosphorus pesticides	pear, grape, eggplant	fiber—CNTs@SiO$_2$	GC–corona discharge ion mobility spectrometric detection	0.5–15 µg/Kg	[147]—2016
organophosphorus pesticides	cucumber, lettuce, apple, tap water	fiber—polypyrrole/montmorillonite nanocomposites	GC-CD-IMS	0.05–10 µg/Kg	[148]—2014
BPA	canned beans, canned corn, canned peas	fiber—polypyrrole nanowire	ion mobility spectrometry	10–150 µg/Kg	[149]—2016
organophosphorous pesticides	fruits	fiber—molecularly imprinted polymer (MIP) with calixarene as template	GC-NPD	0.2–1000 µg/Kg	[150]—2016
multiclass pesticides	vegetables	fiber—Barley husk carbon	GC-MS	0.2–75 µg/Kg	[151]—2017
pyrethroids	vegetables, fruits	fiber—COF-PDA	GC-ECD	1–1000 µg/Kg	[152]—2016
organochlorine pesticides	cucumber	fiber—Covalent organic frameworks (COF)	GC-ECD	0.008–800 ng/kg	[153]—2016
triazole fungicides	vegetable, fruit	fiber—MOF-5/GO hybrid composite	GC–µECD	0.17–500 µg/Kg	[154]—2016
Organochlorine pesticides	vegetables	fiber—ZIF-67	GC–µECD	0.30–50 µg/Kg	[155]—2016
triazines	fruits, vegetables	fiber—ionic liquid (IL)–calixarene	GC-FID	25–5000 µg/Kg	[156]—2014
PAHs	potatoes	fiber—Bis(trifluoromethanesulfonyl)imide-based ionic liquids grafted on graphene oxide	GC-FID	0.05–50 µg/Kg	[158]—2016
parathion	apple, strawberry, celery	fiber—Halloysite nanotubes-titanium dioxide (HNTs-TiO$_2$)	negative corona discharge-ion mobility spectrometer	0.1–25 µg/Kg	[159]—2016
multiclass pesticides	cucumber, pear, green tea	fiber—C$_3$N$_4$ (ZnO/g-C$_3$N$_4$)	GC-MS	3–5000 ng/Kg	[160]—2016

Table 2. *Cont.*

Analytes	Matrix	SPME Approach and Coating Material	Instrumentation	Calibration Range	[Ref] Publishing Year
multiclass pesticides and contaminants	avocado puree	fiber—PDMS/DVB/PDMS	GC×GC-ToF/MS	-	[162]—2017
multiclass pesticides and contaminants	spinach, tomatoes, carrots	fiber—PDMS/DVB/PDMS	GC-MS	-	[163]—2016
multiclass pesticides	grapes	fiber—PDMS-modified PDMS/DVB	GC-ToFMS	1–1000 µg/Kg	[164]—2015
multiclass pesticide	fruits, vegetables	fiber—PDMS	GC-MS	1–500 µg/Kg	[168]—2015
Benzobenzo[a]pyrene	living fish	fiber—mixed-mode/PAN	LC-MS	-	[183]—2018
anesthetics	living fish	fiber—custom-made PDMS	GC-MS	10–5000 µg/Kg	[184]—2017
trihalomethanes	fish	fiber—DVB-CAR-PDMS	GC-ECD	0.35–8 µg/Kg	[185]—2017
PCBs	fish	SBSE—magnetic metal-organic frameworks—Fe_3O_4-MOF-5(Fe)	GC-MS	0.01–500 µg/Kg	[187]—2015
sudan dyes (I, II, III and IV), Rhodamine B	chili oil, chili powder	film—carbon nanotube	desorption corona beam ionization (DCBI)	100–20,000 µg/Kg	[200]—2015
Sudan dyes	chili powder	glass capillary—poly(BMA–EDMA–MAA)	DART-SVP-ToF MS	20–2000 µg/Kg	[201]—2016
PAHs, PCBs and pesticides	edible seaweeds	fiber—PDMS/DVB/PDMS	GC-MS	5–2000 µg/Kg	[202]—2018
triazine herbicides	vegetable oils	magnetic dispersive—1-hexyl-3-methylimidazolium tetrachloroferrate ([C_6mim] [$FeCl_4$]	HPLC-UV	5–1000 µg/L	[197]—2014
phthalates	drinking water, edible vegetable oil	fiber—graphene/polyvinylchloride	GC-FID	0.3–100 µg/L	[196]—2016
sulfonamides	butter	magnetic bar—1-octyl-3-methylimidazolium hexafluorophosphate ([C_8MIM][PF_6^-]	HPLC-UV	6–300 µg/Kg	[198]—2015
PAHs	smoked rice	hollow fiber—MWCNTs	GC-FID	0.02–1000 µg/Kg	[199]—2014

Table 2. *Cont.*

Analytes	Matrix	SPME Approach and Coating Material	Instrumentation	Calibration Range	[Ref] Publishing Year
phenols	honey	fiber—SNW-1	GC-MS	0.1–100 μg/Kg	[188]—2016
organochlorine pesticides, PAHs, PCBs	honey	fiber—PDMS	GC-MS/MS	10–3000 μg/Kg	[189]—2017
phenols	honey	fiber—COF-SNW-1	GC-MS	0.1–100 μg/Kg	[188]—2016
benzoylurea	honey, tea	dispersive ionic liquid (IL)-modified β-cyclodextrin/attapulgite (β-CD/ATP)	HPLC-DAD	5–500 μg/L	[190]—2016
phthalates	tea	fiber—C-NH$_2$-MIL-125	GC-MS	0.05–30 μg/L	[191]—2016
dicofol residues	tea	magnetic dispersive—magnetic molecular imprinted microspheres with DDT as template	GC-ECD	0.2–160 μg/L	[192]—2014
PAHs	tea	film—agarose-chitosan-C$_{18}$	HPLC-UV	1–500 μg/L	[193]—2017
acrylamide	brewed coffee and coffee powder	fiber—nine crosslinked PIL based coatings	GC-MS	0.5–200 μg/Kg	[194]—2016
phthalates	coffee	fiber—crosslinked PIL-based nitinol	GC-MS	-	[195]—2014

4. The Final Endpoint: Bio-Clinical Matrices

Human biomonitoring (HBM), that is the measurement of chemical and/or their metabolites in human tissues and fluids, is a significant means for assessing cumulative exposure to complex mixtures of chemicals and for monitoring chemical hazards in the population. It is also important for understanding the health effects of environmental pollutions and public susceptibility to these compounds. HBM can be used in epidemiological studies in combination with other medical data to show an association between the body burden of pollutants and their consequences on humans [208]. Besides, HBM is a powerful tool for tracking the effectiveness of public health interventions, such as, for example, restrictions on smoking in public places [209]. Considering its usefulness to perform an integrated assessment of environmental exposure, there is increasing awareness for HBM in developed countries that have already started national programs to improve the prevention of disease, injury, and harmful exposures in populations [209]. For these important screening programs, to develop simple, rapid, and reliable methods to quantify the markers of exposure in human body tissues and fluids represents an essential goal. Moreover, it is very necessary to realize automated procedures entailing the benefit of using a small quantity of toxic chemicals, which are not friendly to the environment. In this sense, microextraction approaches can provide a significant contribution to achieving this aim. In fact, many protocols developed in recent years involved the use of microextraction techniques, mainly SPME (Figure 6, Table 3).

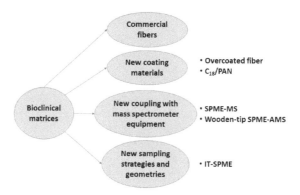

Figure 6. Main solid-phase microextraction geometries and strategies used in the analysis of bio-clinical matrices during the covered period (2014–2019).

Generally speaking, urine is undoubtedly the preferred matrix among the analyzed biological fluids because of its greater biological half-life and its less invasive sampling. This trend is confirmed in the last lustrum since most of the published works on this topic have been directed, as well as to the assay of markers of several pathological conditions [210–212], toward the determination of several contaminants in urine samples [14,74,83,213–219]. Few studies focused on hair [220–222], three papers were published about analysis in blood/serum [29,223,224], and one regarding meconium [225]. Some studies reporting the application of SPME for the analysis of urine have employed commercially available coatings such as Car/PDMS [214,216], PDMS/DVB [215], PDMS [217], and PA [14] for the extraction and further analysis of different contaminants such as VOCs [214,216], aromatic amines [215], organochlorine pesticides [217], and benzothiazoles, benzotriazoles, benzosulfonamides [14]. In all these works, except that regarding the analysis of the polar compounds benzothiazoles, benzotriazoles, benzosulfonamides, SPME was applied in headspace mode in order to minimize the coextraction of matrix interferences and extend the lifetime of employed coatings. In the DI-SPME application proposed by Naccarato et al. a six-fold dilution of urine sample was carried out to avoid the degradation of polyacrylate coating [14]. In another study by Naccarato et al., the overcoated fiber (i.e., PDMS/DVB/PDMS) was evaluated as an analytical sampling tool for the first time in human urine and urinary polycyclic aromatic hydrocarbons with 2–6 aromatic rings were considered as target compounds [74]. The satisfactory results achieved in terms of the lifetime of coatings and validation parameters created not only new alternatives for polycyclic aromatic hydrocarbon exposure assessment but also opened new perspectives for the application of direct immersion solid-phase microextraction to the analysis of bio-clinical matrices. As for food analysis, various coatings were proposed for the analysis of urine, such as C_{18}/PAN [213], layered double hydroxide/graphene (LDH-G) [218], inorganic-organic hybrid nanocomposite [219], and cross-linked PIL [83] for the determination of hydroxylated PAHs as metabolites of PAHs [213,219], organochlorine pesticides [218], and endocrine-disrupting chemicals [83]. In the study proposed by Yang et al. [213], an improved low-cost direct SPME-MS technique with glass capillary was further developed for the determination of five typical OH-PAHs in urine samples using a C18-SPME fiber, which then was inserted into a prefilled glass-capillary with spray solvent to generate ions for MS analysis.

Human hair as an indicator in assessing exposure to organic pollutants is less considered than urine. Recently, PAHs [221], multiclass pesticides, DDTs and PCBs [220,222] were determined in hair by commercial PDMS/DVB fiber [220,222] and a CP-Sil 19CB-based in-tube fiber [221].

As regards other biological fluids, the coupling of SPME with ambient mass spectrometry using a surface coated wooden-tip probe proposed by Deng for the analysis of PFCs in milk samples and already cited in the food section [29] was also employed for the analysis in whole blood. For this matrix, the porous structural surface together with the dual extraction mechanisms demonstrated that the SPME probe has an outstanding enrichment capacity, enhancing sensitivity by approximately 100–500 folds. In another application regarding the analysis in serum, a novel mesoporous graphitic carbon nitride@NiCo$_2$O$_4$ nanocomposite-based fiber was prepared and used for sensitive determination of PCBs and PAHs in headspace mode [224], whereas the commercial PDMS fiber was employed in order to analyze organochlorine pesticides and PCBs levels again in headspace mode [223]. To investigate fetal exposure to volatile organic compounds, a method was developed to identify and quantify BTEX and two chlorinated solvents (trichloroethylene and tetrachloroethylene) in meconium [225]. The protocol is based on SPME extraction in headspace mode carried out by commercial Car/PDMS fiber and following gas chromatography–mass spectrometry analysis.

Table 3. Selected SPME applications in bio-clinical matrices.

Analytes	Matrix	SPME Approach and Coating Material	Instrumentation	Calibration Range	[Ref] Publishing Year
PAHs	urine	fiber—PDMS/DVB/PDMS	GC-MS/MS	0.05–100 µg/L	[74]—2018
OH-PAHs	urine	fiber—C$_{18}$/PAN	nanoESI-MS/MS	0.1–5 µg/L	[213]—2017
endocrine disrupting chemicals (EDCs)	urine	multiple monolithic fiber—1-trimethyl-(4-vinylbenzyl) aminium chloride as monomer	HPLC-DAD	0.1–200 µg/L	[83]—2017
VOCs	urine	fiber—CAR/PDMS	GC-MS	2.9–1500 µg/L	[214]—2016
aromatic amines	urine	fiber—PDMS/DVB	GCxGC-qMS	1–500 ng/L	[215]—2015
VOCs	urine	fiber—CAR/PDMS	GC-MS	2.5–100 µg/L	[216]—2017
organochlorine pesticides	urine	fiber—PDMS	GC-MS	0.5–20 µg/L	[217]—2016
benzothiazoles, benzotriazoles, benzosulfonamides	urine	fiber—PA	GC-MS/MS	1–100 µg/L	[14]—2014
organochlorine pesticides	urine	stir bar—double hydroxide/graphene (LDH-G)	GC-MS	1–200 µg/L	[218]—2017
monohydroxy-PAHs	urine	in tube—inorganic–organic hybrid nanocomposite (zinc oxide/polypyrrole)	LC-MS/MS	0.2–100 µg/L	[219]—2016
multiclass pesticides, PCBs	hair	fiber—PDMS-DVB	GC-MS/MS	0.002–10 µg/Kg	[220]—2015
PAHs	hair	in tube—CP-Sil 19CB (14% cyanopropyl phenyl methylsilicone)	HPLC-FLD	0.02–1 µg/Kg	[221]—2015
DDTs, PCBs	hair	fiber—PDMS/DVB	GC-MS	2.5–50 ng/Kg	[222]—2014
perfluorinated compounds (PFCs)	blood	surface coated wooden-tip probe—n-octadecyldimethyl[3-(trimethoxysilyl)propyl]ammonium chloride	Orbitrap MS	0.5–100 ng/L	[29]—2014
PCBs, PAHs	Serum	fiber—mesoporous graphitic carbon nitride@NiCo$_2$O$_4$ nanocomposite	GC-FID	0.002–100 µg/L.	[224]—2019
organochlorine pesticides, PCBs	Serum	fiber—PDMS	GC-MS	3–100 µg/L	[223]—2014
BTEX, chlorinated solvents	meconium	fiber—CAR/PDMS	GC-MS	0.08–9 (ng)	[225]—2014

5. Concluding Remarks and Future Directions

This review described the most impactful SPME applications in pollutant analysis published in the last five years (2014–2019). The goal of our paper is giving to the reader information about the ongoing research fields involving SPME and its potential future directions. The surveyed papers cover studies that focused on pollutant determination in the path that goes from the different environmental comparts to the bio-clinical matrices passing through the foods. We revised the studies aimed to determine different chemicals including persistent organic pollutants, pesticides, emerging pollutants, and personal care products. These applications underline the growing demands for green and sensitive analytical methods, which have also fostered the development of new SPME devices, coatings, and geometries. As a results, our paper points out how SPME is an analytical approach constantly evolving in multiple directions, that can satisfy the requirements of green analytical chemistry (GAC) [226], while providing ease of use, high-throughput, extraction efficiency for trace analysis, robustness, suitability for in vivo and on-site analysis, and easy coupling to various separation techniques and direct MS analysis.

Regarding the environmental field, the researchers have mainly focused their efforts on the analysis of environmental waters followed by a smaller number of applications on soil and air. In these areas, the SPME has not only been used to set-up new methods, but it was also used as a proper tool in the analyst's hands to carry out eco-biological and health control studies driven by its unique features such as the capability to determine the concentration of the analytes unbound to the matrix and the advancements in on-site sampling devices and modes.

In food analysis, SPME is a widely used technique particularly for drinking water and in other water matrices. The development in the last five years of new coatings that allow improving the fibers in terms of mechanical robustness, selectivity, and resistance to the matrix effect together with the possibility to perform in vivo and ex vivo analysis opened new research directions for pollutant analysis for the next years.

As for the monitoring of pollutants in bio-clinical matrices, SPME has not yet expressed its full potential. The bio-clinical matrices are very complex and although in the last 5 years the SPME was mainly used for pollutant monitoring in urine, the in vivo mode, and to a larger extent, the new direct couplings with the ambient mass spectrometry, are expected to open exciting scenarios in the near future.

Author Contributions: Conceptualization, A.N.; writing—original draft preparation, A.N. and A.T.; writing—review and editing, A.N. and A.T.; visualization, A.N. and A.T.

Funding: This research received no external funding.

Conflicts of Interest: The authors declare no conflict of interest. The funders had no role in the design of the study; in the collection, analyses, or interpretation of data; in the writing of the manuscript, or in the decision to publish the results.

Abbreviations

VOCs	volatile organic compounds
SVOCs	semivolatile organic compounds
DVB/CAR/PDMS	divinylbenzene/carboxen/polydimethylsiloxane
CAR/PDMS	carboxen/polydimethylsiloxane
PDMS	polydimethylsiloxane
PA	polyacrylate
PDMS/DVB	polydimethylsiloxane-divinylbenzene
PDMS/DVB/PDMS	polydimethylsiloxane-divinylbenzene-polydimethylsiloxane
PAHs	polycyclic aromatic hydrocarbons
THMs	trihalomethanes
PCBs	polychlorinated biphenyls

PFBHA	(pentafluorobenzyl)hydroxylamine
MtBSTFA	N-methyl-N-(tert.-butyldimethylsilyl) trifluoroacetamide
OPEs	organophosphate esters
BTEX	benzene, toluene, ethylbenzene and xylenes
PBDEs	polybrominated diphenyl ethers
PM	particulate matter
TWA	Time-Weighted Average sampling
MOF	metal-organic framework
COV	covalent organic frameworks
IL	Ionic liquids
PIL	polymeric ionic liquid
MMF-SPME	multiple monolithic fiber solid-phase microextraction
SPME-TM	Solid-Phase Micro Extraction-Transmission Mode
SPME-TM-DART/MS	Solid-Phase Micro Extraction-Transmission Mode Direct Analysis in Real-Time Mass Spectrometry

References

1. Carter, R.A.A.; West, N.; Heitz, A.; Joll, C.A. An analytical method for the analysis of trihalomethanes in ambient air using solid-phase microextraction gas chromatography-mass spectrometry: An application to indoor swimming pool complexes. *Indoor Air* **2019**, *29*, 499–509. [CrossRef] [PubMed]

2. Saucedo-Lucero, J.O.; Revah, S. Monitoring key organic indoor pollutants and their elimination in a biotrickling biofilter. *Environ. Sci. Pollut. Res.* **2018**, *25*, 9806–9816. [CrossRef] [PubMed]

3. Lucaire, V.; Schwartz, J.J.; Delhomme, O.; Ocampo-Torres, R.; Millet, M. A sensitive method using SPME pre-concentration for the quantification of aromatic amines in indoor air. *Anal. Bioanal. Chem.* **2018**, *410*, 1955–1963. [CrossRef] [PubMed]

4. Ghislain, M.; Beigbeder, J.; Plaisance, H.; Desauziers, V. New sampling device for on-site measurement of SVOC gas-phase concentration at the emitting material surface. *Anal. Bioanal. Chem.* **2017**, *409*, 3199–3210. [CrossRef] [PubMed]

5. Bourdin, D.; Desauziers, V. Development of SPME on-fiber derivatization for the sampling of formaldehyde and other carbonyl compounds in indoor air. *Anal. Bioanal. Chem.* **2014**, *406*, 317–328. [CrossRef]

6. Helin, A.; Rönkkö, T.; Parshintsev, J.; Hartonen, K.; Schilling, B.; Läubli, T.; Riekkola, M.-L. Solid phase microextraction Arrow for the sampling of volatile amines in wastewater and atmosphere. *J. Chromatogr. A* **2015**, *1426*, 56–63. [CrossRef]

7. Ruiz-Jimenez, J.; Zanca, N.; Lan, H.; Jussila, M.; Hartonen, K.; Riekkola, M.L. Aerial drone as a carrier for miniaturized air sampling systems. *J. Chromatogr. A* **2019**, *1597*, 202–208. [CrossRef]

8. Celeiro, M.; Dagnac, T.; Llompart, M. Determination of priority and other hazardous substances in football fields of synthetic turf by gas chromatography-mass spectrometry: A health and environmental concern. *Chemosphere* **2018**, *195*, 201–211. [CrossRef]

9. Baimatova, N.; Kenessov, B.; Koziel, J.A.; Carlsen, L.; Bektassov, M.; Demyanenko, O.P. Simple and accurate quantification of BTEX in ambient air by SPME and GC-MS. *Talanta* **2016**, *154*, 46–52. [CrossRef]

10. Sayed Mohamed Zain, S.M.; Shaharudin, R.; Kamaluddin, M.A.; Daud, S.F. Determination of hydrogen cyanide in residential ambient air using SPME coupled with GC–MS. *Atmos. Pollut. Res.* **2017**, *8*, 678–685. [CrossRef]

11. Van der Veen, I.; de Boer, J. Phosphorus flame retardants: Properties, production, environmental occurrence, toxicity and analysis. *Chemosphere* **2012**, *88*, 1119–1153. [CrossRef] [PubMed]

12. Naccarato, A.; Elliani, R.; Sindona, G.; Tagarelli, A. Multivariate optimization of a microextraction by packed sorbent-programmed temperature vaporization-gas chromatography–tandem mass spectrometry method for organophosphate flame retardant analysis in environmental aqueous matrices. *Anal. Bioanal. Chem.* **2017**, *409*, 7105–7120. [CrossRef]

13. Naccarato, A.; Tassone, A.; Moretti, S.; Elliani, R.; Sprovieri, F.; Pirrone, N.; Tagarelli, A. A green approach for organophosphate ester determination in airborne particulate matter: Microwave-assisted extraction using hydroalcoholic mixture coupled with solid-phase microextraction gas chromatography-tandem mass spectrometry. *Talanta* **2018**, *189*, 657–665. [CrossRef] [PubMed]

14. Naccarato, A.; Gionfriddo, E.; Sindona, G.; Tagarelli, A. Simultaneous determination of benzothiazoles, benzotriazoles and benzosulfonamides by solid phase microextraction-gas chromatography-triple quadrupole mass spectrometry in environmental aqueous matrices and human urine. *J. Chromatogr. A* **2014**, *1338*, 164–173. [CrossRef] [PubMed]

15. Raeppel, C.; Fabritius, M.; Nief, M.; Appenzeller, B.M.R.; Millet, M. Coupling ASE, sylilation and SPME-GC/MS for the analysis of current-used pesticides in atmosphere. *Talanta* **2014**, *121*, 24–29. [CrossRef] [PubMed]

16. Gutiérrez-Serpa, A.; Pacheco-Fernández, I.; Pasán, J.; Pino, V. Metal–Organic Frameworks as Key Materials for Solid-Phase Microextraction Devices—A Review. *Separations* **2019**, *6*, 47. [CrossRef]

17. Li, J.; Li, H.; Zhao, Y.; Wang, S.; Chen, X.; Zhao, R.S. A hollow microporous organic network as a fiber coating for solid-phase microextraction of short-chain chlorinated hydrocarbons. *Microchim. Acta* **2018**, *185*, 416. [CrossRef]

18. Jia, Y.; Su, H.; Wang, Z.; Wong, Y.L.E.; Chen, X.; Wang, M.; Chan, T.W.D. Metal-Organic Framework@Microporous Organic Network as Adsorbent for Solid-Phase Microextraction. *Anal. Chem.* **2016**, *88*, 9364–9367. [CrossRef]

19. Li, J.; Liu, Y.; Su, H.; Elaine Wong, Y.L.; Chen, X.; Dominic Chan, T.W.; Chen, Q. In situ hydrothermal growth of a zirconium-based porphyrinic metal-organic framework on stainless steel fibers for solid-phase microextraction of nitrated polycyclic aromatic hydrocarbons. *Microchim. Acta* **2017**, *184*, 3809–3815. [CrossRef]

20. Zhang, S.; Yang, Q.; Li, Z.; Wang, W.; Wang, C.; Wang, Z. Covalent organic frameworks as a novel fiber coating for solid-phase microextraction of volatile benzene homologues. *Anal. Bioanal. Chem.* **2017**, *409*, 3429–3439. [CrossRef]

21. Riboni, N.; Trzcinski, J.W.; Bianchi, F.; Massera, C.; Pinalli, R.; Sidisky, L.; Dalcanale, E.; Careri, M. Conformationally blocked quinoxaline cavitand as solid-phase microextraction coating for the selective detection of BTEX in air. *Anal. Chim. Acta* **2016**, *905*, 79–84. [CrossRef]

22. Heidari, M.; Bahrami, A.; Ghiasvand, A.R.; Shahna, F.G.; Soltanian, A.R.; Rafieiemam, M. Application of graphene nanoplatelets silica composite, prepared by sol-gel technology, as a novel sorbent in two microextraction techniques. *J. Sep. Sci.* **2015**, *38*, 4225–4232. [CrossRef] [PubMed]

23. Dias, C.M.; Menezes, H.C.; Cardeal, Z.L. Environmental and biological determination of acrolein using new cold fiber solid phase microextraction with gas chromatography mass spectrometry. *Anal. Bioanal. Chem.* **2017**, *409*, 2821–2828. [CrossRef] [PubMed]

24. Kenessov, B.; Koziel, J.A.; Baimatova, N.; Demyanenko, O.P.; Derbissalin, M. Optimization of time-weighted average air sampling by solid-phase microextraction fibers using finite element analysis software. *Molecules* **2018**, *23*, 2736. [CrossRef] [PubMed]

25. Tursumbayeva, M.; Koziel, J.A.; Maurer, D.L.; Kenessov, B.; Rice, S. Development of Time-Weighted Average Sampling of Odorous Volatile Organic Compounds in Air with Solid-Phase Microextraction Fiber Housed inside a GC Glass Liner: Proof of concept. *Molecules* **2019**, *24*, 406. [CrossRef]

26. Carasek, E.; Morés, L.; Merib, J. Basic principles, recent trends and future directions of microextraction techniques for the analysis of aqueous environmental samples. *Trends Environ. Anal. Chem.* **2018**, *19*, e00060. [CrossRef]

27. Gómez-Ríos, G.A.; Gionfriddo, E.; Poole, J.; Pawliszyn, J. Ultrafast Screening and Quantitation of Pesticides in Food and Environmental Matrices by Solid-Phase Microextraction-Transmission Mode (SPME-TM) and Direct Analysis in Real Time (DART). *Anal. Chem.* **2017**, *89*, 7240–7248. [CrossRef]

28. Wang, X.; Li, X.; Li, Z.; Zhang, Y.; Bai, Y.; Liu, H. Online coupling of in-tube solid-phase microextraction with direct analysis in real time mass spectrometry for rapid determination of triazine herbicides in water using carbon-nanotubes-incorporated polymer monolith. *Anal. Chem.* **2014**, *86*, 4739–4747. [CrossRef]

29. Deng, J.; Yang, Y.; Fang, L.; Lin, L.; Zhou, H.; Luan, T. Coupling solid-phase microextraction with ambient mass spectrometry using surface coated wooden-tip probe for rapid analysis of ultra trace perfluorinated compounds in complex samples. *Anal. Chem.* **2014**, *86*, 11159–11166. [CrossRef]

30. Grandy, J.J.; Lashgari, M.; Vander Heide, H.; Poole, J.; Pawliszyn, J. Introducing a mechanically robust SPME sampler for the on-site sampling and extraction of a wide range of untargeted pollutants in environmental waters. *Environ. Pollut.* **2019**, *252*, 825–834. [CrossRef]

31. Bu, Y.; Feng, J.; Sun, M.; Zhou, C.; Luo, C. Facile and efficient poly(ethylene terephthalate) fibers-in-tube for online solid-phase microextraction towards polycyclic aromatic hydrocarbons. *Anal. Bioanal. Chem.* **2016**, *408*, 4871–4882. [CrossRef] [PubMed]

32. Fu, M.; Xing, H.; Chen, X.; Zhao, R.; Zhi, C.; Wu, C.L. Boron nitride nanotubes as novel sorbent for solid-phase microextraction of polycyclic aromatic hydrocarbons in environmental water samples. *Anal. Bioanal. Chem.* **2014**, *406*, 5751–5754. [CrossRef] [PubMed]

33. Yin, L.; Hu, Q.; Mondal, S.; Xu, J.; Ouyang, G. Peanut shell-derived biochar materials for effective solid-phase microextraction of polycyclic aromatic hydrocarbons in environmental waters. *Talanta* **2019**, *202*, 90–95. [CrossRef] [PubMed]

34. Sun, S.; Huang, L.; Xiao, H.; Shuai, Q.; Hu, S. In situ self-transformation metal into metal-organic framework membrane for solid-phase microextraction of polycyclic aromatic hydrocarbons. *Talanta* **2019**, *202*, 145–151. [CrossRef] [PubMed]

35. Wang, G.; Lei, Y.; Song, H. Exploration of metal-organic framework MOF-177 coated fibers for headspace solid-phase microextraction of polychlorinated biphenyls and polycyclic aromatic hydrocarbons. *Talanta* **2015**, *144*, 369–374. [CrossRef]

36. Kong, J.; Zhu, F.; Huang, W.; He, H.; Hu, J.; Sun, C.; Xian, Q.; Yang, S. Sol–gel based metal-organic framework zeolite imidazolate framework-8 fibers for solid-phase microextraction of nitro polycyclic aromatic hydrocarbons and polycyclic aromatic hydrocarbons in water samples. *J. Chromatogr. A* **2019**. [CrossRef]

37. Hu, X.; Liu, C.; Li, J.; Luo, R.; Jiang, H.; Sun, X.; Shen, J.; Han, W.; Wang, L. Hollow mesoporous carbon spheres-based fiber coating for solid-phase microextraction of polycyclic aromatic hydrocarbons. *J. Chromatogr. A* **2017**, *1520*, 58–64. [CrossRef]

38. Bagheri, H.; Soofi, G.; Javanmardi, H.; Karimi, M. A 3D nanoscale polyhedral oligomeric silsesquioxanes network for microextraction of polycyclic aromatic hydrocarbons. *Microchim. Acta* **2018**, *185*, 418. [CrossRef]

39. Guo, M.; Song, W.; Wang, T.; Li, Y.; Wang, X.; Du, X. Phenyl-functionalization of titanium dioxide-nanosheets coating fabricated on a titanium wire for selective solid-phase microextraction of polycyclic aromatic hydrocarbons from environment water samples. *Talanta* **2015**, *144*, 998–1006. [CrossRef]

40. Gutiérrez-Serpa, A.; Napolitano-Tabares, P.I.; Pino, V.; Jiménez-Moreno, F.; Jiménez-Abizanda, A.I. Silver nanoparticles supported onto a stainless steel wire for direct-immersion solid-phase microextraction of polycyclic aromatic hydrocarbons prior to their determination by GC-FID. *Microchim. Acta* **2018**, *185*, 341. [CrossRef]

41. Wang, X.; Sheng, W.R.; Jiao, X.Y.; Zhao, R.S.; Wang, M.L.; Lin, J.M. Zinc(II)-based metal–organic nanotubes coating for high sensitive solid phase microextraction of nitro-polycyclic aromatic hydrocarbons. *Talanta* **2018**, *186*, 561–567. [CrossRef] [PubMed]

42. Liu, Y.L.; Chen, X.F.; Wang, X.; Zhou, J.B.; Zhao, R.S. Sensitive determination of polychlorinated biphenyls in environmental water samples by headspace solid-phase microextraction with bamboo charcoal@iron oxide black fibers prior to gas chromatography with tandem mass spectrometry. *J. Sep. Sci.* **2014**, *37*, 1496–1502. [CrossRef] [PubMed]

43. Sheng, W.R.; Chen, Y.; Wang, S.S.; Wang, X.L.; Wang, M.L.; Zhao, R.S. Cadmium(II)-based metal–organic nanotubes as solid-phase microextraction coating for ultratrace-level analysis of polychlorinated biphenyls in seawater samples. *Anal. Bioanal. Chem.* **2016**, *408*, 8289–8297. [CrossRef] [PubMed]

44. Cheng, H.; Wang, F.; Bian, Y.; Ji, R.; Song, Y.; Jiang, X. Co- and self-activated synthesis of tailored multimodal porous carbons for solid-phase microextraction of chlorobenzenes and polychlorinated biphenyls. *J. Chromatogr. A* **2019**, *1585*, 1–9. [CrossRef]

45. Li, Q.L.; Wang, X.; Liu, Y.L.; Chen, X.F.; Wang, M.L.; Zhao, R.S. Feasibility of metal-organic nanotubes [Cu3(μ3-O)(μ-OH)(triazolate)2]+-coated fibers for solid-phase microextraction of polychlorinated biphenyls in water samples. *J. Chromatogr. A* **2014**, *1374*, 58–65. [CrossRef]

46. Ling, X.; Chen, Z. Immobilization of zeolitic imidazolate frameworks with assist of electrodeposited zinc oxide layer and application in online solid-phase microextraction of Sudan dyes. *Talanta* **2019**, *192*, 142–146. [CrossRef]

47. Pei, M.; Zhu, X.; Huang, X. Mixed functional monomers-based monolithic adsorbent for the effective extraction of sulfonylurea herbicides in water and soil samples. *J. Chromatogr. A* **2018**, *1531*, 13–21. [CrossRef]

48. Zhang, Z.; Mei, M.; Huang, Y.; Huang, X.; Huang, H.; Ding, Y. Facile preparation of a polydopamine-based monolith for multiple monolithic fiber solid-phase microextraction of triazine herbicides in environmental water samples. *J. Sep. Sci.* **2017**, *40*, 733–743. [CrossRef]

49. Prieto, A.; Rodil, R.; Quintana, J.B.; Cela, R.; Möder, M.; Rodríguez, I. Evaluation of polyethersulfone performance for the microextraction of polar chlorinated herbicides from environmental water samples. *Talanta* **2014**, *122*, 264–271. [CrossRef]

50. Bagheri, H.; Amanzadeh, H.; Yamini, Y.; Masoomi, M.Y.; Morsali, A.; Salar-Amoli, J.; Hassan, J. A nanocomposite prepared from a zinc-based metal-organic framework and polyethersulfone as a novel coating for the headspace solid-phase microextraction of organophosphorous pesticides. *Microchim. Acta* **2018**, *185*, 62. [CrossRef]

51. Gutiérrez-Serpa, A.; Rocío-Bautista, P.; Pino, V.; Jiménez-Moreno, F.; Jiménez-Abizanda, A.I. Gold nanoparticles based solid-phase microextraction coatings for determining organochlorine pesticides in aqueous environmental samples. *J. Sep. Sci.* **2017**, *40*, 2009–2021. [CrossRef] [PubMed]

52. Zheng, J.; Liang, Y.; Liu, S.; Jiang, R.; Zhu, F.; Wu, D.; Ouyang, G. Simple fabrication of solid phase microextraction fiber employing nitrogen-doped ordered mesoporous polymer by in situ polymerization. *J. Chromatogr. A* **2016**, *1427*, 22–28. [CrossRef] [PubMed]

53. Wu, J.; Mei, M.; Huang, X. Fabrication of boron-rich multiple monolithic fibers for the solid-phase microextraction of carbamate pesticide residues in complex samples. *J. Sep. Sci.* **2019**, *42*, 878–887. [CrossRef] [PubMed]

54. Pang, J.; Liao, Y.; Huang, X.; Ye, Z.; Yuan, D. Metal-organic framework-monolith composite-based in-tube solid phase microextraction on-line coupled to high-performance liquid chromatography-fluorescence detection for the highly sensitive monitoring of fluoroquinolones in water and food samples. *Talanta* **2019**, *199*, 499–506. [CrossRef]

55. Peng, J.; Liu, D.; Shi, T.; Tian, H.; Hui, X.; He, H. Molecularly imprinted polymers based stir bar sorptive extraction for determination of cefaclor and cefalexin in environmental water. *Anal. Bioanal. Chem.* **2017**, *409*, 4157–4166. [CrossRef]

56. Barahona, F.; Albero, B.; Tadeo, J.L.; Martín-Esteban, A. Molecularly imprinted polymer-hollow fiber microextraction of hydrophilic fluoroquinolone antibiotics in environmental waters and urine samples. *J. Chromatogr. A* **2019**, *1587*, 42–49. [CrossRef]

57. Kazemi, E.; Haji Shabani, A.M.; Dadfarnia, S. Application of graphene oxide-silica composite reinforced hollow fibers as a novel device for pseudo-stir bar solid phase microextraction of sulfadiazine in different matrices prior to its spectrophotometric determination. *Food Chem.* **2017**, *221*, 783–789. [CrossRef]

58. Mei, M.; Huang, X.; Yu, J.; Yuan, D. Sensitive monitoring of trace nitrophenols in water samples using multiple monolithic fiber solid phase microextraction and liquid chromatographic analysis. *Talanta* **2015**, *134*, 89–97. [CrossRef]

59. Li, Q.L.; Huang, F.; Wang, X.L.; Wang, X.; Zhao, R.S. Multiple-helix cobalt(II)-based metal-organic nanotubes on stainless steel fibers for solid-phase microextraction of chlorophenol and nitrophenols from water samples. *Microchim. Acta* **2017**, *184*, 1817–1825. [CrossRef]

60. Gionfriddo, E.; Naccarato, A.; Sindona, G.; Tagarelli, A. Determination of hydrazine in drinking water: Development and multivariate optimization of a rapid and simple solid phase microextraction-gas chromatography-triple quadrupole mass spectrometry protocol. *Anal. Chim. Acta* **2014**, *835*, 37–45. [CrossRef]

61. Li, L.; Guo, R.; Li, Y.; Guo, M.; Wang, X.; Du, X. In situ growth and phenyl functionalization of titania nanoparticles coating for solid-phase microextraction of ultraviolet filters in environmental water samples followed by high performance liquid chromatography-UV detection. *Anal. Chim. Acta* **2015**, *867*, 38–46. [CrossRef] [PubMed]

62. Yang, Y.; Li, Y.; Liu, H.; Wang, X.; Du, X. Electrodeposition of gold nanoparticles onto an etched stainless steel wire followed by a self-assembled monolayer of octanedithiol as a fiber coating for selective solid-phase microextraction. *J. Chromatogr. A* **2014**, *1372*, 25–33. [CrossRef] [PubMed]

63. Zhou, S.; Wang, H.; Jin, P.; Wang, Z.; Wang, X.; Du, X. Electrophoretic deposition strategy for the fabrication of highly stable functionalized silica nanoparticle coatings onto nickel-titanium alloy wires for selective solid-phase microextraction. *J. Sep. Sci.* **2017**, *40*, 4796–4804. [CrossRef] [PubMed]

64. Li, Y.; Zhang, M.; Yang, Y.; Wang, X.; Du, X. Electrochemical in situ fabrication of titanium dioxide-nanosheets on a titanium wire as a novel coating for selective solid-phase microextraction. *J. Chromatogr. A* **2014**, *1358*, 60–67. [CrossRef]

65. Song, W.; Guo, M.; Zhang, Y.; Zhang, M.; Wang, X.; Du, X. Fabrication and application of zinc-zinc oxide nanosheets coating on an etched stainless steel wire as a selective solid-phase microextraction fiber. *J. Chromatogr. A* **2015**, *1384*, 28–36. [CrossRef]

66. Bu, Y.; Feng, J.; Wang, X.; Tian, Y.; Sun, M.; Luo, C. In situ hydrothermal growth of polyaniline coating for in-tube solid-phase microextraction towards ultraviolet filters in environmental water samples. *J. Chromatogr. A* **2017**, *1483*, 48–55. [CrossRef]

67. Wang, H.; Du, J.; Zhen, Q.; Zhang, R.; Wang, X.; Du, X. Selective solid-phase microextraction of ultraviolet filters in environmental water with oriented ZnO nanosheets coated nickel-titanium alloy fibers followed by high performance liquid chromatography with UV detection. *Talanta* **2019**, *191*, 193–201. [CrossRef]

68. Mei, M.; Huang, X. Online analysis of five organic ultraviolet filters in environmental water samples using magnetism-enhanced monolith-based in-tube solid phase microextraction coupled with high-performance liquid chromatography. *J. Chromatogr. A* **2017**, *1525*, 1–9. [CrossRef]

69. Ma, M.; Wang, H.; Zhen, Q.; Zhang, M.; Du, X. Development of nitrogen-enriched carbonaceous material coated titania nanotubes array as a fiber coating for solid-phase microextraction of ultraviolet filters in environmental water. *Talanta* **2017**, *167*, 118–125. [CrossRef]

70. Wang, H.; Song, W.; Zhang, M.; Zhen, Q.; Guo, M.; Zhang, Y.; Du, X. Hydrothermally grown and self-assembled modified titanium and nickel oxide composite nanosheets on Nitinol-based fibers for efficient solid phase microextraction. *J. Chromatogr. A* **2016**, *1468*, 33–41. [CrossRef]

71. Yang, Y.; Guo, M.; Zhang, Y.; Song, W.; Li, Y.; Wang, X.; Du, X. Self-assembly of alkyldithiols on a novel dendritic silver nanostructure electrodeposited on a stainless steel wire as a fiber coating for solid-phase microextraction. *RSC Adv.* **2015**, *5*, 71859–71867. [CrossRef]

72. Li, Y.; Ma, M.; Zhang, M.; Yang, Y.; Wang, X.; Du, X. In situ anodic growth of rod-like TiO2 coating on a Ti wire as a selective solid-phase microextraction fiber. *RSC Adv.* **2014**, *4*, 53820–53827. [CrossRef]

73. Zhang, Y.; Song, W.; Yang, Y.; Guo, M.; Wang, X.; Du, X. Self-assembly of mercaptoundecanol on cedar-like Au nanoparticle coated stainless steel fiber for selective solid-phase microextraction. *Anal. Methods* **2015**, *7*, 7680–7689. [CrossRef]

74. Naccarato, A.; Gionfriddo, E.; Elliani, R.; Pawliszyn, J.; Sindona, G.; Tagarelli, A. Investigating the robustness and extraction performance of a matrix-compatible solid-phase microextraction coating in human urine and its application to assess 2–6-ring polycyclic aromatic hydrocarbons using GC–MS/MS. *J. Sep. Sci.* **2018**, *41*, 929–939. [CrossRef] [PubMed]

75. Liu, S.; Pan, G.; Yang, H.; Cai, Z.; Zhu, F.; Ouyang, G. Determination and elimination of hazardous pollutants by exploitation of a Prussian blue nanoparticles-graphene oxide composite. *Anal. Chim. Acta* **2019**, *1054*, 17–25. [CrossRef] [PubMed]

76. Liu, S.; Xie, L.; Hu, Q.; Yang, H.; Pan, G.; Zhu, F.; Yang, S.; Ouyang, G. A tri-metal centered metal-organic framework for solid-phase microextraction of environmental contaminants with enhanced extraction efficiency. *Anal. Chim. Acta* **2017**, *987*, 38–46. [CrossRef]

77. Cen, J.; Wei, S.; Nan, H.; Xu, J.; Huang, Z.; Liu, S.; Hu, Q.; Yan, J.; Ouyang, G. Incorporation of carbon nanotubes into graphene for highly efficient solid-phase microextraction of benzene homologues. *Microchem. J.* **2018**, *139*, 203–209. [CrossRef]

78. Liu, S.; Hu, Q.; Zheng, J.; Xie, L.; Wei, S.; Jiang, R.; Zhu, F.; Liu, Y.; Ouyang, G. Knitting aromatic polymers for efficient solid-phase microextraction of trace organic pollutants. *J. Chromatogr. A* **2016**, *1450*, 9–16. [CrossRef]

79. Huang, Z.; Liu, S.; Xu, J.; Yin, L.; Zheng, J.; Zhou, N.; Ouyang, G. Porous organic polymers with different pore structures for sensitive solid-phase microextraction of environmental organic pollutants. *Anal. Chim. Acta* **2017**, *989*, 21–28. [CrossRef]

80. Xie, X.; Wang, J.; Zheng, J.; Huang, J.; Ni, C.; Cheng, J.; Hao, Z.; Ouyang, G. Low-cost Scholl-coupling microporous polymer as an efficient solid-phase microextraction coating for the detection of light aromatic compounds. *Anal. Chim. Acta* **2018**, *1029*, 30–36. [CrossRef]

81. Mei, M.; Huang, X.; Yuan, D. Multiple monolithic fiber solid-phase microextraction: A new extraction approach for aqueous samples. *J. Chromatogr. A* **2014**, *1345*, 29–36. [CrossRef] [PubMed]

82. Mei, M.; Huang, X.; Liao, K.; Yuan, D. Sensitive monitoring of benzoylurea insecticides in water and juice samples treated with multiple monolithic fiber solid-phase microextraction and liquid chromatographic analysis. *Anal. Chim. Acta* **2015**, *860*, 29–36. [CrossRef] [PubMed]

83. Pei, M.; Zhang, Z.; Huang, X.; Wu, Y. Fabrication of a polymeric ionic liquid-based adsorbent for multiple monolithic fiber solid-phase microextraction of endocrine disrupting chemicals in complicated samples. *Talanta* **2017**, *165*, 152–160. [CrossRef] [PubMed]

84. Huang, Y.; Lu, M.; Li, H.; Bai, M.; Huang, X. Sensitive determination of perfluoroalkane sulfonamides in water and urine samples by multiple monolithic fiber solid-phase microextraction and liquid chromatography tandem mass spectrometry. *Talanta* **2019**, *192*, 24–31. [CrossRef] [PubMed]

85. Mei, M.; Huang, X.; Luo, Q.; Yuan, D. Magnetism-Enhanced Monolith-Based In-Tube Solid Phase Microextraction. *Anal. Chem.* **2016**, *88*, 1900–1907. [CrossRef]

86. Kabir, A.; Furton, K.G. *Fabric Phase Sorptive Extractor (FPSE)*; US Patent and Trademark Office: Alexandria, VA, USA, 2014.

87. Racamonde, I.; Rodil, R.; Quintana, J.B.; Sieira, B.J.; Kabir, A.; Furton, K.G.; Cela, R. Fabric phase sorptive extraction: A new sorptive microextraction technique for the determination of non-steroidal anti-inflammatory drugs from environmental water samples. *Anal. Chim. Acta* **2015**, *865*, 22–30. [CrossRef]

88. Santana-Viera, S.; Guedes-Alonso, R.; Sosa-Ferrera, Z.; Santana-Rodríguez, J.J.; Kabir, A.; Furton, K.G. Optimization and application of fabric phase sorptive extraction coupled to ultra-high performance liquid chromatography tandem mass spectrometry for the determination of cytostatic drug residues in environmental waters. *J. Chromatogr. A* **2017**, *1529*, 39–49. [CrossRef]

89. Roldán-Pijuán, M.; Lucena, R.; Cárdenas, S.; Valcárcel, M.; Kabir, A.; Furton, K.G. Stir fabric phase sorptive extraction for the determination of triazine herbicides in environmental waters by liquid chromatography. *J. Chromatogr. A* **2015**, *1376*, 35–45. [CrossRef]

90. Lakade, S.S.; Borrull, F.; Furton, K.G.; Kabir, A.; Marcé, R.M.; Fontanals, N. Dynamic fabric phase sorptive extraction for a group of pharmaceuticals and personal care products from environmental waters. *J. Chromatogr. A* **2016**, *1456*, 19–26. [CrossRef]

91. Kenessov, B.; Koziel, J.A.; Bakaikina, N.V.; Orazbayeva, D. Perspectives and challenges of on-site quantification of organic pollutants in soils using solid-phase microextraction. *TrAC Trends Anal. Chem.* **2016**, *85*, 111–122. [CrossRef]

92. Bianchi, F.; Bedini, A.; Riboni, N.; Pinalli, R.; Gregori, A.; Sidisky, L.; Dalcanale, E.; Careri, M. Cavitand-based solid-phase microextraction coating for the selective detection of nitroaromatic explosives in air and soil. *Anal. Chem.* **2014**, *86*, 10646–10652. [CrossRef] [PubMed]

93. Yao, W.; Fan, Z.; Zhang, S. Preparation of metal-organic framework UiO-66-incorporated polymer monolith for the extraction of trace levels of fungicides in environmental water and soil samples. *J. Sep. Sci.* **2019**, *42*, 2679–2686. [CrossRef] [PubMed]

94. Gao, J.; Huang, C.; Lin, Y.; Tong, P.; Zhang, L. In situ solvothermal synthesis of metal-organic framework coated fiber for highly sensitive solid-phase microextraction of polycyclic aromatic hydrocarbons. *J. Chromatogr. A* **2016**, *1436*, 1–8. [CrossRef] [PubMed]

95. Zhang, X.; Zang, X.H.; Wang, J.T.; Wang, C.; Wu, Q.H.; Wang, Z. Porous carbon derived from aluminum-based metal organic framework as a fiber coating for the solid-phase microextraction of polycyclic aromatic hydrocarbons from water and soil. *Microchim. Acta* **2015**, *182*, 2353–2359. [CrossRef]

96. Zhang, N.; Huang, C.; Tong, P.; Feng, Z.; Wu, X.; Zhang, L. Moisture stable Ni-Zn MOF/g-C 3 N 4 nanoflowers: A highly efficient adsorbent for solid-phase microextraction of PAHs. *J. Chromatogr. A* **2018**, *1556*, 37–46. [CrossRef]

97. Zhang, N.; Huang, C.; Feng, Z.; Chen, H.; Tong, P.; Wu, X.; Zhang, L. Metal-organic framework-coated stainless steel fiber for solid-phase microextraction of polychlorinated biphenyls. *J. Chromatogr. A* **2018**, *1570*, 10–18. [CrossRef]

98. Wu, Y.Y.; Yang, C.X.; Yan, X.P. Fabrication of metal-organic framework MIL-88B films on stainless steel fibers for solid-phase microextraction of polychlorinated biphenyls. *J. Chromatogr. A* **2014**, *1334*, 1–8. [CrossRef]

99. Zhang, C.Y.; Yan, Z.G.; Zhou, Y.Y.; Wang, L.; Xie, Y.B.; Bai, L.P.; Zhou, H.Y.; Li, F.S. Embedment of Ag(I)-organic frameworks into silica gels for microextraction of polybrominated diphenyl ethers in soils. *J. Chromatogr. A* **2015**, *1383*, 18–24. [CrossRef]

100. Bakaikina, N.V.; Kenessov, B.; Ul'yanovskii, N.V.; Kosyakov, D.S. Quantification of transformation products of rocket fuel unsymmetrical dimethylhydrazine in soils using SPME and GC-MS. *Talanta* **2018**, *184*, 332–337. [CrossRef]

101. Peruga, A.; Beltrán, J.; López, F.; Hernández, F. Determination of methylisothiocyanate in soil and water by HS-SPME followed by GC-MS-MS with a triple quadrupole. *Anal. Bioanal. Chem.* **2014**, *406*, 5271–5282. [CrossRef]

102. Yegemova, S.; Bakaikina, N.V.; Kenessov, B.; Koziel, J.A.; Nauryzbayev, M. Determination of 1-methyl-1H-1,2,4-triazole in soils contaminated by rocket fuel using solid-phase microextraction, isotope dilution and gas chromatography-mass spectrometry. *Talanta* **2015**, *143*, 226–233. [CrossRef] [PubMed]

103. Škulcová, L.; Hale, S.E.; Hofman, J.; Bielská, L. Laboratory versus field soil aging: Impact on DDE bioavailability and sorption. *Chemosphere* **2017**, *186*, 235–242. [CrossRef] [PubMed]

104. Shen, H.; Li, W.; Graham, S.E.; Starr, J.M. The role of soil and house dust physicochemical properties in determining the post ingestion bioaccessibility of sorbed polychlorinated biphenyls. *Chemosphere* **2019**, *217*, 1–8. [CrossRef] [PubMed]

105. Ma, L.; Yates, S.R. Dissolved organic matter and estrogen interactions regulate estrogen removal in the aqueous environment: A review. *Sci. Total Environ.* **2018**, *640–641*, 529–542. [CrossRef] [PubMed]

106. Guo, M.; Gong, Z.; Allinson, G.; Tai, P.; Miao, R.; Li, X.; Jia, C.; Zhuang, J. Variations in the bioavailability of polycyclic aromatic hydrocarbons in industrial and agricultural soils after bioremediation. *Chemosphere* **2016**, *144*, 1513–1520. [CrossRef] [PubMed]

107. Kumar, R.; Gaurav; Kabir, A.; Furton, K.G.; Malik, A.K. Development of a fabric phase sorptive extraction with high-performance liquid chromatography and ultraviolet detection method for the analysis of alkyl phenols in environmental samples. *J. Sep. Sci.* **2015**, *38*, 3228–3238. [CrossRef]

108. Stanisz, E.; Werner, J.; Matusiewicz, H. Task specific ionic liquid-coated PTFE tube for solid-phase microextraction prior to chemical and photo-induced mercury cold vapour generation. *Microchem. J.* **2014**, *114*, 229–237. [CrossRef]

109. Psillakis, E. Vacuum-assisted headspace solid-phase microextraction: A tutorial review. *Anal. Chim. Acta* **2017**, *986*, 12–24. [CrossRef]

110. Wu, M.; Wang, L.; Zhao, F.; Zeng, B. Ionic liquid polymer functionalized carbon nanotubes-coated polyaniline for the solid-phase microextraction of benzene derivatives. *RSC Adv.* **2015**, *5*, 99483–99490. [CrossRef]

111. Sarafraz-Yazdi, A.; Rounaghi, G.; Vatani, H.; Razavipanah, I.; Amiri, A. Headspace solid phase microextraction of volatile aromatic hydrocarbons using a steel wire coated with an electrochemically prepared nanocomposite consisting of polypyrrole, carbon nanotubes, and titanium oxide. *Microchim. Acta* **2015**, *182*, 217–225. [CrossRef]

112. Song, X.L.; Chen, Y.; Yuan, J.P.; Qin, Y.J.; Zhao, R.S.; Wang, X. Carbon nanotube composite microspheres as a highly efficient solid-phase microextraction coating for sensitive determination of phthalate acid esters in water samples. *J. Chromatogr. A* **2016**, *1468*, 17–22. [CrossRef]

113. Di Pietro Roux, K.C.; Jasinski, É.F.; Merib, J.; Sartorelli, M.L.; Carasek, E. Application of a robust solid-phase microextraction fiber consisting of NiTi wires coated with polypyrrole for the determination of haloanisoles in water and wine. *Anal. Methods* **2016**, *8*, 5503–5510. [CrossRef]

114. Huang, S.; Xu, J.; Tao, X.; Chen, X.; Zhu, F.; Wang, Y.; Jiang, R.; Ouyang, G. Fabrication of polyaniline/silver composite coating as a dual-functional platform for microextraction and matrix-free laser desorption/ionization. *Talanta* **2017**, *172*, 155–161. [CrossRef] [PubMed]

115. Li, Z.; Ma, R.; Bai, S.; Wang, C.; Wang, Z. A solid phase microextraction fiber coated with graphene-poly(ethylene glycol) composite for the extraction of volatile aromatic compounds from water samples. *Talanta* **2014**, *119*, 498–504. [CrossRef]

116. Sarafraz-Yazdi, A.; Yekkebashi, A. Development of a poly(ethylene glycol)-graphene oxide sol-gel coating for solid-phase microextraction of aromatic amines in water samples with a gas chromatography-flame ionization detector method. *New J. Chem.* **2015**, *39*, 1287–1294. [CrossRef]

117. De Toffoli, A.L.; Fumes, B.H.; Lanças, F.M. Packed in-tube solid phase microextraction with graphene oxide supported on aminopropyl silica: Determination of target triazines in water samples. *J. Environ. Sci. Health Part B Pestic. Food Contam. Agric. Wastes* **2018**, *53*, 434–440. [CrossRef] [PubMed]

118. Tan, F.; Zhao, C.; Li, L.; Liu, M.; He, X.; Gao, J. Graphene oxide based in-tube solid-phase microextraction combined with liquid chromatography tandem mass spectrometry for the determination of triazine herbicides in water. *J. Sep. Sci.* **2015**, *38*, 2312–2319. [CrossRef]

119. Li, S.; Lu, C.; Zhu, F.; Jiang, R.; Ouyang, G. Preparation of C18 composite solid-phase microextraction fiber and its application to the determination of organochlorine pesticides in water samples. *Anal. Chim. Acta* **2015**, *873*, 57–62. [CrossRef]

120. Jiang, H.; Li, J.; Jiang, M.; Lu, R.; Shen, J.; Sun, X.; Han, W.; Wang, L. Ordered mesoporous carbon film as an effective solid-phase microextraction coating for determination of benzene series from aqueous media. *Anal. Chim. Acta* **2015**, *888*, 85–93. [CrossRef]

121. Saraji, M.; Shahvar, A. Metal-organic aerogel as a coating for solid-phase microextraction. *Anal. Chim. Acta* **2017**, *973*, 51–58. [CrossRef]

122. Bagheri, H.; Javanmardi, H.; Abbasi, A.; Banihashemi, S. A metal organic framework-polyaniline nanocomposite as a fiber coating for solid phase microextraction. *J. Chromatogr. A* **2016**, *1431*, 27–35. [CrossRef] [PubMed]

123. Xie, L.; Liu, S.; Han, Z.; Jiang, R.; Zhu, F.; Xu, W.; Su, C.; Ouyang, G. Amine-functionalized MIL-53(Al)-coated stainless steel fiber for efficient solid-phase microextraction of synthetic musks and organochlorine pesticides in water samples. *Anal. Bioanal. Chem.* **2017**, *409*, 5239–5247. [CrossRef] [PubMed]

124. Zang, X.; Zhang, X.; Chang, Q.; Li, S.; Wang, C.; Wang, Z. Metal–organic framework UiO-67-coated fiber for the solid-phase microextraction of nitrobenzene compounds from water. *J. Sep. Sci.* **2016**, *39*, 2770–2776. [CrossRef]

125. Zang, X.; Zhang, G.; Chang, Q.; Zhang, X.; Wang, C.; Wang, Z. Metal organic framework MIL-101 coated fiber for headspace solid phase microextraction of volatile aromatic compounds. *Anal. Methods* **2015**, *7*, 918–923. [CrossRef]

126. Zhang, J.; Zhang, W.; Bao, T.; Chen, Z. Polydopamine-based immobilization of zeolitic imidazolate framework-8 for in-tube solid-phase microextraction. *J. Chromatogr. A* **2015**, *1388*, 9–16. [CrossRef] [PubMed]

127. Kang, H.; Mao, Y.; Wang, X.; Zhang, Y.; Wu, J.; Wang, H. Disposable ionic liquid-coated etched stainless steel fiber for headspace solid-phase microextraction of organophosphorus flame retardants from water samples. *RSC Adv.* **2015**, *5*, 41934–41940. [CrossRef]

128. Pacheco-Fernández, I.; Najafi, A.; Pino, V.; Anderson, J.L.; Ayala, J.H.; Afonso, A.M. Utilization of highly robust and selective crosslinked polymeric ionic liquid-based sorbent coatings in direct-immersion solid-phase microextraction and high-performance liquid chromatography for determining polar organic pollutants in waters. *Talanta* **2016**, *158*, 125–133. [CrossRef]

129. Pena-Pereira, F.; Marcinkowski, Ł.; Kloskowski, A.; Namieśnik, J. Ionogel fibres of bis(trifluoromethanesulfonyl) imide anion-based ionic liquids for the headspace solid-phase microextraction of chlorinated organic pollutants. *Analyst* **2015**, *140*, 7417–7422. [CrossRef]

130. Zhang, C.; Anderson, J.L. Polymeric ionic liquid bucky gels as sorbent coatings for solid-phase microextraction. *J. Chromatogr. A* **2014**, *1344*, 15–22. [CrossRef]

131. Yu, H.; Merib, J.; Anderson, J.L. Crosslinked polymeric ionic liquids as solid-phase microextraction sorbent coatings for high performance liquid chromatography. *J. Chromatogr. A* **2016**, *1438*, 10–21. [CrossRef]

132. Feng, J.; Wang, X.; Tian, Y.; Luo, C.; Sun, M. Basalt fibers grafted with a poly(ionic liquids) coating for in-tube solid-phase microextraction. *J. Sep. Sci.* **2018**, *41*, 3267–3274. [CrossRef] [PubMed]

133. Sun, M.; Feng, J.; Bu, Y.; Wang, X.; Duan, H.; Luo, C. Palladium-coated stainless-steel wire as a solid-phase microextraction fiber. *J. Sep. Sci.* **2015**, *38*, 1584–1590. [CrossRef] [PubMed]

134. Wang, X.; Feng, J.; Tian, Y.; Luo, C.; Sun, M. Co-Al bimetallic hydroxide nanocomposites coating for online in-tube solid-phase microextraction. *J. Chromatogr. A* **2018**, *1550*, 1–7. [CrossRef] [PubMed]

135. Feng, J.; Tian, Y.; Wang, X.; Luo, C.; Sun, M. Basalt fibers functionalized with gold nanoparticles for in-tube solid-phase microextraction. *J. Sep. Sci.* **2018**, *41*, 1149–1155. [CrossRef]

136. Pena-Pereira, F.; Marcinkowski, Ł.; Kloskowski, A.; Namieśnik, J. Silica-based ionogels: Nanoconfined ionic liquid-rich fibers for headspace solid-phase microextraction coupled with gas chromatography-barrier discharge ionization detection. *Anal. Chem.* **2014**, *86*, 11640–11648. [CrossRef]

137. Jiang, H.; Li, J.; Hu, X.; Shen, J.; Sun, X.; Han, W.; Wang, L. Ordered mesoporous silica film as a novel fiber coating for solid-phase microextraction. *Talanta* **2017**, *174*, 307–313. [CrossRef]

138. Bagheri, H.; Akbarinejad, A.; Aghakhani, A. A highly thermal-resistant electrospun-based polyetherimide nanofibers coating for solid-phase microextraction Microextraction Techniques. *Anal. Bioanal. Chem.* **2014**, *406*, 2141–2149. [CrossRef]

139. Bagheri, H.; Roostaie, A. Roles of inorganic oxide nanoparticles on extraction efficiency of electrospun polyethylene terephthalate nanocomposite as an unbreakable fiber coating. *J. Chromatogr. A* **2015**, *1375*, 8–16. [CrossRef]

140. Sarafraz-Yazdi, A.; Yekkebashi, A. A non-ionic surfactant-mediated sol-gel coating for solid-phase microextraction of benzene, toluene, ethylbenzene and o-xylene in water samples using a gas chromatography-flame ionization detector. *New J. Chem.* **2014**, *38*, 4486–4493. [CrossRef]

141. Saraji, M.; Mehrafza, N. A simple approach for the preparation of simazine molecularly imprinted nanofibers via self-polycondensation for selective solid-phase microextraction. *Anal. Chim. Acta* **2016**, *936*, 108–115. [CrossRef]

142. Mirabelli, M.F.; Wolf, J.C.; Zenobi, R. Direct Coupling of Solid-Phase Microextraction with Mass Spectrometry: Sub-pg/g Sensitivity Achieved Using a Dielectric Barrier Discharge Ionization Source. *Anal. Chem.* **2016**, *88*, 7252–7258. [CrossRef] [PubMed]

143. Feng, J.; Sun, M.; Li, L.; Wang, X.; Duan, H.; Luo, C. Multiwalled carbon nanotubes-doped polymeric ionic liquids coating for multiple headspace solid-phase microextraction. *Talanta* **2014**, *123*, 18–24. [CrossRef] [PubMed]

144. Wu, M.; Wang, L.; Zeng, B.; Zhao, F. Ionic liquid polymer functionalized carbon nanotubes-doped poly(3,4-ethylenedioxythiophene) for highly efficient solid-phase microextraction of carbamate pesticides. *J. Chromatogr. A* **2016**, *1444*, 42–49. [CrossRef] [PubMed]

145. Ai, Y.; Zhang, J.; Zhao, F.; Zeng, B. Hydrophobic coating of polyaniline-poly(propylene oxide) copolymer for direct immersion solid phase microextraction of carbamate pesticides. *J. Chromatogr. A* **2015**, *1407*, 52–57. [CrossRef] [PubMed]

146. Cavaliere, B.; Monteleone, M.; Naccarato, A.; Sindona, G.; Tagarelli, A. A solid-phase microextraction-gas chromatographic approach combined with triple quadrupole mass spectrometry for the assay of carbamate pesticides in water samples. *J. Chromatogr. A* **2012**, *1257*, 149–157. [CrossRef] [PubMed]

147. Saraji, M.; Jafari, M.T.; Mossaddegh, M. Carbon nanotubes@silicon dioxide nanohybrids coating for solid-phase microextraction of organophosphorus pesticides followed by gas chromatography-corona discharge ion mobility spectrometric detection. *J. Chromatogr. A* **2016**, *1429*, 30–39. [CrossRef]

148. Jafari, M.T.; Saraji, M.; Sherafatmand, H. Polypyrrole/montmorillonite nanocomposite as a new solid phase microextraction fiber combined with gas chromatography-corona discharge ion mobility spectrometry for the simultaneous determination of diazinon and fenthion organophosphorus pesticides. *Anal. Chim. Acta* **2014**, *814*, 69–78. [CrossRef]

149. Kamalabadi, M.; Mohammadi, A.; Alizadeh, N. Polypyrrole nanowire as an excellent solid phase microextraction fiber for bisphenol A analysis in food samples followed by ion mobility spectrometry. *Talanta* **2016**, *156–157*, 147–153. [CrossRef]

150. Li, J.W.; Wang, Y.L.; Yan, S.; Li, X.J.; Pan, S.Y. Molecularly imprinted calixarene fiber for solid-phase microextraction of four organophosphorous pesticides in fruits. *Food Chem.* **2016**, *192*, 260–267. [CrossRef]

151. Liang, W.; Wang, J.; Zang, X.; Dong, W.; Wang, C.; Wang, Z. Barley husk carbon as the fiber coating for the solid-phase microextraction of twelve pesticides in vegetables prior to gas chromatography–mass spectrometric detection. *J. Chromatogr. A* **2017**, *1491*, 9–15. [CrossRef]

152. Wu, M.; Chen, G.; Liu, P.; Zhou, W.; Jia, Q. Polydopamine-based immobilization of a hydrazone covalent organic framework for headspace solid-phase microextraction of pyrethroids in vegetables and fruits. *J. Chromatogr. A* **2016**, *1456*, 34–41. [CrossRef] [PubMed]

153. Wu, M.; Chen, G.; Ma, J.; Liu, P.; Jia, Q. Fabrication of cross-linked hydrazone covalent organic frameworks by click chemistry and application to solid phase microextraction. *Talanta* **2016**, *161*, 350–358. [CrossRef] [PubMed]

154. Zhang, S.; Yang, Q.; Wang, W.; Wang, C.; Wang, Z. Covalent Bonding of Metal-Organic Framework-5/Graphene Oxide Hybrid Composite to Stainless Steel Fiber for Solid-Phase Microextraction of Triazole Fungicides from Fruit and Vegetable Samples. *J. Agric. Food Chem.* **2016**, *64*, 2792–2801. [CrossRef] [PubMed]

155. Zhang, S.; Yang, Q.; Li, Z.; Wang, W.; Wang, C.; Wang, Z. Zeolitic imidazole framework templated synthesis of nanoporous carbon as a novel fiber coating for solid-phase microextraction. *Analyst* **2016**, *141*, 1127–1135. [CrossRef] [PubMed]

156. Tian, M.; Cheng, R.; Ye, J.; Liu, X.; Jia, Q. Preparation and evaluation of ionic liquid-calixarene solid-phase microextraction fibres for the determination of triazines in fruit and vegetable samples. *Food Chem.* **2014**, *145*, 28–33. [CrossRef]

157. Gionfriddo, E.; Naccarato, A.; Sindona, G.; Tagarelli, A. A reliable solid phase microextraction-gas chromatography-triple quadrupole mass spectrometry method for the assay of selenomethionine and selenomethylselenocysteine in aqueous extracts: Difference between selenized and not-enriched selenium potatoes. *Anal. Chim. Acta* **2012**, *747*, 58–66. [CrossRef]

158. Hou, X.; Guo, Y.; Liang, X.; Wang, X.; Wang, L.; Wang, L.; Liu, X. Bis(trifluoromethanesulfonyl)imide-based ionic liquids grafted on graphene oxide-coated solid-phase microextraction fiber for extraction and enrichment of polycyclic aromatic hydrocarbons in potatoes and phthalate esters in food-wrap. *Talanta* **2016**, *153*, 392–400. [CrossRef]

159. Saraji, M.; Jafari, M.T.; Mossaddegh, M. Halloysite nanotubes-titanium dioxide as a solid-phase microextraction coating combined with negative corona discharge-ion mobility spectrometry for the determination of parathion. *Anal. Chim. Acta* **2016**, *926*, 55–62. [CrossRef]

160. Zhang, N.; Gao, J.; Huang, C.; Liu, W.; Tong, P.; Zhang, L. In situ hydrothermal growth of ZnO/g-C3N4 nanoflowers coated solid-phase microextraction fibers coupled with GC-MS for determination of pesticides residues. *Anal. Chim. Acta* **2016**, *934*, 122–131. [CrossRef]

161. Souza Silva, É.A.; Pawliszyn, J. Optimization of fiber coating structure enables direct immersion solid phase microextraction and high-throughput determination of complex samples. *Anal. Chem.* **2012**, *84*, 6933–6938. [CrossRef]

162. De Grazia, S.; Gionfriddo, E.; Pawliszyn, J. A new and efficient Solid Phase Microextraction approach for analysis of high fat content food samples using a matrix-compatible coating. *Talanta* **2017**, *167*, 754–760. [CrossRef] [PubMed]

163. Naccarato, A.; Pawliszyn, J. Matrix compatible solid phase microextraction coating, a greener approach to sample preparation in vegetable matrices. *Food Chem.* **2016**, *206*, 67–73. [CrossRef] [PubMed]

164. Souza-Silva, É.A.; Pawliszyn, J. Direct immersion solid-phase microextraction with matrix-compatible fiber coating for multiresidue pesticide analysis of grapes by gas chromatography-time-of-flight mass spectrometry (DI-SPME-GC-ToFMS). *J. Agric. Food Chem.* **2015**, *63*, 4464–4477. [CrossRef] [PubMed]

165. Brereton, R.G. *Chemometrics: Data Analysis for the Laboratory and Chemical Plant*; John Wiley & Sons, Ltd.: Chichester, UK, 2003; ISBN 0471489778.

166. Naccarato, A.; Furia, E.; Sindona, G.; Tagarelli, A. Multivariate class modeling techniques applied to multielement analysis for the verification of the geographical origin of chili pepper. *Food Chem.* **2016**, *206*, 217–222. [CrossRef] [PubMed]

167. Di Donna, L.; Mazzotti, F.; Naccarato, A.; Salerno, R.; Tagarelli, A.; Taverna, D.; Sindona, G. Secondary metabolites of Olea europaea leaves as markers for the discrimination of cultivars and cultivation zones by multivariate analysis. *Food Chem.* **2010**, *121*, 492–496. [CrossRef]

168. Abdulra'uf, L.B.; Tan, G.H. Chemometric approach to the optimization of HS-SPME/GC-MS for the determination of multiclass pesticide residues in fruits and vegetables. *Food Chem.* **2015**, *177*, 267–273. [CrossRef]

169. Wang, X.; Li, X.; Bai, Y.; Liu, H. Just dip it: Online coupling of "dip-it" polymer monolith microextraction with plasma assisted laser desorption ionization mass spectrometry. *Chem. Commun.* **2015**, *51*, 4615–4618. [CrossRef]

170. Gómez-Ríos, G.A.; Vasiljevic, T.; Gionfriddo, E.; Yu, M.; Pawliszyn, J. Towards on-site analysis of complex matrices by solid-phase microextraction-transmission mode coupled to a portable mass spectrometer: Via direct analysis in real time. *Analyst* **2017**, *142*, 2928–2935. [CrossRef]

171. Asiabi, H.; Yamini, Y.; Seidi, S.; Esrafili, A.; Rezaei, F. Electroplating of nanostructured polyaniline-polypyrrole composite coating in a stainless-steel tube for on-line in-tube solid phase microextraction. *J. Chromatogr. A* **2015**, *1397*, 19–26. [CrossRef]

172. de Souza Freitas, L.A.; Vieira, A.C.; Mendonça, J.A.F.R.; Figueiredo, E.C. Molecularly imprinted fibers with renewable surface for solid-phase microextraction of triazoles from grape juice samples followed by gas chromatography mass spectrometry analysis. *Analyst* **2014**, *139*, 626–632. [CrossRef]

173. Wu, M.; Chen, G.; Liu, P.; Zhou, W.; Jia, Q. Preparation of porous aromatic framework/ionic liquid hybrid composite coated solid-phase microextraction fibers and their application in the determination of organochlorine pesticides combined with GC-ECD detection. *Analyst* **2016**, *141*, 243–250. [CrossRef] [PubMed]

174. Pelit, F.O.; Pelit, L.; Dizdaş, T.N.; Aftafa, C.; Ertaş, H.; Yalçinkaya, E.E.; Türkmen, H.; Ertaş, F.N. A novel polythiophene - ionic liquid modified clay composite solid phase microextraction fiber: Preparation, characterization and application to pesticide analysis. *Anal. Chim. Acta* **2015**, *859*, 37–45. [CrossRef] [PubMed]

175. Viñas, P.; Pastor-Belda, M.; Torres, A.; Campillo, N.; Hernández-Córdoba, M. Use of oleic-acid functionalized nanoparticles for the magnetic solid-phase microextraction of alkylphenols in fruit juices using liquid chromatography-tandem mass spectrometry. *Talanta* **2016**, *151*, 217–223. [CrossRef] [PubMed]

176. Mirabelli, M.F.; Gionfriddo, E.; Pawliszyn, J.; Zenobi, R. A quantitative approach for pesticide analysis in grape juice by direct interfacing of a matrix compatible SPME phase to dielectric barrier discharge ionization-mass spectrometry. *Analyst* **2018**, *143*, 891–899. [CrossRef]

177. Lan, H.; Pan, D.; Sun, Y.; Guo, Y.; Wu, Z. Thin metal organic frameworks coatings by cathodic electrodeposition for solid-phase microextraction and analysis of trace exogenous estrogens in milk. *Anal. Chim. Acta* **2016**, *937*, 53–60. [CrossRef]

178. Merib, J.; Nardini, G.; Carasek, E. Use of Doehlert design in the optimization of extraction conditions in the determination of organochlorine pesticides in bovine milk samples by HS-SPME. *Anal. Methods* **2014**, *6*, 3254–3260. [CrossRef]

179. Lin, W.; Wei, S.; Jiang, R.; Zhu, F.; Ouyang, G. Calibration of the complex matrix effects on the sampling of polycyclic aromatic hydrocarbons in milk samples using solid phase microextraction. *Anal. Chim. Acta* **2016**, *933*, 117–123. [CrossRef]

180. Lv, F.; Gan, N.; Cao, Y.; Zhou, Y.; Zuo, R.; Dong, Y. A molybdenum disulfide/reduced graphene oxide fiber coating coupled with gas chromatography–mass spectrometry for the saponification-headspace solid-phase microextraction of polychlorinated biphenyls in food. *J. Chromatogr. A* **2017**, *1525*, 42–50. [CrossRef]

181. Joshi, M.D.; Ho, T.D.; Cole, W.T.S.; Anderson, J.L. Determination of polychlorinated biphenyls in ocean water and bovine milk using crosslinked polymeric ionic liquid sorbent coatings by solid-phase microextraction. *Talanta* **2014**, *118*, 172–179. [CrossRef]

182. Pang, J.; Yuan, D.; Huang, X. On-line combining monolith-based in-tube solid phase microextraction and high-performance liquid chromatography- fluorescence detection for the sensitive monitoring of polycyclic aromatic hydrocarbons in complex samples. *J. Chromatogr. A* **2018**, *1571*, 29–37. [CrossRef]

183. Roszkowska, A.; Yu, M.; Bessonneau, V.; Bragg, L.; Servos, M.; Pawliszyn, J. Metabolome Profiling of Fish Muscle Tissue Exposed to Benzo[a]pyrene Using in Vivo Solid-Phase Microextraction. *Environ. Sci. Technol. Lett.* **2018**, *5*, 431–435. [CrossRef]

184. Huang, S.; Xu, J.; Wu, J.; Hong, H.; Chen, G.; Jiang, R.; Zhu, F.; Liu, Y.; Ouyang, G. Rapid detection of five anesthetics in tilapias by in vivo solid phase microextraction coupling with gas chromatography-mass spectrometry. *Talanta* **2017**, *168*, 263–268. [CrossRef] [PubMed]

185. Delvaux Júnior, N.A.; de Queiroz, M.E.L.R.; Neves, A.A.; Oliveira, A.F.; da Silva, M.R.F.; Faroni, L.R.A.; Heleno, F.F. Headspace solid phase microextraction-gas chromatography for the determination of trihalomethanes in fish. *Microchem. J.* **2017**, *133*, 539–544. [CrossRef]

186. Hashemi-Moghaddam, H.; Ahmadifard, M. Novel molecularly imprinted solid-phase microextraction fiber coupled with gas chromatography for analysis of furan. *Talanta* **2016**, *150*, 148–154. [CrossRef] [PubMed]

187. Lin, S.; Gan, N.; Qiao, L.; Zhang, J.; Cao, Y.; Chen, Y. Magnetic metal-organic frameworks coated stir bar sorptive extraction coupled with GC-MS for determination of polychlorinated biphenyls in fish samples. *Talanta* **2015**, *144*, 1139–1145. [CrossRef] [PubMed]

188. Wang, W.; Wang, J.; Zhang, S.; Cui, P.; Wang, C.; Wang, Z. A novel Schiff base network-1 nanocomposite coated fiber for solid-phase microextraction of phenols from honey samples. *Talanta* **2016**, *161*, 22–30. [CrossRef]

189. Al-Alam, J.; Fajloun, Z.; Chbani, A.; Millet, M. A multiresidue method for the analysis of 90 pesticides, 16 PAHs, and 22 PCBs in honey using QuEChERS–SPME. *Anal. Bioanal. Chem.* **2017**, *409*, 5157–5169. [CrossRef]

190. Yang, M.; Wu, X.; Xi, X.; Zhang, P.; Yang, X.; Lu, R.; Zhou, W.; Zhang, S.; Gao, H.; Li, J. Using β-cyclodextrin/attapulgite-immobilized ionic liquid as sorbent in dispersive solid-phase microextraction to detect the benzoylurea insecticide contents of honey and tea beverages. *Food Chem.* **2016**, *197*, 1064–1072. [CrossRef]

191. Liang, W.; Wang, J.; Zang, X.; Wang, C.; Wang, Z. A porous carbon derived from amino-functionalized material of Institut Lavoisier as a solid-phase microextraction fiber coating for the extraction of phthalate esters from tea. *J. Sep. Sci.* **2016**, *39*, 1331–1338. [CrossRef]

192. Cheng, X.; Yan, H.; Wang, X.; Sun, N.; Qiao, X. Vortex-assisted magnetic dispersive solid-phase microextraction for rapid screening and recognition of dicofol residues in tea products. *Food Chem.* **2014**, *162*, 104–109. [CrossRef]

193. Ng, N.T.; Sanagi, M.M.; Wan Ibrahim, W.N.; Wan Ibrahim, W.A. Agarose-chitosan-C18 film micro-solid phase extraction combined with high performance liquid chromatography for the determination of phenanthrene and pyrene in chrysanthemum tea samples. *Food Chem.* **2017**, *222*, 28–34. [CrossRef] [PubMed]

194. Cagliero, C.; Nan, H.; Bicchi, C.; Anderson, J.L. Matrix-compatible sorbent coatings based on structurally tuned polymeric ionic liquids for the determination of acrylamide in brewed coffee and coffee powder using solid-phase microextraction. *J. Chromatogr. A* **2016**, *1459*, 17–23. [CrossRef] [PubMed]

195. Ho, T.D.; Toledo, B.R.; Hantao, L.W.; Anderson, J.L. Chemical immobilization of crosslinked polymeric ionic liquids on nitinol wires produces highly robust sorbent coatings for solid-phase microextraction. *Anal. Chim. Acta* **2014**, *843*, 18–26. [CrossRef] [PubMed]

196. Amanzadeh, H.; Yamini, Y.; Moradi, M.; Asl, Y.A. Determination of phthalate esters in drinking water and edible vegetable oil samples by headspace solid phase microextraction using graphene/polyvinylchloride nanocomposite coated fiber coupled to gas chromatography-flame ionization detector. *J. Chromatogr. A* **2016**, *1465*, 38–46. [CrossRef]

197. Wang, Y.; Sun, Y.; Xu, B.; Li, X.; Jin, R.; Zhang, H.; Song, D. Magnetic ionic liquid-based dispersive liquid-liquid microextraction for the determination of triazine herbicides in vegetable oils by liquid chromatography. *J. Chromatogr. A* **2014**, *1373*, 9–16. [CrossRef]

198. Wu, L.; Song, Y.; Hu, M.; Xu, X.; Zhang, H.; Yu, A.; Ma, Q.; Wang, Z. Determination of sulfonamides in butter samples by ionic liquid magnetic bar liquid-phase microextraction high-performance liquid chromatography. *Anal. Bioanal. Chem.* **2015**, *407*, 569–580. [CrossRef]

199. Matin, A.A.; Biparva, P.; Gheshlaghi, M. Gas chromatographic determination of polycyclic aromatic hydrocarbons in water and smoked rice samples after solid-phase microextraction using multiwalled carbon nanotube loaded hollow fiber. *J. Chromatogr. A* **2014**, *1374*, 50–57. [CrossRef]

200. Chen, D.; Huang, Y.Q.; He, X.M.; Shi, Z.G.; Feng, Y.Q. Coupling carbon nanotube film microextraction with desorption corona beam ionization for rapid analysis of Sudan dyes (I-IV) and Rhodamine B in chilli oil. *Analyst* **2015**, *140*, 1731–1738. [CrossRef]

201. Li, X.; Li, Z.; Wang, X.; Nie, H.; Zhang, Y.; Bai, Y.; Liu, H. Monolith dip-it: A bifunctional device for improving the sensitivity of direct analysis in real time mass spectrometry. *Analyst* **2016**, *141*, 4947–4952. [CrossRef]

202. Zhang, L.; Gionfriddo, E.; Acquaro, V.; Pawliszyn, J. Direct immersion solid-phase microextraction analysis of multi-class contaminants in edible seaweeds by gas chromatography-mass spectrometry. *Anal. Chim. Acta* **2018**, *1031*, 83–97. [CrossRef]

203. Jian, J.M.; Guo, Y.; Zeng, L.; Liang-Ying, L.; Lu, X.; Wang, F.; Zeng, E.Y. Global distribution of perfluorochemicals (PFCs) in potential human exposure source–A review. *Environ. Int.* **2017**, *108*, 51–62. [CrossRef] [PubMed]

204. Monteleone, M.; Naccarato, A.; Sindona, G.; Tagarelli, A. A rapid and sensitive assay of perfluorocarboxylic acids in aqueous matrices by headspace solid phase microextraction-gas chromatography-triple quadrupole mass spectrometry. *J. Chromatogr. A* **2012**, *1251*, 160–168. [CrossRef] [PubMed]

205. Ouyang, G.; Oakes, K.D.; Bragg, L.; Wang, S.; Liu, H.; Cui, S.; Servos, M.R.; Dixon, D.G.; Pawliszyn, J. Sampling-rate calibration for rapid and nonlethal monitoring of organic contaminants in fish muscle by solid-phase microextraction. *Environ. Sci. Technol.* **2011**, *45*, 7792–7798. [CrossRef] [PubMed]

206. Ouyang, G.; Vuckovic, D.; Pawliszyn, J. Nondestructive sampling of living systems using in vivo solid-phase microextraction. *Chem. Rev.* **2011**, *111*, 2784–2814. [CrossRef]

207. Wang, H.; Sun, W.; Zhang, J.; Yang, X.; Lin, T.; Ding, L. Desorption corona beam ionization source for mass spectrometry. *Analyst* **2010**, *135*, 688–695. [CrossRef]
208. World Health Organization Regional Office for Europe. *Human Biomonitoring: Facts and Figures*; WHO: Geneva, Switzerland, 2015.
209. Centers for Disease Control and Prevention—National Biomonitoring Program. Available online: https://www.cdc.gov/biomonitoring/ (accessed on 1 November 2019).
210. Souza-Silva, É.A.; Reyes-Garcés, N.; Gómez-Ríos, G.A.; Boyaci, E.; Bojko, B.; Pawliszyn, J. A critical review of the state of the art of solid-phase microextraction of complex matrices III. Bioanalytical and clinical applications. *TrAC Trends Anal. Chem.* **2015**, *71*, 249–264. [CrossRef]
211. Naccarato, A.; Gionfriddo, E.; Elliani, R.; Sindona, G.; Tagarelli, A. A fast and simple solid phase microextraction coupled with gas chromatography-triple quadrupole mass spectrometry method for the assay of urinary markers of glutaric acidemias. *J. Chromatogr. A* **2014**, *1372*, 253–259. [CrossRef]
212. Naccarato, A.; Elliani, R.; Cavaliere, B.; Sindona, G.; Tagarelli, A. Development of a fast and simple gas chromatographic protocol based on the combined use of alkyl chloroformate and solid phase microextraction for the assay of polyamines in human urine. *J. Chromatogr. A* **2018**, *1549*, 1–13. [CrossRef]
213. Yang, B.C.; Fang, S.F.; Wan, X.J.; Luo, Y.; Zhou, J.Y.; Li, Y.; Li, Y.J.; Wang, F.; Huang, O.P. Quantification of monohydroxylated polycyclic aromatic hydrocarbons in human urine samples using solid-phase microextraction coupled with glass-capillary nanoelectrospray ionization mass spectrometry. *Anal. Chim. Acta* **2017**, *973*, 68–74. [CrossRef]
214. Antonucci, A.; Vitali, M.; Avino, P.; Manigrasso, M.; Protano, C. Sensitive multiresidue method by HS-SPME/GC-MS for 10 volatile organic compounds in urine matrix: A new tool for biomonitoring studies on children. *Anal. Bioanal. Chem.* **2016**, *408*, 5789–5800. [CrossRef]
215. Lamani, X.; Horst, S.; Zimmermann, T.; Schmidt, T.C. Determination of aromatic amines in human urine using comprehensive multi-dimensional gas chromatography mass spectrometry (GCxGC-qMS). *Anal. Bioanal. Chem.* **2015**, *407*, 241–252. [CrossRef] [PubMed]
216. Song, H.N.; Kim, C.H.; Lee, W.Y.; Cho, S.H. Simultaneous determination of volatile organic compounds with a wide range of polarities in urine by headspace solid-phase microextraction coupled to gas chromatography/mass spectrometry. *Rapid Commun. Mass Spectrom.* **2017**, *31*, 613–622. [CrossRef] [PubMed]
217. Koureas, M.; Karagkouni, F.; Rakitskii, V.; Hadjichristodoulou, C.; Tsatsakis, A.; Tsakalof, A. Serum levels of organochlorine pesticides in the general population of Thessaly, Greece, determined by HS-SPME GC-MS method. *Environ. Res.* **2016**, *148*, 318–321. [CrossRef] [PubMed]
218. Sajid, M.; Basheer, C.; Daud, M.; Alsharaa, A. Evaluation of layered double hydroxide/graphene hybrid as a sorbent in membrane-protected stir-bar supported micro-solid-phase extraction for determination of organochlorine pesticides in urine samples. *J. Chromatogr. A* **2017**, *1489*, 1–8. [CrossRef]
219. Wang, S.L.; Xu, H. Inorganic–organic hybrid coating material for the online in-tube solid-phase microextraction of monohydroxy polycyclic aromatic hydrocarbons in urine. *J. Sep. Sci.* **2016**, *39*, 4610–4620. [CrossRef]
220. Hardy, E.M.; Duca, R.C.; Salquebre, G.; Appenzeller, B.M.R. Multi-residue analysis of organic pollutants in hair and urine for matrices comparison. *Forensic Sci. Int.* **2015**, *249*, 6–19. [CrossRef]
221. Yamamoto, Y.; Ishizaki, A.; Kataoka, H. Biomonitoring method for the determination of polycyclic aromatic hydrocarbons in hair by online in-tube solid-phase microextraction coupled with high performance liquid chromatography and fluorescence detection. *J. Chromatogr. B Anal. Technol. Biomed. Life Sci.* **2015**, *1000*, 187–191. [CrossRef]
222. Tzatzarakis, M.N.; Barbounis, E.G.; Kavvalakis, M.P.; Vakonaki, E.; Renieri, E.; Vardavas, A.I.; Tsatsakis, A.M. Rapid method for the simultaneous determination of DDTs and PCBs in hair of children by headspace solid phase microextraction and gas chromatography-mass spectrometry (HSSPME/GC-MS). *Drug Test. Anal.* **2014**, *6*, 85–92. [CrossRef]
223. Flores-Ramírez, R.; Ortiz-Pérez, M.D.; Batres-Esquivel, L.; Castillo, C.G.; Ilizaliturri-Hernández, C.A.; Díaz-Barriga, F. Rapid analysis of persistent organic pollutants by solid phase microextraction in serum samples. *Talanta* **2014**, *123*, 169–178. [CrossRef]
224. Zhang, J.; Li, W.; Zhu, W.; Qin, P.; Lu, M.; Zhang, X.; Miao, Y.; Cai, Z. Mesoporous graphitic carbon nitride@NiCo 2 O 4 nanocomposite as a solid phase microextraction coating for sensitive determination of environmental pollutants in human serum samples. *Chem. Commun.* **2019**, *55*, 10019–10022. [CrossRef]

Separations **2019**, *6*, 54

225. Meyer-Monath, M.; Beaumont, J.; Morel, I.; Rouget, F.; Tack, K.; Lestremau, F. Analysis of BTEX and chlorinated solvents in meconium by headspace-solid-phase microextraction gas chromatography coupled with mass spectrometry. *Anal. Bioanal. Chem.* **2014**, *406*, 4481–4490. [CrossRef] [PubMed]

226. de la Guardia, M.; Garrigues, S. *Handbook of Green Analytical Chemistry*; John Wiley & Sons, Ltd.: Chichester, UK, 2012; ISBN 9780470972014.

Review

Returning to Nature for the Design of Sorptive Phases in Solid-Phase Microextraction

Gabriela Mafra [1], María Teresa García-Valverde [2], Jaime Millán-Santiago [2], Eduardo Carasek [1], Rafael Lucena [2,*] and Soledad Cárdenas [2]

[1] Departamento de Química, Universidade Federal de Santa Catarina, Florianopolis, SC 88040900, Brazil; gabip_mafra@hotmail.com (G.M.); eduardo.carasek@ufsc.br (E.C.)

[2] Departamento de Química Analítica, Instituto Universitario de Investigación en Química Fina y Nanoquímica IUNAN, Universidad de Córdoba, Campus de Rabanales, Edificio Marie Curie (anexo), E-14071 Cordoba, Spain; q72gavam@uco.es (M.T.G.-V.); q52misaj@uco.es (J.M.-S.); qa1caarm@uco.es (S.C.)

* Correspondence: rafael.lucena@uco.es

Received: 20 October 2019; Accepted: 24 December 2019; Published: 29 December 2019

Abstract: Green analytical chemistry principles aim to minimize the negative impact of analytical procedures in the environment, which can be considered both at close (to ensure the safety of the analysts) and global (to conserve our natural resources) levels. These principles suggest, among other guidelines, the reduction/minimization of the sample treatment and the use of renewable sources when possible. The first aspect is largely fulfilled by microextraction, which is considered to be among the greenest sample treatment techniques. The second consideration is attainable if natural products are used as raw materials for the preparation of new extraction phases. This strategy is in line with the change in our production system, which is being gradually moved from a linear model (take–make–dispose) to a circular one (including reusing and recycling as key terms). This article reviews the potential of natural products as sorbents in extraction and microextraction techniques from the synergic perspectives of two research groups working on the topic. The article covers the use of unmodified natural materials and the modified ones (although the latter has a less green character) to draw a general picture of the usefulness of the materials.

Keywords: green chemistry; circular economy; natural products; sorbents; cork; cotton; pollen; seeds; paper; wood

---

1. Introduction

The irrational fear of chemicals, called chemophobia, is caused by the negative perspective among the general public of the impact of chemistry in our health and environment [1]. While fighting this chemophobia by intensive teaching at different levels [2,3] (including the general public as a target, too) of the benefits that chemistry provides to our societies, chemists must be aware of the potential risks they deal with, to design effective strategies for their control and minimization. In the environmental protection context, analytical chemistry plays a role, since it allows the detection of environmental pollution and permits the monitorization of the remediation protocols. However, this positive contribution must be complemented by the reduction of the collateral impact of analytical procedures, which is the primary goal of green analytical chemistry (GAC) [4–6].

In 2012, Professor Namieśnik et al. theorized about the main guidelines of GAC, providing 12 general principles to be followed in order to reduce the potentially deleterious effects of analytical procedures [7]. The application of these principles is desirable as long as the main aim of analytical chemistry, providing useful and reliable information, is fulfilled. For example, the first principle recommends the direct analysis of samples avoiding in that way the sample treatment. Although this principle identifies one of the trends of current research in analytical sciences, it is difficult to be applied when complex samples containing the analytes at very low concentrations are processed. In such scenarios, the simplification of the sample treatment and the reduction of the sources applied (reagents, energy) can be a more practical objective, at least currently. Microextraction techniques fulfill the latter criteria [8], and they are considered among the greenest sample treatment techniques [9].

Microextraction techniques have evolved in the last decade following some key trends. Among them, the development of new extraction phases can be highlighted, considering the context of this review article. In this evolution, the tenth (use of renewable resources) and eleventh (replace or remove toxic reagents) principles of GAC are especially relevant [7]. In the liquid microextraction context, environmentally friendly solvents [10,11] such as CyreneTM [12] and deep eutectic solvents [13] are clear examples of this progress.

The paradigm of our production system, which up to now has been based on a linear "take–make–dispose" model, is progressively changed to a circular model [14] where reusing, repairing, refurbishing, and recycling appear as key terms. The use of surpluses of natural products as raw materials for the preparation of new sorbents is an interesting contribution of analytical chemistry for changing the production model. This review article, which combines the vision of two research groups working in the topic, tries to draw the general picture of the potential of natural products for the synthesis of new sorptive phases in solid phase extraction and solid phase microextraction. The article will cover strategies with different green characteristics, as some of the natural materials can be used with minimal modifications, but others require a chemical adjustment depending on the analytes to be extracted.

2. Cork

Cork is defined as the outside bark of the *Quercus suber* L., which is commonly known as cork oak tree. This evergreen oak can be found in southwest Europe and northwest Africa and grows up to 20 m height. Due to its cellular structure and chemical composition, cork exhibits some physical properties such as a high coefficient of friction, resilience, high energy absorption, excellent insulation properties, impermeability, low conductivity, and low density, which makes it an excellent material for a variety of applications. It is mainly used as wine bottle stopper; nevertheless, various other applications have been attributed to cork and its derivatives such as flooring and walls coverings, acoustic and vibrating insulation, ecoceramics, and ecodesign [15,16].

Cork has unique microscopic features compared to other lignocellulosic materials. Its hollow polyhedral prismatic cells may present honeycomb or brick wall structures when observed from radial or axial directions, respectively. On average, cork cells are 45 mm tall and have 15–20 mm of face and 1–2 mm of thickness. The chemical composition of cork varies according to seasonality and territory but mainly consists of hydrophobic biopolymers such as suberin ($\pm$40%) and lignin ($\pm$24%), the hydrophilic polysaccharides cellulose and hemicellulose ($\pm$20%), and 15% of other extractives e.g., waxes and tannins. The main cork constituent comprises phenolic, long-chain, and hydroxy fatty acids, which are linked by ester groups framing a polyester structure [17]. Moreover, granules and cork powders exhibit surface charge according to the environment pH. The point of zero-charge values between 2.1 and 4.6 can be reached, corresponding to acidic range. Meanwhile, about 40% of the total acid groups correspond to strong acids and 50% correspond to the overall phenolic OH groups. Therefore, its formidable characteristics are promising resources with potential application on adsorption technologies [18]. Herewith cork is a natural, cheap, renewable, fully sustainable, and biodegradable raw material with a very relevant advantage over other carbonaceous materials to be explored as a sorbent in many applications [19].

Since it was first described as an adsorbent in 2005, [20] its use in environmental applications for the removal of a variety of organic and inorganic pollutants has gained considerable attention, and a large number of research articles, as well as reviews, covering this approach have been published [17,21–26]. The cork employment in sample preparation for microextraction purposes was firstly reported in 2011 [27] and has been increasing over the years. In the first study, powdered activated carbons (AC)

Separations **2020**, *7*, 2

from cork waste were supported for bar adsorptive microextraction (BAμE) as novel adsorbent phases for the determination of clofibric acid and ibuprofen in environmental and biological matrices [27]. The ACs were prepared by the chemical and physical activation of raw waste cork with K_2CO_3 at 700 °C for 1 h and steam at 750 °C for 1 h, respectively. For the concentrations used in the study, both carbons completely removed the two target compounds.

Further, cork was successfully applied as a coating for solid phase microextraction (SPME) devices in the determination of ultra-trace levels of organochlorine pesticides and polycyclic aromatic hydrocarbons (PAHs) in water samples, respectively, by gas chromatography [28,29]. The preparation of the fibers was performed as follows: the cork powder (200 mesh) was immobilized into wires of NiTi (0.2 mm thickness and 2 cm length) containing epoxy glue. Then, the devices were placed into a heating block for 90 min at 180 °C and conditioned at 260 °C for 60 min in the gas chromatograph (GC) inlet port before using. The natural features of the cork were modified due the heating indicating that the biosorbent suffered thermal decomposition at high temperatures. According to the chemical analysis, at 200 °C the partial decomposition of suberin, waxes and other extractives occurred. Over 90% of the polysaccharides were degraded at 250 °C, and lignin started to decompose between 250 and 300 °C. Nevertheless, the cork coatings showed similar or better extraction efficiencies than polydimethylsiloxane/divinylbenzene (PDMS/DVB) and divinylbenzene/carboxen/polydimethylsiloxane (DVB/CAR/PDMS) commercial fibers.

Regarding the recent publications, raw cork-based approaches have been highlighted in microextraction methodologies whereas they exhibit some unique analytical features that allow for "green", sustainable, and efficient procedures that are relevant to the current environmental concerns [30–38]. Table 1 points out the analytical features of the recent applications using raw cork-based methodologies for the extraction of different analytes from various matrices. Raw powder cork is produced from cork stoppers after cleaning with ultrapure water and overnight drying at 110 °C. Further, the powder is prepared using a sandpaper, and the resulting material is sifted to ensure 200 mesh granulometry. Afterward, the resulting powder is conditioned with acetonitrile, and it is ready to be applied as sorbent phase.

Table 1. Applications of raw cork-based microextraction techniques for different analytes and matrices. (Reference period: 2015–2019).

Technique	Raw Cork Format	Analytes	Matrix	Desorption Volume (µL)	LOQ (µg/L)	Instrumentation	Ref.
BAµE	Powder	Benzophenone, Trichlocarban and Parabens	Lagoon water	250	1.6–20	LC-DAD	[30]
BAµE	Powder	Cancer biomarkers	Urine	100	250–300	LC-DAD	[31]
DPX	Powder	10 Pharmaceuticals	Urine	85	5–10	LC-DAD	[32]
TF-SPME	Powder	Endocrine Disruptors Compounds	River water	300	0.8–15	LC-DAD	[33]
RDSE	Powder	Parabens	River water	3000	0.8	LC-MS/MS	[34]
DPX	Powder	Pb and Cd	Water	300	0.3–4.1	HR-CS GFAAS	[35]
DPX	Powder	Parabens and UV filters	Lake water	100	2.0–4.3	LC-DAD	[36]
RDSE	Laminar	Hormones	Wastewater	5000	0.01–0.062	GC-MS	[37]
RDSE	Laminar	20 Pesticides, PAHs and UV filters	River water	1000	0.3–4.8	GC-MS	[38]

BAµE: Bar Adsorptive Microextraction; **DPX**: Disposable Pipette Extraction; **TF-SPME**: Thin-Film Solid Phase Microextraction; **RDSE**: Rotating Disk Sorptive Extraction; **PAHs**, polycyclic aromatic hydrocarbons; **LC**, liquid chromatography; **DAD**, diode array detection; **HR-CS GFAAS**, high resolution continuum source graphite furnace atomic absorption spectrometer; **GC**, gas chromatography; **MS**, mass spectrometry.

Raw cork powder has been successfully applied in different microextraction approaches such as bar adsorptive microextraction [30,31], disposable pipette extraction [32,35,36], thin film-solid phase microextraction [33], and rotating disk sorptive extraction [34] as a biosorbent for the reliable determination of organic micropollutants, toxic metals, UV filters, endocrine disruptors, and compounds in aqueous samples as well as pharmaceuticals and lung cancer biomarkers in human urine. Cork exhibits significant hydrophobicity and a number of aromatic rings that can undergo effective π–π interactions with the analytes and substantially enhance the preconcentration ability of the extraction procedures. The last cork-based applications have been focused on improving the mass transfer using laminar cork for rotating disk sorptive extraction (RDSE) methodologies, demonstrating an interesting new configuration for high-throughput procedures [37,38].

Studies comparing the extraction efficiency of cork-based microextraction techniques with commercial sorbents such as C18, nylon, Oasis® HLB (Hydrophilic-Lipophilic Balance), and DVB have been proposed in some applications. In a recent study, the recovery results showed that the cork reaches higher sorption efficiency than C18, DVB, and nylon, and achieves very similar recoveries to those of Oasis® HLB in which recoveries were between 67% and 98% for Oasis® HLB, while the cork reached values between 63% and 89% [37]. In another study, on applying the optimized conditions for all sorbents, positive results were obtained for the cork-based methodology where using the same amount of sample and sorbent, the renewable sorbent provided better results when compared with the commercial C18 [34]. Therefore, cork proved to be an excellent alternative to the synthetic phases, presenting the advantage of achieving similar efficiency with a cost-effective benefit. Moreover, cork-based devices have been demonstrating an incredible performance regarding reproducibility and reusability. On Dispersive Pipette Extraction (DPX) applications, studies were conducted to evaluate the cleaning step of the pipette tip and the cork stability under several extraction cycles. The results showed that a single DPX cork-based tip maintained around 80% of the extraction efficiency with good precision (relative standard deviation lower than 20%) for all analytes with up to 15 extraction/desorption cycles [32]. In addition, an efficient cleaning of the DPX device was achieved after four cycles with the desorption solvent, enabling the reutilization of the device without carryover [36].

The advances in cork-based techniques have led to remarkable improvements with regard to environmentally friendly aspects, in particular because cork harnessed as biosorbent is originated from cork stoppers that would be discarded and are reused for the development of several analytical methodologies. Moreover, the strategy of combining this cheap and natural biosorbent with high-throughput strategies [33,38] that are able to perform fast and efficient extractions are promising trends that should be further investigated.

3. Cotton

Raw cotton fibers are mainly composed of cellulose (about 95% of the naturally occurring material). Cellulose is a plentiful, inexpensive, and biodegradable material that has been used for many purposes. The non-cellulosic constituents comprise proteins, amino acids, other nitrogen-containing compounds, wax, pectic substances, organic acids, sugars, inorganic salts, and a minimal amount of pigments. Raw fibers may be treated with selective solvents to remove the naturally occurring non-cellulosic materials, resulting in a material with cellulose content over 99% [39].

Cellulose, found in plant walls, is the most abundant raw material on Earth. It is a 1→4 linked linear polymer of ß-D-glucopyranose, which is interlinked with strong intermolecular/intramolecular hydrogen bonds besides hydrophobic bonds. This fact is possible due to the high content of hydroxyl groups on the polymer surface, providing a hydrophilic character. For this reason, the functionalization of the fibers with different groups is compulsory for being used in the microextraction context as sorbent as well as a support for nanocomposites [40]. The chemical structure indicates that the 2-OH, 3-OH, and 6-OH are the potentially available sites for the same chemical reactions that occur with alcohols. However, it must be noted that in cotton, not all the OH groups are accessible for reaction. Besides, the reactivity of the hydroxyl groups of cellulose may change depending on the swelling pretreatment, the reagents employed, and the reaction conditions. Some procedures have been carried out to achieve the correct functionalization of the fibers and therefore the applicability of the material. Etherification reactions, particularly condensation reactions, produce the most stable cotton derivatives. Hydroxyl groups of cotton cellulose may be functionalized with carboxylic acid, acyl halides, anhydrides, isocyanates, and ketenes to produce cellulose esters [41–43]. This variation provides wrinkle resistance, water repellence, flame resistance, and antimicrobial action, as well as resistance to alkaline and acidic conditions. In this way, cotton fibers may be modified with biologically active conjugates such as proteins or peptides by glycine esterification [44,45]. Accordingly, Edwards et al. employed the peptide-cellulosic material as a biosensor of human serine protease, monitoring the fluorescence produced by the reaction. Furthermore, cotton fibers have been treated with 4-formylphenylboronic acid to obtain a boronate affinity adsorbent for the determination of nucleosides from urine samples. In this case, the microextraction process was simplified drawing upon the in-pipette-tip solid phase extraction (SPE), exhibiting good selectivity, capacity, and accuracy [46]. On the other hand, cotton has been altered through graft copolymerization with polyacrylonitrile (PAN) for selective extraction via the imprinting process of copper ions from aqueous solutions [47]. In the same way, carbon-based nanomaterials such as carbon nanotubes or graphene have been incorporated into cotton fibers, being the last one employed as sorbent for the determination of multiclass pesticide residues from water samples [48], along with a large number of applications. Apart from the strategies mentioned above, many attempts, including sulfonation of the cotton, modification of the cotton surface with ion-imprinted polymers, organic ligands, and surfactants have been made to overcome the lack of selectivity of the material [49].

On another note, raw cotton has been commonly employed in the production of activated carbon fibers (ACFs or CFs) as an alternative to synthetic precursors such as PAN, viscose/rayon, phenolic, asphalt, and polyamide fibers. Typically, this green and easy modification of raw cotton consists of the pyrolysis of the cellulose fibers in an inert atmosphere, approximately at 400–700 °C, being used for many years to remove dyes and oil from environmental samples [50,51]. Figure 1 shows the macroscopic appearance of raw cotton (Figure 1a) and CFs (Figure 1b), which maintain the fibrous structure (Figure 1c) of the original substrate. Denoted as carbon fibers aerogels (CFAs) in some cases, these materials have been employed in various fields including energy storage, adsorption, thermal insulation, and flame retardancy [52]. In the microextraction context, CFAs are usually modified following the carbonization process in order to enhance the selectivity of the sorbent material. For this reason, CFAs coated with chitosan and dopamine–polyethylenimine complex were used to remove nanopollutants such as citrate-capped gold and silver nanoparticles from water samples [53]. In some cases, activation agents such as $ZnCl_2$ [54], H_3PO_4 [55], KOH or NaOH [56], K_2CO_3, $AlCl_3$, and Na_2HPO_4 [57] are used for the obtention of fibers with better strength, yield, and adsorption capacities. ACFs were used for the isolation of dyes (methylene blue, crystal violet, or Alizarin Red S) and nitrobenzene from aqueous samples [58–61], in addition to the determination of chlorophenols from urine samples [62]. In the last case, the material was immobilized in a syringe barrel allowing the dispersion of the sorbent in the sample matrix, resulting in good accuracy, sensitivity, and precision values in a simple extraction procedure. Moreover, magnetic CFs have been employed for the determination of bisphenol compounds from environmental samples [63]. On the other hand, a relation between the pyrolysis degree (concerning time and temperature) with the polarity of the resulting CFs has been recently accomplished. Thereby, the pyrolysis parameters may be tailored according to the analytical problem, increasing in this way the selectivity of the extraction process [64].

Figure 1. (**a**) Raw cotton; (**b**) Carbon fibers; (**c**) Scanning electron microscopy picture of carbon fibers where the fibrous structure is observable.

In recent years, cotton waste has been employed as a novel source in the development of cellulosic-based sorbents in order to obtain a high-added-value product at low cost. A million tons of cotton cloths are produced annually, increasing at the same time the generation of their waste. Nowadays, environmental concern has gained great importance, arising the consciousness about recycling and resource utilization. For this reason, microextraction applications using waste products, such as cotton cloths waste, are increasingly appearing in scientific publications [65–67]. Cotton cloths waste has been used for the production of nanocellulose materials [68], including activated and porous carbon [69,70]. There are two main types of nanocellulose materials arising from cotton fibers, viz. cellulose nanofibers (CNF) and cellulose nanocrystals (CNC), which differ in their dimensions, functions, and preparation methods. Generally, the production of CNF consists of mechanical treatments, while acid hydrolysis is the primary chemical process used to produce CNC [71]. These nanomaterials reveal a host of advantages such as high surface area-to-volume ratio, large aspect ratio (typically 20–70), high strength, and thermal stability, due to their nanometric dimensions together with a high degree of molecular order [72]. For this reason, CNC and CNF have been used in the microextraction context, among other applications, for isolating fluoroquinolones from egg samples as well as crystal violet dyes and magnetic nanoparticles from water samples, respectively [73,74].

The main applications of cotton in the microextraction context are summarized in Table 2.

Table 2. Applications of cotton as sorbent material in microextraction techniques for different analytes and matrices. (Reference period: 2015–2018).

Technique	Material	Analytes	Matrix	LOD	Instrumentation	Ref.
In-pipette-tip SPE	Cotton fibers modified with 4-formylphenylboronic acid	Nucleosides	Urine	5.1 and 6.1 ng/mL	LC-UV	[46]
SPE under stirring	Graphene-coated cotton fibers	Multiclass pesticide residues	Water	Low µg/L	GC-MS	[48]
D-µSPE	Carbon fibers	Chlorophenols	Urine	0.1–0.9 µg/L	GC-MS	[62]
D-µSPE	Magnetic cellulose-based carbon fibers	Bisphenol analogues	Environmental samples	0.56–0.83 ng/mL	LC-UV	[63]
D-µSPE	Carbon fibers	Pollutants of different polarities	Water	Low ng/mL	HS-GC-MS	[64]
Magnetic D-µSPE	Fe_3O_4@CCNs@MIPs	Fluoroquinolones	Egg	3.6–18.4 ng g^{-1}	LC-DAD	[73]

SPE: solid phase extraction; **D-µSPE**: dispersive micro-solid phase extraction; **Fe₃O₄@CCNs@MIPs**, molecularly imprinted polymers coated on magnetic carboxylated cellulose nanocrystals, **LC**: liquid chromatography; **UV**: Ultraviolet detection; **GC**: gas chromatography; **MS**: mass spectrometry; **HS**: head space; **CCNs**: carboxylated cellulose nanocrystals; **MIPs**: molecularly imprinted polymers.

4. Pollen

Pollen grains are produced by higher plants to contain and spread the male genetic material [75]. The grains, which have a size in the 10–150 μm depending on the species, present a very resistant outer wall (called exine) to protect the genetic content. The resistance to non-oxidative deterioration procedures is mainly provided by sporopollenin [76]. The particle size, the superficial area, and the OH-rich surface make pollen grain a sustainable, cheap, and green sorbent.

Although pollen was proposed as a sorbent for environmental application in 2011 [77], its use for analytical sample preparation was firstly reported in 2014 by Professor Feng's research group [78]. In this initial approach, pine pollen instead of bee pollen was selected, since it can be obtained in a higher amount, cheaper, and cleaner (free of hormones and pesticides). The untreated pollen, for which only a washing step was necessary, was packed in a conventional SPE cartridge. The size (30–40 μm) allowed a good but not excessive packaging of the sorbent. The highly hydrophilic surface of pollen made its application as hydrophilic interaction sorbent possible in such a way that the water that adsorbed over the outer surface was actually responsible for the analyte extraction. In this initial approach, 16 plant growth regulators were extracted from different fruit and vegetables. Then, this extraction format was extrapolated to the extraction of trans-resveratrol in peanut oils [79].

The OH-rich surface of pollen, which is responsible for its hydrophilic nature, opens the door to their easy chemical modification to include special extractive groups that broaden its applicability as sorbent. Mohamad et al. have proposed a double derivatization of sporopollenin spores to synthesize magnetic and selective sorbents [80]. In an initial step, β-cyclodextrin (β-CD) is immobilized over the surface of the spore using toluene diisocyanate as the linker. These β-CDs, which develop a host–guest interaction mechanism with different compounds according to their chemical structure and size, provide a selective interaction with several drugs. In addition, the porous surface of sporopollenin, which is crossed with abundant channels, was exploited to entrap magnetic nanoparticles, which are synthesized by the simple precipitation of Fe (II) and Fe (III) in an alkaline medium. A similar approach, but using cyanopropyltriethoxysilane as the extractive group, has been recently proposed for the isolation of some drugs from water samples [81]. However, in this case, the double derivatization is done in a different order. The spore (Figure 2a) is initially covered with the magnetic nanoparticles (Figure 2b), and the sorptive phase is finally coated over the magnetic spore (Figure 2c).

Figure 2. (a) Spore; (b) Spore covered with magnetic nanoparticles; (c) Final composite after the coating with the sorptive phase. Reproduced from reference [81] with permission of Elsevier, 2019.

The main applications of pollen and related materials in the microextraction context are summarized in Table 3.

Separations **2020**, 7, 2

Table 3. Applications of pollen as sorbent material in microextraction techniques for different analytes and matrices. (Reference period: 2015–2018).

Technique	Material	Analytes	Matrix	LOD	Instrumentation	Ref.
HILIC-SPE	Raw pollen	Plant growth regulators	Fruit and vegetables	0.01–1.1 µg/kg	UHPLC-MS/MS	[78]
NP-SPE	Raw pollen	Trans-resveratrol	Peanut oil	2.7 ng/g	LC-UV	[79]
Magnetic SPE	Sporollenin modified with cyclodextrin	Non-steroidal autoinflammatory drugs	Water	0.16–0.37 ng/mL	LC-UV	[80]
Magnetic SPE	Sporollenin modified with CNPrTEOS	Non-steroidal autoinflammatory drugs	Water	0.21–0.51 µg/L	LC-UV	[81]

HILIC-SPE: hydrophilic interaction solid phase extraction; **NP-SPE**: normal phase solid phase extraction; **CNPrTEOS**: cyanopropyl-triethoxysilane; **UHPLC**: Ultra high-pressure liquid chromatography; **MS**: mass spectrometry; **LC**: liquid chromatography; **UV**: Ultraviolet detection.

5. Agricultural By-Products

As previously noticed, the use of biomass as an extractant for inorganic and organic compounds is considered as a promising alternative to conventional sorbents. Among the existing choices, the use of natural products usually considered as waste such as fruit peels for cations and anions removal from waters has been extensively described [82,83]. These sorbents are effective and economical with a clear beneficial effect on reducing the amount of waste to be eliminated.

The retention is based on the presence of residual hydroxyl, carboxyl, or amine groups of cellulose or lignin, which exhibit chelating or ion-exchange properties. It has been further demonstrated that once retained, the metal ions can be removed from the sorbent by an acidic treatment, opening the door to evaluate their use as extractant phases with analytical aims. This section will describe the potential of agricultural by-products such as fruit and vegetable peels as a sorbent for the isolation and preconcentration of inorganic and organic compounds from waters.

Vegetable old cell walls are enriched with lignin, which is a phenolic polymer of hydrophobic nature whose aromatic moieties have been identified as responsible for interacting with metals [84]. Amine groups of cellulose proteins and glycoproteins synergically contribute to adsorption [85]. Increasing the superficial area of any sorbent results in a better capacity for analytes retention. In the case of fruit and vegetable peels, chemical treatment such as mercerization can be used to modify the surface of the peel to increase the number of hydroxyl groups available for interaction, thus enhancing the chelating/ion exchange capacity [86]. Concerning the solid-phase extraction of cationic species from waters, banana peel and Sophia seeds have been proposed as sorbents. Cadmium (II) has been extracted from environmental and industrial wastewaters [87]. In this specific application, once dried and crushed, the peels were passed through a 120-mesh sieve (125 μm). Then, activation of the superficial carboxylic groups was carried out using acidic methanol. The esterification of the acidic groups was corroborated by infrared spectroscopy. Only 100 mg of the banana peel was needed to efficiently preconcentrate cadmium (II) by ion exchange with an up to 10 times reusability cycle. Untreated banana peel has also been proposed for the solid-phase extraction of copper and lead from river waters [88]. In this application, dried banana peel was pulverized using a ball mill and further sieved to select the fraction between 35 and 45 μm for metals preconcentration using 20 mg of solid. To minimize potential interferents, the organic fraction of the sample was eliminated by oxidation, being the extraction procedure carried out at acidic pH. An enrichment factor of 20 was achieved in this case, this being value corroborated by the analysis of a standard reference material. Descurania Sophia seeds have also been proposed as sorbent for the isolation and preconcentration of cadmium (II) from water and rice flour [89]. Seeds were commercially available and utilized as received, with the only requirements being washing and sieving. The extraction of cadmium was accomplished in acidic medium using 150 mg of sorbent. The selectivity study carried out by the authors demonstrated that no interference from other divalent and trivalent ions was identified. Electrostatic and coordinative interactions between carboxylic groups and cadmium were responsible for the isolation. The enrichment factor obtained after the analytical method was 20. Accuracy was corroborated by analyzing a certified reference material.

The interaction of organic compounds with biopeels has also been described in the literature. In fact, methylene blue [90] and direct red 12B [91] were removed from water samples using garlic peel. However, the use of these materials for the solid-phase extraction of organic compounds usually requires an additional treatment of the biopeel. In this context, Zhao et al. have proposed the oxidation of the garlic peel with nitric acid to increase the surface acidic functional groups [92]. In this way, the sorption capacity was increased by a factor of 10 for quinolone antibiotics. The authors systematically studied the effect of the oxidation of garlic peel in terms of porosity and functional group distribution. Concerning the superficial morphology, the scanning electron microscopy analysis demonstrated that while the garlic peel exhibits a compact net structure, the oxidized one showed a corroded one and smaller pore irregularly distribution on the surface. The infrared spectra pointed out that after the acidic treatment, some unreactive groups were transformed into carboxylic moieties, while a weaker absorption band was observed in the aromatic ring region, which indicates their decomposition during the treatment. Moreover, the evaluation of the cellulose, hemicellulose, and lignin contents also indicates an increase of the former in the oxidized garlic peel, this fact correlatating with the higher retention for quinolones on the modified sorbent.

The elimination of dyes, pigments, and other colorants using activated carbon is probably the most effective remediation procedure due to the almost irreversible interaction established between the sorbent and the analyte. Agricultural by-products have been identified as an environmentally friendly source of activated carbon, which is usually generated by carbonization at high temperatures [93]. Following this idea, several carbon-based sorbents have been prepared using banana and pomelo peels as starting materials. Four relevant examples will be briefly presented.

Li et al. prepared a hierarchical porous carbon by the treatment of banana peels at 160 °C and further carbonization at 900 °C under an inert atmosphere [94]. The solid showed an intrinsic microporous structure with the presence of meso and macropores, which provides a high surface area (561.8 m^2/g). The formation of graphitized carbon during the synthesis allows the interaction with aromatic compounds via π-stacking. Therefore, the authors evaluate the potential of the hierarchical porous carbon synthesized as a sorbent for carbamate pesticides potentially present in cucumber and watermelon samples. Cartridge SPE was selected as an extraction mode by packing 10 mg of the solid. The enrichment factors obtained were in the range of 80–114 depending on the carbamate and the sample, which resulted in detection limits between 0.05 and 0.30 ng/g.

Pomelo peels have also been used as a precursor material to obtain nanoporous carbon [95]. In this approach, chemical activation with KOH was applied. The grounded and dried pomelo peel was precarbonized at 450 °C for 2 h in an inert atmosphere and thoroughly mixed with 1 M KOH aqueous solution. After a thermal threaten (up to 800 °C), the nanoporous carbon was activated being ready to use as a sorbent phase in SPME fiber. For this aim, the solid was immobilized onto a stainless-steel wire via physical coating approach and further protected with a silicone sealant. The SPME fiber was evaluated for the headspace extraction of benzene homologs from waters and soil before their determination by gas chromatography-mass spectrometry. As evaluated by the authors, their approach resulted in better sensitivity and comparable selectivity as regards reported methods for the same analytical problem.

Probably, dispersive microextraction can be identified as the simplest and most efficient approach among miniaturized sample treatment techniques [96]. The use of an extractant phase dispersed in the sample matrix facilitates the interaction with the analytes, thus enhancing the efficiency of the whole process. However, the recovery of the extractant enriched with the analytes is challenging. Dispersive micro solid-phase extraction usually requires the implementation of filtration and centrifugation steps, which are usually tedious and negatively affect the method sample throughput. This limitation can be overcome by using superparamagnetic sorbents which can be separated from the sample matrix by means of an external magnet, which clearly simplifies the whole analytical process. Magnetic carbon sorbents can also be prepared using agricultural by-products. Two approaches have been very recently proposed based on the use of pomelo peels. The one-pot synthesis pathway is very similar, using either a mixture of FeCl$_3$–FeCl$_2$ [97] or FeCl$_3$–urea [98] as precursors of the Fe$_3$O$_4$ magnetic core of the nanocomposite. Both methods are characterized by the mild conditions used during the synthesis, with temperatures not exceeding 80 °C or 180 °C, respectively. Once obtained, the solids are activated with an organic media and used for the extraction of fluoroquinolones and parabens from waters [97] or triazole fungicides from fruits [98]. The amount of sorbent required for the extraction was in the low milligram level (20–50 mg) with excellent sensitivity and precision. Besides, the results of the proposed approaches showed that they were more competitive in terms of costs, time, and greener considerations.

The main applications of agriculture by-products in the microextraction context are summarized in Table 4.

Table 4. Application of agricultural by-products as sorbent material in microextraction techniques for different analytes and matrices. (Reference period: 2008–2018).

Technique	Material	Analytes	Matrix	LOD	Instrumentation	Ref.
Dispersive SPE	Banana peel	Cadmium	Environmental and industrial wastewaters	1.7 µg/L	FAAS	[87]
SPE	Banana peel	Copper, Lead	River water	–	FAAS	[88]
SPE	Descurainia Sophia seeds	Cadmium	Water rice flour	1.0 µg/L	FAAS	[89]
SPE	Garlic peel	Quinolone antibiotics	Water	0.65–0.85 µg/L	LC-DAD	[92]
SPE	Banana peel	Carbamate pesticides	Cucumber watermelon	0.05–0.20 ng/g	LC-DAD	[94]
SPME	Pomelo peel	Benzene homologues	Water	0.05–0.18 ng/L	GC-MS	[95]
			Soil	0.11–0.18 ng/Kg		
Magnetic-SPE	Pomelo peel	Parabens	Water	0.011–0.053 µg/L	LC-DAD	[97]
		Fluoroquinolones		0.012–0.46 µg/L		
Magnetic-SPE	Pomelo peel	Triazoles fungicides	Fruits	0.12–0.55 µg/Kg	GC-MS	[98]

SPE: solid phase extraction; **SPME**: solid phase microextraction; **FAAS**: flame atomic absorption spectroscopy; **LC**, liquid chromatography; **LC**, liquid chromatography; **DAD**, diode array detection; **GC**, gas chromatography; **MS**, mass spectrometry.

6. Trends, Natural Products for Simplifying the Analytical Workflow

The classical analytical workflow comprises the isolation/enrichment of the targets from the sample matrix to obtain a clean extract that is finally analyzed by chromatography. This approach provides a high level of sensitivity and selectivity, but the sample throughput is usually limited by the chromatographic cycle. The elimination of the chromatographic separation, by the direct combination of the microextraction step with the instrumental technique, appears as an attractive alternative. However, avoiding the chromatographic separation compromises the method selectivity, and this loss can be offset by improving the selectivity on the analyte isolation by using a selective instrumental technique such as high-resolution mass spectrometry (MS) or by combining both strategies. Gómez-Ríos and Mirabelli have recently reviewed the potential of the SPME-MS combination promoting as well, changing the classic perspective about chemical analysis [99]. This comprehensive and inspiring review divides this combination into four main groups, depending on the sorptive phase employed namely: fiber/tip, in-tube, mesh, and substrate spray. SPME substrate spray approaches are very versatile, comprising different supports such as coated blades [100–102], paper [103,104], or wooden tips [105,106]. The latter configurations, which make use of natural substrates, are named as paper spray and wooden tip spray, respectively. In both approaches, the substrate can be used for the direct ionization of the sample [107] or the off-line coupling with a microextraction technique [108]. However, the substrate can also be modified with a sorptive phase for the isolation of the target analytes prior to their direct analysis by MS [103]. Although the discussion of the microextraction–MS coupling is beyond the scope of this article, the description of the synthesis of sorptive phases based on paper and wood is relevant and it will be briefly discussed below. The selected developments have been used under the classical or direct analytical workflows.

Paper is a cellulose-processed material that shares some of the characteristics of cotton but presents a flat configuration. This geometry opens the door to its application under the thin film microextraction technique. Although bare paper can be used for extraction [109], it is usually modified to boost its extraction capability. This modification can be done by the covalent bonding [110] or by the deposition of a thin layer of sorptive phase [111]. The coating of paper with polymers of both synthetic [112] and natural origins [113] appears as an interesting way to synthesize versatile sorptive phases. Conventional coatings in microextraction, such as PDMS [114], have been recently complemented by other approaches.

In 2017, Ríos-Gómez et al. proposed the simple modification of paper by dip coating for the extraction of methadone from biological samples [111]. This process is based on the previous dissolution of a polymer in a volatile solvent and the immersion of paper in this solution. The evaporation of the solvent creates a thin film of the polymer over the paper whose thickness depends on the polymer concentration in the original solution and the number of dips developed during the synthesis. The use of polyamides in combination with a template molecule has been used for the fabrication of molecularly imprinted papers [115]. If some nanoparticles are included in the polymer solution, they can be incorporated into the coating, providing additional characteristics [116]. Also, the dip coating has been proposed to cover paper with a pure film of carbon nanohorn suprastructures that can be used for the extraction of drugs from biological matrices [117]. The SEM micrograph of Figure 3 shows how the dahlias (the ordered aggregates of carbon nanohorns) are combined to form a homogeneous coating over the paper.

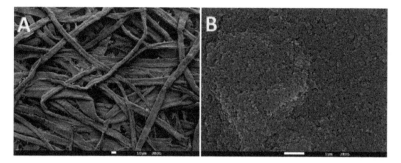

Figure 3. SEM images obtained for (**A**) a bare paper and (**B**) a paper modified with suprastructures of carbon nanohorns. Reprinted from [117].

Wood is a mixture of natural materials such as lignin, cellulose, and hemicellulose [118]. This lignocellulosic material, in the form of a tip or stick, has been used for the development of microextraction phases. The OH-rich surface of wood opens the door to its easy modification by anchoring appropriate groups in order to enhance the interaction with the analytes. Deng et al. proposed a simple silanization, followed by a sulfonation, of wooden tip to prepare a mixed-mode extractant phase that is capable of extracting acidic drugs for water samples [119]. The silanization mechanism also permits the introduction of C18 (using trimethoxyoctadecylsilane) and amine groups (using 3-aminopropyltriethoxysilane), increasing the versatility of these phases [106]. These sorptive phases are not selective at all, and their applicability to complex matrices can be somewhat limited. In this sense, the coating of the wooden tips with molecularly imprinted polymers has allowed the determination of analytes in complex samples such as fish [120] and milk [121]. Recently, Abdel-Rehim et al. have proposed the modification of wooden sticks with a composite based on graphene oxide, making the applicability of these materials even broader [122].

7. Conclusions

Green chemistry tries to minimize the impact of chemicals in the environment, considering both the local and global context. This main objective can be extended to all the chemistry fields, including analytical chemistry, and it requires the previous identification of the impacts in order to provide some alternatives to minimize or avoid these deleterious effects. The principles of GAC provide general guidelines that can be applied to different stages of the analytical process. Some of these principles suggest the simplification of the sample treatment and the use of renewable resources. Both topics have been considered in this review article.

The description of the potential of natural materials as sorbents or substrates in solid-phase microextraction has been the main aim of this article. The principal materials, their characteristics, and their applications have been presented to inspire the readers for further research. Some of the described developments, especially those based on bare natural material, can be used for environmental remediation if they are adapted for a large scale.

In order to avoid green marketing, some challenges in this field must be indicated. The use of renewable sources for the design of new sorbents only reduces the environmental impact if these materials are applied without any chemical modification. However, if this chemical derivatization is required (for example to improve the sorption capacity or selectivity), it must involve no reagents (this is the case of pyrolysis) or a low amount of them. In addition, the proposed materials should be compared with commercial existing products to clearly demonstrate their superiority.

In the next years, intensive research on the topic is expected. This research will cover the use of natural materials as precursors but also the use of natural materials as inspiration for the design of smart and environmentally friendly materials.

Funding: The Spanish Ministry of Economy and Competitiveness is gratefully acknowledged for funding (Grant CTQ2017-83175R).

Acknowledgments: The authors would like to thank and recognize the work of all their group members, including senior and young researchers, who have been working on the topic during all these years. The authors are grateful to the Brazilian governmental agency Coordenação de Aperfeiçoamento de Pessoal de Nível Superior for the scholarship supported by the Programa Institucional de Internacionalização of the Universidade Federal de Santa Catarina (CAPES/PRINT-UFSC, Project number 88887.310569/2018-00).

Conflicts of Interest: The authors declare no conflict of interest.

References

1. Smith, R.B.; Karousos, N.G.; Cowham, E.; Davis, J.; Billington, S. Covert Approaches to Countering Adult Chemophobia. *J. Chem. Educ.* **2008**, *85*, 379. [CrossRef]
2. Chalupa, R.; Nesměrák, K. Analytical chemistry as a tool for suppressing chemophobia: An introduction to the 5E-principle. *Monatshefte für Chemie-Chemical Monthly* **2018**, *149*, 1527–1534. [CrossRef]
3. Valcárcel, M.; Christian, G.D.; Lucena, R. Teaching Social Responsibility in Analytical Chemistry. *Anal. Chem.* **2013**, *85*, 6152–6161. [CrossRef] [PubMed]
4. Armenta, S.; Garrigues, S.; de la Guardia, M. Green analytical chemistry. *TrAC Trends Anal. Chem.* **2008**, *27*, 497–511. [CrossRef]
5. Koel, M.; Kaljurand, M. *Green Analytical Chemistry*; RSC Publishing: Cambridge, UK, 2010; ISBN 978-1-84755-872-5.
6. De la Guardia, M.; Garrigues, S. *Handbook of Green Analytical Chemistry*; John Wiley & Sons: Chichester, UK, 2012; ISBN 9780470972014.
7. Gałuszka, A.; Migaszewski, Z.; Namieśnik, J. The 12 principles of green analytical chemistry and the SIGNIFICANCE mnemonic of green analytical practices. *TrAC Trends Anal. Chem.* **2013**, *50*, 78–84. [CrossRef]
8. Valcárcel, M.; Cárdenas, S.; Lucena, R. Microextraction techniques. *Anal. Bioanal. Chem.* **2014**, *406*, 1999–2000. [CrossRef]
9. Armenta, S.; Garrigues, S.; de la Guardia, M. The role of green extraction techniques in Green Analytical Chemistry. *TrAC Trends Anal. Chem.* **2015**, *71*, 2–8. [CrossRef]
10. Pacheco-Fernández, I.; Pino, V. Green solvents in analytical chemistry. *Curr. Opin. Green Sustain. Chem.* **2019**, *18*, 42–50. [CrossRef]
11. Płotka-Wasylka, J.; Rutkowska, M.; Owczarek, K.; Tobiszewski, M.; Namieśnik, J. Extraction with environmentally friendly solvents. *TrAC Trends Anal. Chem.* **2017**, *91*, 12–25. [CrossRef]
12. Marino, T.; Galiano, F.; Molino, A.; Figoli, A. New frontiers in sustainable membrane preparation: Cyrene™ as green bioderived solvent. *J. Membr. Sci.* **2019**, *580*, 224–234. [CrossRef]
13. de los Ángeles, M.; Boiteux, J.; Espino, M.; Gomez, F.J.V.; Silva, M.F. Natural deep eutectic solvents-mediated extractions: The way forward for sustainable analytical developments. *Anal. Chim. Acta* **2018**, *1038*, 1–10. [CrossRef]
14. Kirchherr, J.; Reike, D.; Hekkert, M. Conceptualizing the circular economy: An analysis of 114 definitions. *Resour. Conserv. Recycl.* **2017**, *127*, 221–232. [CrossRef]
15. Silva, S.P.; Sabino, M.A.; Fernandes, E.M.; Correlo, V.M.; Boesel, L.F.; Reis, R.L. Cork: Properties, capabilities and applications. *Int. Mater. Rev.* **2005**, *50*, 345–365. [CrossRef]
16. Lagorce-Tachon, A.; Karbowiak, T.; Loupiac, C.; Gaudry, A.; Ott, F.; Alba-Simionesco, C.; Gougeon, R.D.; Alcantara, V.; Mannes, D.; Kaestner, A.; et al. The cork viewed from the inside. *J. Food Eng.* **2015**, *149*, 214–221. [CrossRef]
17. Pintor, A.M.A.; Ferreira, C.I.A.; Pereira, J.C.; Correia, P.; Silva, S.P.; Vilar, V.J.P.; Botelho, C.M.S.; Boaventura, R.A.R. Use of cork powder and granules for the adsorption of pollutants: A review. *Water Res.* **2012**, *46*, 3152–3166. [CrossRef]
18. Monteiro, M.K.S.; Paiva, S.S.M.; da Silva, D.R.; Vilar, V.J.P.; Martínez-Huitle, C.A.; dos Santos, E.V. Novel cork-graphite electrochemical sensor for voltammetric determination of caffeine. *J. Electroanal. Chem.* **2019**, *839*, 283–289. [CrossRef]
19. Novais, R.M.; Caetano, A.P.F.; Seabra, M.P.; Labrincha, J.A.; Pullar, R.C. Extremely fast and efficient methylene blue adsorption using eco-friendly cork and paper waste-based activated carbon adsorbents. *J. Clean. Prod.* **2018**, *197*, 1137–1147. [CrossRef]

20. Domingues, V.; Alves, A.; Cabral, M.; Delerue-Matos, C. Sorption behaviour of bifenthrin on cork. *J. Chromatogr. A* **2005**, *1069*, 127–132. [CrossRef]
21. Olivella, M.À.; Jové, P.; Oliveras, A. The use of cork waste as a biosorbent for persistent organic pollutants–Study of adsorption/desorption of polycyclic aromatic hydrocarbons. *J. Environ. Sci. Health Part A* **2011**, *46*, 824–832. [CrossRef]
22. de Aguiar, T.R.; Guimarães Neto, J.O.A.; Şen, U.; Pereira, H. Study of two cork species as natural biosorbents for five selected pesticides in water. *Heliyon* **2019**, *5*, e01189. [CrossRef]
23. Mallek, M.; Chtourou, M.; Portillo, M.; Monclús, H.; Walha, K.; ben Salah, A.; Salvadó, V. Granulated cork as biosorbent for the removal of phenol derivatives and emerging contaminants. *J. Environ. Manag.* **2018**, *223*, 576–585. [CrossRef] [PubMed]
24. Castellar, J.A.C.; Formosa, J.; Fernández, A.I.; Jové, P.; Bosch, M.G.; Morató, J.; Brix, H.; Arias, C.A. Cork as a sustainable carbon source for nature-based solutions treating hydroponic wastewaters—Preliminary batch studies. *Sci. Total. Environ.* **2019**, *650*, 267–276. [CrossRef] [PubMed]
25. Pirozzi, C.; Pontoni, L.; Fabbricino, M.; Bogush, A.; Campos, L.C. Effect of organic matter release from natural cork used on bisphenol a removal from aqueous solution. *J. Clean. Prod.* **2020**, *244*, 118675. [CrossRef]
26. Silva, B.; Martins, M.; Rosca, M.; Rocha, V.; Lago, A.; Neves, I.C.; Tavares, T. Waste-based biosorbents as cost-effective alternatives to commercial adsorbents for the retention of fluoxetine from water. *Sep. Purif. Technol.* **2020**, *235*, 116139. [CrossRef]
27. Neng, N.R.; Mestre, A.S.; Carvalho, A.P.; Nogueira, J.M.F. Cork-based activated carbons as supported adsorbent materials for trace level analysis of ibuprofen and clofibric acid in environmental and biological matrices. *J. Chromatogr. A* **2011**, *1218*, 6263–6270. [CrossRef]
28. Neves Dias, A.; Simão, V.; Merib, J.; Carasek, E. Use of green coating (cork) in solid-phase microextraction for the determination of organochlorine pesticides in water by gas chromatography-electron capture detection. *Talanta* **2015**, *134*, 409–414. [CrossRef]
29. Dias, A.N.; Simão, V.; Merib, J.; Carasek, E. Cork as a new (green) coating for solid-phase microextraction: Determination of polycyclic aromatic hydrocarbons in water samples by gas chromatography–mass spectrometry. *Anal. Chim. Acta* **2013**, *772*, 33–39. [CrossRef]
30. Dias, A.N.; da Silva, A.C.; Simão, V.; Merib, J.; Carasek, E. A novel approach to bar adsorptive microextraction: Cork as extractor phase for determination of benzophenone, triclocarban and parabens in aqueous samples. *Anal. Chim. Acta* **2015**, *888*, 59–66. [CrossRef]
31. Oenning, A.L.; Morés, L.; Dias, A.N.; Carasek, E. A new configuration for bar adsorptive microextraction (BAμE) for the quantification of biomarkers (hexanal and heptanal) in human urine by HPLC providing an alternative for early lung cancer diagnosis. *Anal. Chim. Acta* **2017**, *965*, 54–62. [CrossRef]
32. Mafra, G.; Spudeit, D.; Brognoli, R.; Merib, J.; Carasek, E. Expanding the applicability of cork as extraction phase for disposable pipette extraction in multiresidue analysis of pharmaceuticals in urine samples. *J. Chromatogr. B* **2018**, *1102–1103*, 159–166. [CrossRef]
33. Morés, L.; Dias, A.N.; Carasek, E. Development of a high-throughput method based on thin-film microextraction using a 96-well plate system with a cork coating for the extraction of emerging contaminants in river water samples. *J. Sep. Sci.* **2018**, *41*, 697–703. [CrossRef] [PubMed]
34. Vieira, C.M.S.; Mazurkievicz, M.; Lopez Calvo, A.M.; Debatin, V.; Micke, G.A.; Richter, P.; Rosero-Moreano, M.; da Rocha, E.C. Exploiting green sorbents in rotating-disk sorptive extraction for the determination of parabens by high-performance liquid chromatography with tandem electrospray ionization triple quadrupole mass spectrometry. *J. Sep. Sci.* **2018**, *41*, 4047–4054. [CrossRef] [PubMed]
35. Cadorim, H.R.; Schneider, M.; Hinz, J.; Luvizon, F.; Dias, A.N.; Carasek, E.; Welz, B. Effective and High-Throughput Analytical Methodology for the Determination of Lead and Cadmium in Water Samples by Disposable Pipette Extraction Coupled with High-Resolution Continuum Source Graphite Furnace Atomic Absorption Spectrometry (HR-CS GF AAS). *Anal. Lett.* **2019**, *52*, 2133–2149. [CrossRef]
36. Morés, L.; da Silva, A.C.; Merib, J.; Dias, A.N.; Carasek, E. A natural and renewable biosorbent phase as a low-cost approach in disposable pipette extraction technique for the determination of emerging contaminants in lake water samples. *J. Sep. Sci.* **2019**, *42*, 1404–1411. [CrossRef]
37. Manzo, V.; Goya-Pacheco, J.; Arismendi, D.; Becerra-Herrera, M.; Castillo-Aguirre, A.; Castillo-Felices, R.; Rosero-Moreano, M.; Carasek, E.; Richter, P. Cork sheet as a sorptive phase to extract hormones from water by rotating-disk sorptive extraction (RDSE). *Anal. Chim. Acta* **2019**, *1087*, 1–10. [CrossRef]

38. Vieira, C.M.S.; Mafra, G.; Brognoli, R.; Richter, P.; Rosero-Moreano, M.; Carasek, E. A high throughput approach to rotating-disk sorptive extraction (RDSE) using laminar cork for the simultaneous determination of multiclass organic micro-pollutants in aqueous sample by GC-MS. *Talanta* **2019**, 120459. [CrossRef]

39. Menachem, L. *Handbook of Fiber Chemistry*; CRC Press: Boca Raton, FL, USA, 2006; ISBN 9780824725655.

40. Heidari, N.; Ghiasvand, A.; Abdolhosseini, S. Amino-silica/graphene oxide nanocomposite coated cotton as an efficient sorbent for needle trap device. *Anal. Chim. Acta* **2017**, *975*, 11–19. [CrossRef]

41. Hong, K.H. Preparation and properties of phenolic compound/BTCA treated cotton fabrics for functional textile applications. *Cellulose* **2015**, *22*, 2129–2136. [CrossRef]

42. Ragab, S.; El Nemr, A. Zirconyl chloride as a novel and efficient green Lewis acid catalyst for direct acetylation of cotton cellulose in the presence and absence of solvent. *J. Polym. Res.* **2019**, *26*, 156. [CrossRef]

43. Harms, H.; Bernt, I.; Roggenstein, W. Regenerated Cellulose fiber 2013. International Application No. PCT/EP2012/072387, 6 June 2013.

44. Edwards, J.; Fontenot, K.; Prevost, N.; Pircher, N.; Liebner, F.; Condon, B. Preparation, Characterization and Activity of a Peptide-Cellulosic Aerogel Protease Sensor from Cotton. *Sensors* **2016**, *16*, 1789. [CrossRef]

45. Edwards, J.V.; Prevost, N.T.; Condon, B.; French, A.; Wu, Q. Immobilization of lysozyme-cellulose amide-linked conjugates on cellulose I and II cotton nanocrystalline preparations. *Cellulose* **2012**, *19*, 495–506. [CrossRef]

46. Gao, L.; Wei, Y. Fabrication of boronate-decorated polyhedral oligomeric silsesquioxanes grafted cotton fiber for the selective enrichment of nucleosides in urine. *J. Sep. Sci.* **2016**, *39*, 2365–2373. [CrossRef] [PubMed]

47. Monier, M.; Ibrahim, A.A.; Metwally, M.M.; Badawy, D.S. Surface ion-imprinted amino-functionalized cellulosic cotton fibers for selective extraction of Cu(II) ions. *Int. J. Biol. Macromol.* **2015**, *81*, 736–746. [CrossRef] [PubMed]

48. Montesinos, I.; Sfakianaki, A.; Gallego, M.; Stalikas, C.D. Graphene-coated cotton fibers as a sorbent for the extraction of multiclass pesticide residues from water and their determination by gas chromatography with mass spectrometry. *J. Sep. Sci.* **2015**, *38*, 836–843. [CrossRef]

49. Karimi, M.; Dadfarnia, S.; Shabani, A.M.H. Application of Deep Eutectic Solvent Modified Cotton as a Sorbent for Online Solid-Phase Extraction and Determination of Trace Amounts of Copper and Nickel in Water and Biological Samples. *Biol. Trace Elem. Res.* **2017**, *176*, 207–215. [CrossRef]

50. Li, Y.; Zhu, X.; Ge, B.; Men, X.; Li, P.; Zhang, Z. Versatile fabrication of magnetic carbon fiber aerogel applied for bidirectional oil–water separation. *Appl. Phys. A* **2015**, *120*, 949–957. [CrossRef]

51. Yue, X.; Jiang, F.; Zhang, D.; Lin, H.; Chen, Y. Preparation of adsorbent based on cotton fiber for removal of dyes. *Fibers Polym.* **2017**, *18*, 2102–2110. [CrossRef]

52. Zuo, L.; Zhang, Y.; Zhang, L.; Miao, Y.-E.; Fan, W.; Liu, T. Polymer/Carbon-Based Hybrid Aerogels: Preparation, Properties and Applications. *Materials (Basel)* **2015**, *8*, 6806–6848. [CrossRef]

53. Liu, R.-L.; Mao, S.; Wang, Y.; Wang, L.; Ge, Y.-H.; Xu, X.-Y.; Fu, Q. A mussel-inspired hybrid copolymer adhered to chitosan-coated micro-sized carbon fiber aerogels for highly efficient nanoparticle scavenging. *Environ. Sci. Nano* **2017**, *4*, 2164–2174. [CrossRef]

54. Chiu, K.-L.; Ng, D.H.L. Synthesis and characterization of cotton-made activated carbon fiber and its adsorption of methylene blue in water treatment. *Biomass Bioenergy* **2012**, *46*, 102–110. [CrossRef]

55. Duan, X.; Srinivasakannan, C.; Wang, X.; Wang, F.; Liu, X. Synthesis of activated carbon fibers from cotton by microwave induced H3PO4 activation. *J. Taiwan Inst. Chem. Eng.* **2017**, *70*, 374–381. [CrossRef]

56. Sun, Y.; Yue, Q.; Gao, B.; Li, Q.; Huang, L.; Yao, F.; Xu, X. Preparation of activated carbon derived from cotton linter fibers by fused NaOH activation and its application for oxytetracycline (OTC) adsorption. *J. Colloid Interface Sci.* **2012**, *368*, 521–527. [CrossRef]

57. Hina, K.; Zou, H.; Qian, W.; Zuo, D.; Yi, C. Preparation and performance comparison of cellulose-based activated carbon fibres. *Cellulose* **2018**, *25*, 607–617. [CrossRef]

58. Li, Z.; Jia, Z.; Ni, T.; Li, S. Adsorption of methylene blue on natural cotton based flexible carbon fiber aerogels activated by novel air-limited carbonization method. *J. Mol. Liq.* **2017**, *242*, 747–756. [CrossRef]

59. Wanassi, B.; Ben Hariz, I.; Ghimbeu, C.M.; Vaulot, C.; Jeguirim, M. Green Carbon Composite-Derived Polymer Resin and Waste Cotton Fibers for the Removal of Alizarin Red S Dye. *Energies* **2017**, *10*, 1321. [CrossRef]

60. Abd-Elhamid, A.I.; Nayl, A.A.; El. Shanshory, A.A.; Soliman, H.M.A.; Aly, H.F. Decontamination of organic pollutants from aqueous media using cotton fiber–graphene oxide composite, utilizing batch and filter adsorption techniques: A comparative study. *RSC Adv.* **2019**, *9*, 5770–5785. [CrossRef]

61. Wu, Y.; Qi, H.; Li, B.; Zhanhua, H.; Li, W.; Liu, S. Novel hydrophobic cotton fibers adsorbent for the removal of nitrobenzene in aqueous solution. *Carbohydr. Polym.* **2017**, *155*, 294–302. [CrossRef]

62. García-Valverde, M.T.; Lucena, R.; Cárdenas, S.; Valcárcel, M. In-syringe dispersive micro-solid phase extraction using carbon fibres for the determination of chlorophenols in human urine by gas chromatography/mass spectrometry. *J. Chromatogr. A* **2016**, *1464*, 42–49. [CrossRef]

63. Zhang, D.; Zhang, L.; Liu, T. A magnetic cellulose-based carbon fiber hybrid as a dispersive solid-phase extraction material for the simultaneous detection of six bisphenol analogs from environmental samples. *Analyst* **2018**, *143*, 3100–3106. [CrossRef]

64. García-Valverde, M.; Ledesma-Escobar, C.; Lucena, R.; Cárdenas, S. Tunable Polarity Carbon Fibers, a Holistic Approach to Environmental Protection. *Molecules* **2018**, *23*, 1026. [CrossRef]

65. Mehmandost, N.; Soriano, M.L.; Lucena, R.; Goudarzi, N.; Chamjangali, M.A.; Cardenas, S. Recycled polystyrene-cotton composites, giving a second life to plastic residues for environmental remediation. *J. Environ. Chem. Eng.* **2019**, *7*, 103424. [CrossRef]

66. Cheng, H.; Song, Y.; Bian, Y.; Ji, R.; Wang, F.; Gu, C.; Yang, X.; Jiang, X. Sustainable synthesis of nanoporous carbons from agricultural waste and their application for solid-phase microextraction of chlorinated organic pollutants. *RSC Adv.* **2018**, *8*, 15915–15922. [CrossRef]

67. Silva, T.L.; Cazetta, A.L.; Souza, P.S.C.; Zhang, T.; Asefa, T.; Almeida, V.C. Mesoporous activated carbon fibers synthesized from denim fabric waste: Efficient adsorbents for removal of textile dye from aqueous solutions. *J. Clean. Prod.* **2018**, *171*, 482–490. [CrossRef]

68. Wang, Z.; Yao, Z.; Zhou, J.; Zhang, Y. Reuse of waste cotton cloth for the extraction of cellulose nanocrystals. *Carbohydr. Polym.* **2017**, *157*, 945–952. [CrossRef]

69. Boudrahem, N.; Delpeux-Ouldriane, S.; Khenniche, L.; Boudrahem, F.; Aissani-Benissad, F.; Gineys, M. Single and mixture adsorption of clofibric acid, tetracycline and paracetamol onto Activated carbon developed from cotton cloth residue. *Process. Saf. Environ. Prot.* **2017**, *111*, 544–559. [CrossRef]

70. Wang, S.; Wei, M.; Xu, Q.; Jia, H. Functional porous carbons from waste cotton fabrics for dyeing wastewater purification. *Fibers Polym.* **2016**, *17*, 212–219. [CrossRef]

71. Blanco, A.; Monte, M.C.; Campano, C.; Balea, A.; Merayo, N.; Negro, C. Nanocellulose for Industrial Use. In *Handbook of Nanomaterials for Industrial Applications*; Elsevier: Amsterdam, The Netherlands, 2018; pp. 74–126.

72. Harper, B.J.; Clendaniel, A.; Sinche, F.; Way, D.; Hughes, M.; Schardt, J.; Simonsen, J.; Stefaniak, A.B.; Harper, S.L. Impacts of chemical modification on the toxicity of diverse nanocellulose materials to developing zebrafish. *Cellulose* **2016**, *23*, 1763–1775. [CrossRef]

73. Wang, Y.-F.; Wang, Y.-G.; Ouyang, X.-K.; Yang, L.-Y. Surface-Imprinted Magnetic Carboxylated Cellulose Nanocrystals for the Highly Selective Extraction of Six Fluoroquinolones from Egg Samples. *ACS Appl. Mater. Interfaces* **2017**, *9*, 1759–1769. [CrossRef]

74. Gopakumar, D.A.; Pasquini, D.; Henrique, M.A.; de Morais, L.C.; Grohens, Y.; Thomas, S. Meldrum's Acid Modified Cellulose Nanofiber-Based Polyvinylidene Fluoride Microfiltration Membrane for Dye Water Treatment and Nanoparticle Removal. *ACS Sustain. Chem. Eng.* **2017**, *5*, 2026–2033. [CrossRef]

75. Bradley, R.S. Pollen. In *Paleoclimatology*; Elsevier: Amsterdam, The Netherlands, 2015; pp. 405–451.

76. Domínguez, E.; Mercado, J.A.; Quesada, M.A.; Heredia, A. Pollen sporopollenin: Degradation and structural elucidation. *Sex. Plant Reprod.* **1999**, *12*, 171–178. [CrossRef]

77. Thio, B.J.R.; Clark, K.K.; Keller, A.A. Magnetic pollen grains as sorbents for facile removal of organic pollutants in aqueous media. *J. Hazard. Mater.* **2011**, *194*, 53–61. [CrossRef] [PubMed]

78. Lu, Q.; Wu, J.-H.; Yu, Q.-W.; Feng, Y.-Q. Using pollen grains as novel hydrophilic solid-phase extraction sorbents for the simultaneous determination of 16 plant growth regulators. *J. Chromatogr. A* **2014**, *1367*, 39–47. [CrossRef] [PubMed]

79. Lu, Q.; Zhao, Q.; Yu, Q.-W.; Feng, Y.-Q. Use of Pollen Solid-Phase Extraction for the Determination of trans -Resveratrol in Peanut Oils. *J. Agric. Food Chem.* **2015**, *63*, 4771–4776. [CrossRef] [PubMed]

80. Syed Yaacob, S.F.F.; Kamboh, M.A.; Wan Ibrahim, W.A.; Mohamad, S. New sporopollenin-based β-cyclodextrin functionalized magnetic hybrid adsorbent for magnetic solid-phase extraction of nonsteroidal anti-inflammatory drugs from water samples. *R. Soc. Open Sci.* **2018**, *5*, 171311. [CrossRef]

81. Abd Wahib, S.M.; Wan Ibrahim, W.A.; Sanagi, M.M.; Kamboh, M.A.; Abdul Keyon, A.S. Magnetic sporopollenin-cyanopropyltriethoxysilane-dispersive micro-solid phase extraction coupled with high performance liquid chromatography for the determination of selected non-steroidal anti-inflammatory drugs in water samples. *J. Chromatogr. A* **2018**, *1532*, 50–57. [CrossRef]

82. Kurniawan, A.; Kosasih, A.N.; Febrianto, J.; Ju, Y.-H.; Sunarso, J.; Indraswati, N.; Ismadji, S. Evaluation of cassava peel waste as lowcost biosorbent for Ni-sorption: Equilibrium, kinetics, thermodynamics and mechanism. *Chem. Eng. J.* **2011**, *172*, 158–166. [CrossRef]

83. Mallampati, R.; Valiyaveettil, S. Apple Peels—A Versatile Biomass for Water Purification? *ACS Appl. Mater. Interfaces* **2013**, *5*, 4443–4449. [CrossRef]

84. Gonzalez, M.H.; Araújo, G.C.L.; Pelizaro, C.B.; Menezes, E.A.; Lemos, S.G.; de Sousa, G.B.; Nogueira, A.R.A. Coconut coir as biosorbent for Cr(VI) removal from laboratory wastewater. *J. Hazard. Mater.* **2008**, *159*, 252–256. [CrossRef]

85. Das, S.K.; Guha, A.K. Biosorption of chromium by Termitomyces clypeatus. *Colloids Surf. B Biointerfaces* **2007**, *60*, 46–54. [CrossRef]

86. Liu, W.; Liu, Y.; Tao, Y.; Yu, Y.; Jiang, H.; Lian, H. Comparative study of adsorption of Pb(II) on native garlic peel and mercerized garlic peel. *Environ. Sci. Pollut. Res.* **2014**, *21*, 2054–2063. [CrossRef]

87. Memon, J.R.; Memon, S.Q.; Bhanger, M.I.; Memon, G.Z.; El-Turki, A.; Allen, G.C. Characterization of banana peel by scanning electron microscopy and FT-IR spectroscopy and its use for cadmium removal. *Colloids Surf. B Biointerfaces* **2008**, *66*, 260–265. [CrossRef] [PubMed]

88. Castro, R.S.D.; Caetano, L.; Ferreira, G.; Padilha, P.M.; Saeki, M.J.; Zara, L.F.; Martines, M.A.U.; Castro, G.R. Banana Peel Applied to the Solid Phase Extraction of Copper and Lead from River Water: Preconcentration of Metal Ions with a Fruit Waste. *Ind. Eng. Chem. Res.* **2011**, *50*, 3446–3451. [CrossRef]

89. Khodarahmi, M.; Eftekhari, M.; Gheibi, M.; Chamsaz, M. Preconcentration of trace levels of cadmium (II) ion using Descurainia Sophia seeds as a green adsorbent for solid phase extraction followed by its determination by flame atomic absorption spectrometry. *J. Food Meas. Charact.* **2018**, *12*, 1485–1492. [CrossRef]

90. Hameed, B.H.; Ahmad, A.A. Batch adsorption of methylene blue from aqueous solution by garlic peel, an agricultural waste biomass. *J. Hazard. Mater.* **2009**, *164*, 870–875. [CrossRef]

91. Asfaram, A.; Fathi, M.R.; Khodadoust, S.; Naraki, M. Removal of Direct Red 12B by garlic peel as a cheap adsorbent: Kinetics, thermodynamic and equilibrium isotherms study of removal. *Spectrochim. Acta Part A Mol. Biomol. Spectrosc.* **2014**, *127*, 415–421. [CrossRef]

92. Zhao, Y.; Li, W.; Liu, J.; Huang, K.; Wu, C.; Shao, H.; Chen, H.; Liu, X. Modification of garlic peel by nitric acid and its application as a novel adsorbent for solid-phase extraction of quinolone antibiotics. *Chem. Eng. J.* **2017**, *326*, 745–755. [CrossRef]

93. Ahmad, M.A.; Alrozi, R. Removal of malachite green dye from aqueous solution using rambutan peel-based activated carbon: Equilibrium, kinetic and thermodynamic studies. *Chem. Eng. J.* **2011**, *171*, 510–516. [CrossRef]

94. Li, M.; Jiao, C.; Yang, X.; Wang, C.; Wu, Q.; Wang, Z. Solid phase extraction of carbamate pesticides with banana peel derived hierarchical porous carbon prior to high performance liquid chromatography. *Anal. Methods* **2017**, *9*, 593–599. [CrossRef]

95. Wang, W.; Zhang, L.; Li, Z.; Zhang, S.; Wang, C.; Wang, Z. A nanoporous carbon material derived from pomelo peels as a fiber coating for solid-phase microextraction. *RSC Adv.* **2016**, *6*, 113951–113958. [CrossRef]

96. Chisvert, A.; Cárdenas, S.; Lucena, R. Dispersive micro-solid phase extraction. *TrAC Trends Anal. Chem.* **2019**, *112*, 226–233. [CrossRef]

97. Huang, Y.; Peng, J.; Huang, X. One-pot preparation of magnetic carbon adsorbent derived from pomelo peel for magnetic solid-phase extraction of pollutants in environmental waters. *J. Chromatogr. A* **2018**, *1546*, 28–35. [CrossRef] [PubMed]

98. Ren, K.; Zhang, W.; Cao, S.; Wang, G.; Zhou, Z. Carbon-Based Fe3O4 Nanocomposites Derived from Waste Pomelo Peels for Magnetic Solid-Phase Extraction of 11 Triazole Fungicides in Fruit Samples. *Nanomaterials* **2018**, *8*, 302. [CrossRef] [PubMed]

99. Gómez-Ríos, G.A.; Mirabelli, M.F. Solid Phase Microextraction-mass spectrometry: Metanoia. *TrAC Trends Anal. Chem.* **2019**, *112*, 201–211. [CrossRef]

100. Gómez-Ríos, G.A.; Pawliszyn, J. Development of Coated Blade Spray Ionization Mass Spectrometry for the Quantitation of Target Analytes Present in Complex Matrices. *Angew. Chem. Int. Ed.* **2014**, *53*, 14503–14507. [CrossRef]

101. Gómez-Ríos, G.A.; Tascon, M.; Reyes-Garcés, N.; Boyacı, E.; Poole, J.; Pawliszyn, J. Quantitative analysis of biofluid spots by coated blade spray mass spectrometry, a new approach to rapid screening. *Sci. Rep.* **2017**, *7*, 16104. [CrossRef]

102. Gómez-Ríos, G.A.; Tascon, M.; Pawliszyn, J. Coated blade spray: Shifting the paradigm of direct sample introduction to MS. *Bioanalysis* **2018**, *10*, 257–271. [CrossRef]

103. Pereira, I.; Rodrigues, M.F.; Chaves, A.R.; Vaz, B.G. Molecularly imprinted polymer (MIP) membrane assisted direct spray ionization mass spectrometry for agrochemicals screening in foodstuffs. *Talanta* **2018**, *178*, 507–514. [CrossRef]

104. Espy, R.D.; Teunissen, S.F.; Manicke, N.E.; Ren, Y.; Ouyang, Z.; van Asten, A.; Cooks, R.G. Paper Spray and Extraction Spray Mass Spectrometry for the Direct and Simultaneous Quantification of Eight Drugs of Abuse in Whole Blood. *Anal. Chem.* **2014**, *86*, 7712–7718. [CrossRef]

105. Hu, B.; So, P.-K.; Chen, H.; Yao, Z.-P. Electrospray Ionization Using Wooden Tips. *Anal. Chem.* **2011**, *83*, 8201–8207. [CrossRef]

106. Hu, B.; So, P.-K.; Yang, Y.; Deng, J.; Choi, Y.-C.; Luan, T.; Yao, Z.-P. Surface-Modified Wooden-Tip Electrospray Ionization Mass Spectrometry for Enhanced Detection of Analytes in Complex Samples. *Anal. Chem.* **2018**, *90*, 1759–1766. [CrossRef]

107. Hu, B.; Yao, Z. Detection of native proteins using solid-substrate electrospray ionization mass spectrometry with nonpolar solvents. *Anal. Chim. Acta* **2018**, *1004*, 51–57. [CrossRef] [PubMed]

108. Fang, L.; Deng, J.; Yu, Y.; Yang, Y.; Wang, X.; Liu, H.; Luan, T. Coupling liquid-phase microextraction with paper spray for rapid analysis of malachite green, crystal violet and their metabolites in complex samples using mass spectrometry. *Anal. Methods* **2016**, *8*, 6651–6656. [CrossRef]

109. Meng, X.; Liu, Q.; Ding, Y. Paper-based solid-phase microextraction for analysis of 8-hydroxy-2'-deoxyguanosine in urine sample by CE-LIF. *Electrophoresis* **2017**, *38*, 494–500. [CrossRef] [PubMed]

110. Saraji, M.; Farajmand, B. Chemically modified cellulose paper as a thin film microextraction phase. *J. Chromatogr. A* **2013**, *1314*, 24–30. [CrossRef] [PubMed]

111. Ríos-Gómez, J.; Lucena, R.; Cárdenas, S. Paper supported polystyrene membranes for thin film microextraction. *Microchem. J.* **2017**, *133*, 90–95. [CrossRef]

112. Ríos-Gómez, J.; García-Valverde, M.T.; López-Lorente, Á.I.; Toledo-Neira, C.; Lucena, R.; Cárdenas, S. Polymeric ionic liquid immobilized onto paper as sorptive phase in microextraction. *Anal. Chim. Acta* **2019**. [CrossRef]

113. Hashemian, Z.; Khayamian, T.; Saraji, M. Anticodeine aptamer immobilized on a Whatman cellulose paper for thin-film microextraction of codeine from urine followed by electrospray ionization ion mobility spectrometry. *Anal. Bioanal. Chem.* **2014**, *407*. [CrossRef]

114. Kim, E.-A.; Lim, Y.Y. Effective preconcentration of volatile organic compounds from aqueous solutions with polydimethylsiloxane-coated filter paper. *Microchem. J.* **2019**, *145*, 979–987. [CrossRef]

115. Díaz-Liñán, M.C.; López-Lorente, A.I.; Cárdenas, S.; Lucena, R. Molecularly imprinted paper-based analytical device obtained by a polymerization-free synthesis. *Sens. Actuators B Chem.* **2019**, *287*, 138–146. [CrossRef]

116. Ríos-Gómez, J.; Ferrer-Monteagudo, B.; López-Lorente, Á.I.; Lucena, R.; Luque, R.; Cárdenas, S. Efficient combined sorption/photobleaching of dyes promoted by cellulose/titania-based nanocomposite films. *J. Clean. Prod.* **2018**, *194*, 167–173. [CrossRef]

117. Ríos-Gómez, J.; Fresco-Cala, B.; García-Valverde, M.; Lucena, R.; Cárdenas, S. Carbon Nanohorn Suprastructures on a Paper Support as a Sorptive Phase. *Molecules* **2018**, *23*, 1252. [CrossRef] [PubMed]

118. Dotan, A. Biobased Thermosets. In *Handbook of Thermoset Plastics*; Elsevier: Amsterdam, The Netherlands, 2014; pp. 577–622.

119. Deng, J.; Yu, T.; Yao, Y.; Peng, Q.; Luo, L.; Chen, B.; Wang, X.; Yang, Y.; Luan, T. Surface-coated wooden-tip electrospray ionization mass spectrometry for determination of trace fluoroquinolone and macrolide antibiotics in water. *Anal. Chim. Acta* **2017**, *954*, 52–59. [CrossRef] [PubMed]

120. Huang, Y.; Ma, Y.; Hu, H.; Guo, P.; Miao, L.; Yang, Y.; Zhang, M. Rapid and sensitive detection of trace malachite green and its metabolite in aquatic products using molecularly imprinted polymer-coated wooden-tip electrospray ionization mass spectrometry. *RSC Adv.* **2017**, *7*, 52091–52100. [CrossRef]

121. Liu, Y.; Yang, Q.; Chen, X.; Song, Y.; Wu, Q.; Yang, Y.; He, L. Sensitive analysis of trace macrolide antibiotics in complex food samples by ambient mass spectrometry with molecularly imprinted polymer-coated wooden tips. *Talanta* **2019**, *204*, 238–247. [CrossRef] [PubMed]
122. Karimiyan, H.; Hadjmohammadi, M.R.; Kunjali, K.L.; Moein, M.M.; Dutta, J.; Abdel-Rehim, M. Graphene Oxide/Polyethylene Glycol-Stick for Thin Film Microextraction of β-Blockers from Human Oral Fluid by Liquid Chromatography-Tandem Mass Spectrometry. *Molecules* **2019**, *24*, 3664. [CrossRef]

Review

Recent Advances in In Vivo SPME Sampling

Nicolò Riboni [1,2], **Fabio Fornari** [1], **Federica Bianchi** [1,2,*] and **Maria Careri** [1,2]

[1] Dipartimento di Scienze Chimiche, della Vita e della Sostenibilità Ambientale, Università di Parma, Parco Area delle Scienze 17/A, 43124 Parma, Italy; nicolo.riboni@studenti.unipr.it (N.R.); fabio.fornari2@studenti.unipr.it (F.F.); careri@unipr.it (M.C.)

[2] Centro Interdipartimentale per l'Energia e l'Ambiente (CIDEA), Università di Parma, Parco Area delle Scienze, 43124 Parma, Italy

[*] Correspondence: federica.bianchi@unipr.it; Tel./Fax: +39-0521-905446

Received: 4 November 2019; Accepted: 3 January 2020; Published: 15 January 2020

Abstract: In vivo solid-phase microextraction (SPME) has been recently proposed for the extraction, clean-up and preconcentration of analytes of biological and clinical concern. Bioanalysis can be performed by sampling exo- or endogenous compounds directly in living organisms with minimum invasiveness. In this context, innovative and miniaturized devices characterized by both commercial and lab-made coatings for in vivo SPME tissue sampling have been proposed, thus assessing the feasibility of this technique for biomarker discovery, metabolomics studies or for evaluating the environmental conditions to which organisms can be exposed. Finally, the possibility of directly interfacing SPME to mass spectrometers represents a valuable tool for the rapid quali- and quantitative analysis of complex matrices. This review article provides a survey of in vivo SPME applications focusing on the extraction of tissues, cells and simple organisms. This survey will attempt to cover the state-of- the-art from 2014 up to 2019.

Keywords: solid-phase microextraction; in vivo extraction; tissue analysis; cells; simple organisms

---

1. Introduction

Solid-phase microextraction (SPME) [1] is a widely used extraction technique recently applied for in vivo and ex vivo analysis. Performing ex vivo SPME extraction means that analytes are extracted from samples collected from living organisms, whereas in vivo sampling is directly performed on living organisms using SPME both in the headspace (HS) and in the direct immersion (DI) mode [2]. It is known that in bioanalysis a plethora of endo- and exogenous compounds has to be monitored in a variety of matrices. Ideally, SPME should allow sampling, analyte pre-concentration and extraction to be performed in one single step, with no or very limited solvent consumption and minimum invasiveness. Taking into account the reduced amount of sample required for the analysis, another advantage of in vivo SPME is the low adverse effects on living organisms. In addition, the possibility of directly interfacing SPME to mass spectrometers represents a valuable tool for the rapid quali- and quantitative analysis of complex matrices [3–6]. The development of in vivo/ex vivo SPME-based methods can be of paramount importance in medicine and veterinary medicine, when rapid decisions need to be taken during or immediately after surgery in order to establish the proper therapeutic protocol [7,8]. Metabolomic studies are another field of interest: in fact, detecting metabolites is critical for interpreting the health status or disease conditions of living organisms [9,10]. Analogously, detection of pollutants deriving from both anthropogenic and natural sources in living plants and animals can be useful to achieve information about the environmental conditions to which the organisms are exposed [11].

SPME coatings play a crucial role for in vivo applications: both commercial coatings, such as polydimethylsiloxane (PDMS), polyacrylate (PA) and divinylbenzene (DVB), and lab-made fibers based on the use of biocompatible coatings like C_{18}, polydopamine (PDA), molecularly imprinted polymers (MIPs), mixed C_{18} and cation exchange particles, polyacrylonitrile (PAN), hydrophilic lipophilic balanced particles (HLB) [1,12–20] have been proposed with the final aim of improving both method sensitivity and selectivity. Novel geometry of SPME, like the thin-film microextraction blades (TF-SPME) [18] or biocompatible surface coated probes (BSCP) [21,22] have been also developed to provide higher sensitivity and reduced analysis time due both to the high surface area-to-volume ratio and to the possibility of a direct mass spectrometry (MS) coupling. In this context, many ex vivo SPME studies could be implemented for in vivo applications, in order to capture short-living and labile compounds, avoiding sample degradation [10,23–27].

The aim of this survey is to cover the recent studies regarding in vivo SPME focusing on the SPME extraction of tissues, cells and simple organisms. This survey will attempt to cover the state-of-the-art from 2014 up to 2019.

2. In Vivo SPME Extraction of Mammal Tissues

One of the major problems associated to tissue sampling is related to the adverse effects that can be produced during its collection. The use of miniaturized devices for in vivo SPME sampling can minimize these effects, allowing the direct analysis of tissues located in different body areas.

In this context, interesting devices have been recently developed for extraction of neurotransmitters performing in vivo brain sampling. Lendor et al. have developed a SPME-based miniaturized probe, having hydrophilic lipophilic balanced particles with strong cation exchange groups (HLB-SCX) SPME coating and a layer of biocompatible PAN, for the chemical biopsy of rat brain [17]. Brain sampling is assisted by a software-controlled driving system equipped with a needle able to promote probe penetration. The presence of a guiding cannula preserves the coating from contamination until the probe reaches the brain area to be sampled. The developed solid-phase microextraction-liquid chromatography-tandem mass spectrometry (SPME-LC-MS/MS) protocol in a surrogate brain matrix proved to be suitable for determining neurochemicals at physiological levels. Finally, the proof-of-concept in vivo application was performed on macaque brain, extracting several neurochemicals simultaneously from three brain areas. Very recently, in another study reliable measurements of different neuromodulators like glutamate, dopamine, acetylcholine and choline have been simultaneously made by in vivo SPME sampling within the frontal cortex and striatum of macaque monkeys during goal-directed behavior [28].

In comparison to microdialysis-mass spectrometry, which is the most common method for determining multiple neuromodulators in awake behaving animals, the proposed in vivo SPME sampling combines the high enrichment and does not destroy the tissue during the positioning of both the probe and the guiding cannula, thus avoiding the damage-induced release of neuromodulators (Figure 1). Finally, an additional advantage of the proposed approach relies on the highest affinity of the used SPME coating towards hydrophobic compounds. The developed SPME-LC-MS/MS protocol allowed the effective determination of the neuromodulators at different concentration levels, thus being useful for a better understanding of the neuromodulatory system. In vivo brain sampling using the same SPME probe has been also carried out by Reyes-Garces et al. [29] with the aim of performing the untargeted in vivo analysis of rodent's brain after deep brain stimulation (DBS). Metabolite changes occurring in brain hippocampi after 3 h of DBS and after 8 days of daily DBS therapy were evaluated. Findings demonstrated that acute DBS was able to produce changes in the levels of several metabolites like citrulline, phosphor- and glycosphingolipids, whose concentration levels increased after the therapy. By contrast, after chronic DBS, a decrease in the corticosterone levels were observed.

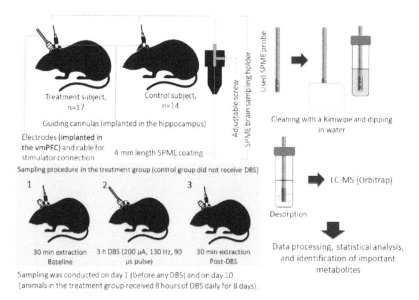

Figure 1. General schematic of the in vivo solid-phase microextraction (SPME) brain sampling and sample analysis procedure. Reprinted with permission from [29].

Taking into account that liver is the main metabolic organ of mammals, in vivo SPME has been applied also for the selective capture of luteolin and its metabolites in rat liver [15]. In vivo sampling is proposed as valid alternative to the use of liver microsomes and homogenates since these approaches can cause serious damages or animal death due to the high invasiveness. Owing to the presence of cavities having high affinity for specific analytes, the use of MIP-based coatings has been proposed to enhance SPME selectivity with respect to commercial fibers. In this study, a molecularly imprinted polymer-solid-phase microextraction (MIP-SPME) coating was devised and applied for the LC-MS/MS analysis of the target analytes. The MIP-SPME fiber was prepared using luteolin, acrylamide and ethylene glycol dimethacrylate as template, functional monomer and cross-linker, respectively. As for luteolin metabolites, three compounds were identified, i.e., apigenin, chrysoeriol and diosmetin, thus proposing in vivo sampling as a promising tool for assessing the real metabolic pathway of target compounds. Since MIPs are usually incompatible with macromolecules, requiring a preliminary clean-up, a restricted molecularly imprinted solid-phase microextraction (RAMIPs-SPME) coating has been proposed by Wang and coworkers for the selective determination of hesperetin and its metabolites in rat livers [30]. Being able of selectively adsorbing analytes from complex matrices and eliminating macromolecules, the use of RAMIP-based material offered the advantages of both MIPs and restricted access materials. The compounds extracted by in vivo RAMIPs-SPME were analyzed by ultra-performance-liquid chromatography-tandem mass spectrometry (UPLC-MS/MS), showing the highest affinity and enrichment capability of the developed coating with respect to both other MIPs and commercially available PDMS and DVB fibers.

Since the determination of the concentration of anticancer drugs could improve the efficacy of chemotherapic treatments reducing adverse effects on patients, recently Roszkowska et al. have developed an in vivo SPME-LC-MS/MS protocol for the quantitation of doxorubicin in lung tissue [31]. Preliminary experiments carried out using the ex vivo SPME approach allowed to optimize the operative conditions for doxorubicin extraction using lamb lungs as surrogate matrix. Validation proved the reliability of the developed protocol, obtaining a quantitation limit (LOQ) of 2.5 µg/g, a good precision with relative standard deviation (RSD) < 14.7% and a good linearity in the 2.5–50 µg/g range. Then, in vivo SPME sampling was performed on real pig lung samples to detect doxorubicin after in vivo lung perfusion, proving the capability of in vivo SPME for therapeutic drug monitoring in clinical studies, opening the possibility to perform sampling several times in different areas of the organ, without the need of biopsies.

In the field of cancer research, untargeted metabolite analysis on resected tumors could be used as a new diagnostic approach able to characterize endogenous metabolites, thus being potentially useful for biomarker discovery. Performing ex vivo SPME sampling on tumors allows sample availability for additional analyses like histological testing, thus obtaining a complete pattern of information about a specific disease. A very interesting study has been proposed by Zhang and coworkers, who developed a disposable handheld device, the MasSpec Pen, for the real time sampling of tissues [32].

The device was characterized by a pen-sized handheld device directly integrated into a laboratory-built MS interface. The biocompatible sampling probe allowed the time and volume-controlled extraction of molecules from tissue by means of water droplets. After a few seconds of extraction, the droplets were transported from the MasSpec Pen to the mass spectrometer for molecular analysis. Preliminary experiments were performed by ex vivo sampling on tissue sections of more than 200 patients, then the MasSpec Pen was tested for in vivo tissue analysis in mice using a murine model of human breast cancer. Under anesthesia, the skin overlying the tumors was removed, and several tissue regions, i.e., multiple positions of the top of the tumor, the core of the tumor after partial tumor resection, and adjacent normal soft connective tissue, were analyzed. A distinctive molecular profile was observed between adjacent normal soft connective tissue regions and tumor regions. No observable macroscopic or microscopic damages of the tissue regions analyzed were detected. Furthermore, no apparent effects to the health of the animals were observed caused by the MasSpec Pen analysis during surgery, thus suggesting the effectiveness of the device for in vivo molecular evaluation and cancer diagnosis.

An overview of the discussed applications is reported in Table 1.

Table 1. Summary of applications of in vivo SPME for mammal tissues.

Analyte	Matrix	Coating	SPME	Detection Technique	LOQs	RSD%	Ref.
Neurotransmitters	Macaque brain	HLB-SCX/PAN	Miniaturized recessed stainless-steel probe	LC-MS/MS	25–20,000 ng/mL	<11	[17]
Neuromodulators	Macaque brain	HLB-SCX/PAN	Miniaturized recessed stainless steel probe	LC-MS/MS	25–20,000 ng/mL	<11	[28]
Untargeted metabolomics after DBS	Rodent brain	C_{18} and mixed mode	Commercially available fibers	LC-MS/MS	-	<30 (cut-off)	[29]
Luteolin and its metabolites	Rat liver	MIP	Homemade stainless-steel fiber	LC-MS/MS	0.05–0.21 µg/mL	<3.2	[15]
Hesperetin and its metabolites	Rat liver	RAMIP	Homemade stainless-steel fiber	UPLC-MS/MS	0.05 µg/mL	<7.0	[30]
Doxorubicin	Mammals lung tissue	Biocompatible mixed-mode	Commercially available fibers	LC-MS/MS	2.5 µg/g	<21.5	[31]

- Not declared.

3. In Vivo SPME Extraction of Fish Tissues

In vivo analysis of fish samples is an emerging strategy for monitoring the health of aquatic ecosystems and water contamination from both natural sources and anthropogenic pollutants [33]. In fact, fish could absorb contaminants through their gills, skin, or gastrointestinal tract [33–35]. In vivo tissue monitoring of pharmaceuticals [36–41], persistent pollutants [42–44], pesticides [45] and antibacterial agents [46] provides valuable information regarding their concentration in the ecosystem, bioaccumulation levels and metabolism. In particular, lipophilic pollutants can easily diffuse through biological membranes and accumulate in fish tissues and organs [47–50]. The increased concentration levels of toxic compounds and the possibility of additive effects related to the accumulation of multiple contaminants can result in physiological disorders and alteration of the normal metabolism, affecting reproductive, immune, nervous, cardiovascular and endocrine systems [33–35,51]. In addition, compounds accumulated in fish tissues could be transferred to other consumers in the food chain, leading to biomagnification phenomena [35,52–54]. Standard methods used for the assessment of the bioconcentration, metabolism and elimination of targeted compounds in fish and for environmental monitoring require sampling of tens of individuals; moreover, analyses are usually performed from ex vivo tissues [55].

Due to the high complexity of the matrix, extraction has to be carried out in order to remove the possible interfering species and to concentrate the target compounds. To this purpose, several sample preparation techniques have been proposed among which SPME, liquid extraction (LE), Soxhlet extraction, pressurized liquid extraction, microwave-assisted extraction and Quick Easy Cheap Effective Rugged Safe extraction (QuEChERS) [56–58]. Sampled tissues are usually homogenized and processed using organic solvents, leading to a challenging identification of compounds naturally present in the living systems, due to phenomena such as cellular degradation, chemical alterations, enzymatic activity and aggregation processes [59,60].

In vivo SPME, integrating sampling, extraction, and enrichment of the analytes into a single step is able to overcome these limitations and therefore has been proposed for both target and untargeted analysis of chemical compounds in fish tissues [2]. Usually the sampling is performed by inserting the fiber in the dorsal-epaxial muscle of the anesthetized or immobilized fish to a depth of about 2 cm (Figure 2). This approach proved to be the best solution since the sampling of the dorsal-epaxial muscle reflects the overall composition of the tissue due to the uniform distribution of the analytes [61]. Sampling duration ranges between 1 and 20 min, thus resulting in the possibility to both observe short-term events occurring in dynamic biological systems and capture highly reactive compounds in living organisms. In addition, long-time processes such as compounds uptake, metabolism and elimination can be monitored onto the individual test subject, strongly reducing sample size and allowing for the calculation of inter-sample variability with the possibility of highlighting inflammation and disease states of abnormal samples [51,60].

Figure 2. In vivo SPME sampling of Tilapia brain (top) and dorsal-epaxial muscle (bottom). Reprinted with permission from [41].

In vivo SPME target analysis has been focused on tracing the uptake and elimination of persistent organic pollutants (POPs), personal care products (PCPs) and pharmaceuticals used in aquaculture. Xu et al. [45] proposed a simple and time-efficient method to trace the uptake and elimination kinetics of both organochlorine (OCPs) and organophosphorus (OPPs) pesticides from the dorsal-epaxial muscle of tilapias (*Oreochromis mossambicus*) and pomfrets (*Piaractus brachypomus*). The extraction was performed using homemade PDMS-coated fibers. The uptake and elimination of the pesticides were monitored via gas chromatography-mass spectrometry (GC-MS) targeting the unaltered pesticides. The use of in vivo SPME allowed to monitor the fast elimination processes of OPPs, guaranteeing an accurate determination of fast changing species without the enzyme quenching steps required in the ex vivo process. These analyses resulted in the calculation of the elimination kinetics (k_e) and the bioconcentration factors (BCFs), which were consistent with those reported in United States Environmental Protection Agency (US EPA) databases. Subsequently, the metabolism of fenthion was monitored via solid phase microextraction-liquid chromatography-mass spectrometry (SPME-LC-MS) using thicker PDMS fibers, leading to the identification of fenthion sulfoxide, fenthoxon and fenthoxon sulfoxide. The elimination kinetics of fenthion and its metabolites was monitored along the time, assessing a different persistence of the species in the muscle compartment.

Trace analysis of PCPs was performed on rainbow trout (*Oncorhynchus mykiss*) [43]. The extraction from the dorsal-epaxial muscle was performed using C_{18} SPME fiber probes, followed by GC-MS analysis to detect targeted UV filters and polycyclic aromatic musks. Method calibration was performed in vivo, whereas validation parameters, i.e., extraction time profile, detection limits (LODs), LOQs, linearity and repeatability were obtained ex vivo due to the inter-fish variation. Analyte time profile and sampling rates presented significant differences between the in vivo and in vitro applications due to the physiological activity of the living organisms. The use of C_{18} SPME fiber allowed the extraction of small molecules able to penetrate and be adsorbed onto the embedded particles, thus excluding the large matrix-derived biomolecules and strongly reducing interfering phenomena. Uptake and elimination of synthetic musks (SMs) in tilapias were also studied by Chen et al. [44] using sampling-rate calibration for the quantification of the analytes [62]. In particular, musk xylene (MX), musk ketone (MK), galaxolide™ (HHCB), and tonalide™ (AHTN) were investigated. The analytes presented different uptake and bioconcentration factors: nitro musks, hypothesized as potential carcinogenic substances, showed greater bioaccumulation potential (BCFs 989 ± 56 and 241 ± 73 for MX and MK, respectively) than polycyclic musks (67 ± 15 and 99 ± 28 for HHCB and AHTN). Elimination kinetics presented the same trend present in Ocaña-Rios [43] for all the analyzed compounds, with an initial rapid elimination of the SMs, followed by a slower concentration decrease.

In-muscle detection of pharmaceuticals used in aquaculture was investigated by Huang [36] and Tang [46], targeting anesthetics and fluoroquinolones respectively. Both studies deal with health safety, focusing on the elimination of potentially harmful pharmaceuticals from edible fish. Huang proposed the use of in vivo SPME for a rapid in situ sampling of anesthetics in living fish, since they could be metabolized or degraded during fish samples transportation to the lab [36]. Due to the rapid metabolism of anesthetics, in order to obtain a better estimation of anesthetics concentrations, SPME was proposed as valid alternative to standard methods requiring multiple sample preparation steps, i.e., fish euthanasia, tissues removal and homogenization. Method development and validation were performed ex vivo analyzing homogenized fish muscle, whereas elimination study was performed in vivo. The concentration of five anesthetics was monitored for 5 h by exposing for 10 min homemade PDMS fibers in the dorsal-epaxial muscle of tilapias. The study demonstrated a rapid metabolism of the anesthetics, with half-life times ranging between 44 and 150 min and a decline of 10% of their concentration within the first 10 min. The concentration decline profile was demonstrated to be different compared to that obtained by spiking the analytes in homogenized tissue samples due the physiological activity. The proposed method exhibited lower LODs (in the 1.7–9.4 ng/g range) and reduced analysis times compared to traditional ex vivo methods, strongly simplifying sample preparation step.

Tang [46] focused the study on target analysis of 5 fluoroquinolones (FQs) on cultured pufferfish (*Takifugu obscurus*). Due to the high economic value of pufferfish and its major consumption in East-Asia, FQs are often used in its cultivation to prevent pathogenic infection. Despite their intense use in veterinary disease treatment, these antibacterial agents are known to accumulate in fish tissues and are considered a potential health risk for human for seafood consumption. In the study, an in vivo SPME-LC-MS/MS method was developed and validated to assess the concentration levels of FQs in the dorsal-epaxial muscle of immature pufferfish using homemade biocompatible SPME fibers coated by PAN-C_{18}. PAN is usually chosen as binder for stationary phase immobilization due to its biocompatibility, high chemical and mechanical stability [1]. The octadecyl silica was selected because of its good extraction efficiency toward a wide range of compounds. The developed coating proved to be characterized by higher extraction capabilities compared to PDMS (9–31 times) and comparable efficiency to commercial C_{18} fibers. Method optimization and validation were performed using spiked water samples. Good linearity and LOQs lower than those reported in the standard LE method were obtained. No significant difference was observed when the in vivo SPME-LC-MS/MS method was compared with the official liquid extraction-liquid chromatography-tandem mass spectrometry (LE-LC-MS/MS) method.

In order to obtain a more efficient extraction of the analytes from the fish matrix, researchers are developing new biocompatible coatings designed to provide enhanced enrichment of target compounds, while eliminating possible interferences. Additional features of these materials rely on the improved wettability, high surface area, presence of specific functional groups able to provide stable chemical interactions, tunable pore sizes [1]. The developed phases are based on the use of new functionalized polymeric fiber coatings [14,63], polymeric-coated nanoparticles [37,38], functionalized nanotubes [39], metal organic frameworks (MOFs) [40] and polyelectrolyte dispersed in microcapsules [41]. Biocompatible polystyrene-polydopamine-glutaraldehyde (PS@PDA-GA) coating has been developed for sampling analytes in semisolid tissues and accelerate sampling kinetics thanks to the increased surface area [14,63]. The coating of the device is designed in order to expel the air trapped in the wettable 3D-interconnected pores in presence of the tissue fluid, thus allowing the full accessibility of the whole surface. By the use of this SPME coating, sampling equilibrium is reached within few minutes, boosting the speed of the analysis and simplifying method calibration. This coating was tested for the extraction of tetrodotoxin (TTX) from pufferfish [63] and pharmaceuticals from tilapias muscle [14].

Chen et al. [63] developed a rapid in vivo SPME-LC-MS/MS method for the detection of TTX in pufferfish muscle using electrospun (PS@PDA-GA) fibers. Electrospinning was proposed since it allowed a fine control of fiber diameter, morphology and orientation of the micro/nanofibers, obtaining fully exposed surface active sites and high permeability [64]. The developed coating was characterized by higher extraction capabilities compared to commercially available PDMS (nearly 120 times) and PA (about 20 times) fibers. Spiked water solutions were used for the optimization of the extraction and desorption conditions, whereas method validation was performed on homogenized pufferfish muscle spiked with TTX. The developed SPME-LC-MS/MS method exhibited a wide linearity range, good repeatability (RSDs < 12.1%) and lower LOQ (7.3 ng/g) compared to the official method (LOQ: 50 ng/g). Animal studies were performed by applying the in vivo sampling on fish divided in a control group and five different sample groups fed with increasing amount of TTX (1–80 MU/g·body mass/day). Method accuracy was assessed by comparing the concentration of two groups obtained by using the developed method with those of the official method, showing no significant difference. Backwards, when the analysis was performed on fish cultured with lower dosage of TTX, only the in vivo SPME-LC-MS/MS method was able to detect the target toxin, proving its superior detection capabilities compared to the official LE-based method.

The PS@PDA-GA coated-fibers were also tested for the extraction of pharmaceuticals from immature tilapias [14]. The coating was deposited onto electrospun fibers inserted inside a syringe needle, which was withdrawn during fiber exposure. PS@PDA-GA coated-fibers extraction efficiency of pharmaceuticals was compared in vitro with those of electrospun PS and PDMS coated fibers at equilibrium, resulting in signals at least 4.4 and 26 times higher respectively. In addition, the hydrophobic surface of the PS@PDA-GA coated-fibers proved to circumvent the adhesion of biological macromolecules. LODs for the target pharmaceuticals were in the 1.1–8.9 ng/g range, whereas RSDs for inter-fiber repeatability were in the 5.9–14.3% range. Finally, the developed fibers were tested for extracting pharmaceuticals from tilapia dorsal-epaxial muscle with a 10 min extraction, resulting in satisfactory sensitivity and accuracy. Fish exposed to fluoxetine and norfluoxetine were analyzed by both the SPME-LC-MS/MS and the LE-LC-MS/MS resulting in comparable mean concentration levels.

Qiu has proposed different coatings deposited onto electrospun fibers for the extraction of pharmaceuticals from fish tissues [37–39]. Quartz fiber (QF) coated by gluing poly(diallyldimethilammonium chloride) (PDDA) assembled graphene oxide (GO)-coated C_{18} composite particles (C_{18}@GO@PDDA) with polyaniline (PANI) and modified with polynorepinephrine (pNE) were used (Figure 3) [37]. This biocompatible coating was devised in order to avoid both the absorption of biomacromolecules and rejection reactions when the fiber is exposed inside the living tissue. C_{18} silica nanoparticles were chosen for extracting hydrophobic compounds, whereas GO was proposed due to the large surface area and the possible π-π interactions with the aromatic compounds as well as the high extraction capabilities towards hydrophilic molecules. PDDA is a cationic polyelectrolyte agent able to interact with acidic compounds. PANI and pNE were selected since they allow coating of any surface creating a bioinspired layer. The developed SPME fibers were tested for the extraction of 10 acidic pharmaceuticals from tilapia muscle. The extraction capabilities were compared ex vivo with commercially available fibers resulting in extraction 8.0–81.7 and 2.7–23.3 times higher respectively for PDMS and PA. LODs were in the 0.13–8.44 ng/g range. Linearity was demonstrated up to a range of 1–5000 ng/g and an inter-fiber repeatability in the 2.6–11.5 ng/g range was proved. The in vivo analysis was performed on living tilapias monitoring the uptake of the target pharmaceuticals along a period of 96 h.

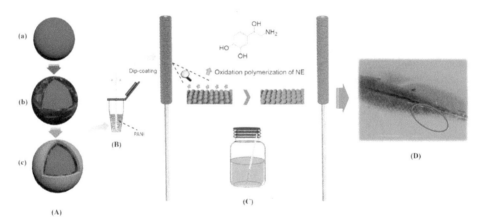

Figure 3. Schematic representation of the graphene oxide -coated C_{18} composite particles (C_{18}@GO@PDDA) coated fibers. (**A**) Preparation of the C_{18}@GO@PDDA particles. (**B**) Dip-coating preparation of the custom-made fiber with polyaniline (PANI) (**C**) Bioinspired modification by pNE. (**D**) In vivo sampling in fish dorsal-epaxial muscle. Reprinted with permission from [37].

For monitoring neutral, acidic and basic pharmaceuticals in living fish and vegetables, biocompatible copolymer poly(lactic acid-caprolactone) (PLCL) containing sulfonated γ-Al_2O_3 nanoparticles, sheathed with norepinephrine has been proposed [38] (sulfonated Al_2O_3@PLCL/pNE SPME fiber—Figure 4). The PLCL copolymer was chosen to be fully biocompatible, while maintaining a sufficient mechanical strength to be used for target monitoring of immature tilapias muscle and spinach (*Basella alba* L.) stem. Sulfonation allowed for the interaction between the fiber coating and the amino groups of basic sulphanilamide pharmaceuticals, thus improving their extraction from the living systems. The extraction capabilities of the developed fibers were 36–85 and 4–15 times higher than the PDMS fibers for the basic and the acidic/neutral pharmaceuticals, respectively. The fibers were tested in vivo obtaining LODs at nanogram of pharmaceuticals per gram of tissue level. Accuracy of the SPME-LC-MS/MS method was compared with that of the standard LE-LC-MS/MS method, demonstrating no significant difference between the obtained results, except for the sulfafurazole, which was detected only by SPME extraction.

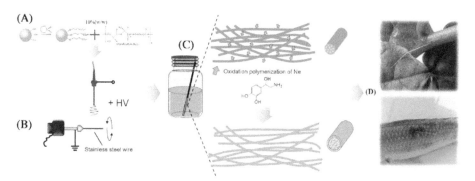

Figure 4. Flow diagram of the preparation and application of the novel SPME fiber. (**A**) Sulfonation of γ-Al$_2$O$_3$ nanoparticles, (**B**) electrospinning of doped poly(lactic acid-caprolactone) (PLCL) solution on a stainless-steel wire, (**C**) polymerization of norepinephrine on the surfaces of the spun nanofibers, (**D**) in vivo SPME sampling in vegetable and fish. Reprinted with permission from [38].

A coating obtained by functionalization of carbon nanotubes (CNT) with polypyrrole (PPY) and pNE has been proposed for the electrosorption-enhanced extraction of ionized acidic pharmaceutical from fish muscle [39]. PPY was chosen to obtain a biocompatible coating and to increase the conductivity of the extractive phase. CNT were used because of their 3D interconnected structure and the possibility to establish π-π and hydrophobic interactions with the target compounds. The advantage of the proposed method relies on the electrosorption-enhanced extraction, requiring the application of a low-power electric field to move the ionized analytes toward the coating via electrophoresis and complementary charge attraction, significantly improving the extraction efficiency and speed. The sampling device consists of a conductive SPME fiber connected with the working electrode, four opposite parallel stainless steel electrodes surrounding the fiber and connected with the counter electrode, and another uncoated electrospun needle connected with the reference electrode (Figure 5). The three-electrode system provided a stable electric field, resulting in enhanced extraction kinetics and accelerating the diffusion rates of the ionized analytes. The sampling time is reduced to 1 min compared to the 20 min required by the common SPME process, obtaining comparable or better extraction efficiencies for the target pharmaceuticals in deionized water. LODs in the 0.12–0.25 ng/g range and RSDs < 9.50% for inter-fiber repeatability were obtained. The proposed system was finally tested for the extraction of ionized pharmaceuticals from mature tilapias. The concentration of the ionized pharmaceuticals was monitored over a period of 360 h, allowing repeated long-time monitoring on living fish. The BCF values, in the 1.84–16.18 range, reached stability after 168 h of exposure.

MOFs have been also proposed as SPME coating for the in vivo monitoring of antibiotics (ABs) in fish muscle [40]. The monitoring of ABs in aquatic ecosystem is of paramount importance due to their worldwide massive use and the related spreading of antibiotic resistant bacteria and allergic sensitization. MOFs are particularly appealing due to their high surface area, tunable pore size, and adjustable internal surface properties obtained by changing both the metal ions center and organic ligand repeating units. In this study, a MIL-101(Cr)-NH$_2$ was proposed as SPME coating because of the large porosity and the excellent stability in both water and organic solvents. SPME extraction was optimized in terms of extraction and desorption time on six model ABs in water solution. LODs at ng/L level were obtained with a satisfactory repeatability (RSDs < 10%). The performance of developed fibers was compared with commercially available PDMS, PDMS/DVB, C_{18} and PA fibers, showing enhanced extraction capabilities for all the analytes except in the case of tilmicosin (C_{18} presented higher enhanced normalized peak area) and trimethoprim (no significant difference compared with PDMS/DVB). The ABs were monitored in living tilapias dorsal-epaxial muscle, obtaining low inter-fiber RSDs (<14.5%) and LODs in the 0.18–1.12 ng/g. The sampling rates (in the 11–69 ng/min range) were used for calculating the concentrations of ABs in the fish tissue, achieving results comparable with those obtained by using the reference LE method applied onto homogenized tissue samples, thus demonstrating the suitability of the developed SPME-LC-MS/MS method for the ABs in vivo monitoring.

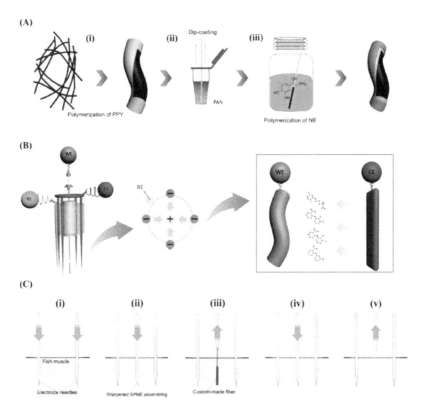

Figure 5. Schematic representation of: coating synthesis (**A**), proposed sampling device (**B**) and electrosorption-enhanced SPME with the device for ionized pharmaceuticals (**C**). Reprinted with permission from [39].

Polyelectrolyte microcapsules dispersed in silicone rubber were tested for SPME monitoring of antidepressants, i.e., fluoxetine and its metabolite norfluoxetine, in brains of living tilapias [41]. Differently from conventional fibers, extracting only neutral species, this coating was able to interact with both neutral and protonated analytes, thus increasing sampling efficiency. In addition, the use of microcapsules boosted the kinetic of sampling. Thanks to these features, it was possible to miniaturize the fiber dimension, allowing the sampling of immature fish brain. The competition effect between the two ionized analytes was negligible at biological concentration levels, whereas salting-out effect was significant in phosphate buffer solution. The two target analytes were monitored in vivo in both fish muscle and brain at environmentally relevant concentrations. Sampling rate calibration was used to determine the concentration of the antidepressants in the fish tissue. The results were comparable with those obtained by the LE method, demonstrating a high inter-sample variability. As expected, the concentration of the analytes in brain were from 4.4 to 9.2 times higher than those in the dorsal-epaxial muscle.

Untargeted analysis of exposome has shifted the focus from a bottom-up to a top-down approach in order to understand the impact of multiple and simultaneous exposures to environmental contaminants and detect modifications in the profile of endogenous compounds [65]. Direct in vivo SPME extraction has been proposed for monitoring fish tissues in a nonlethal manner, using coatings able to extract a wide range of low-molecular-weight compounds [10,50,51,60,66]. In addition, the use of SPME for in vivo monitoring has allowed the sampling of very labile and highly reactive species, which could be degraded during tissue samples transportation, storage and handling [60]. Since both endogenous and exogenous compounds can be detected, chemometric techniques have to be applied to highlight different contribution and detect abnormal samples [50,51,60,66,67].

Roszkowska [66] studied the metabolome profile associated to benzo[α]pyrene (BaP) exposition using in vivo solid-phase microextraction-liquid chromatography-high resolution mass spectrometry (SPME-LC-HRMS) analysis. It is recognized that the presence of BaP and its metabolites cause modification of cellular metabolism with carcinogenic, mutagenic, and cytotoxic effects, exacerbated by its bioaccumulation in biological tissues [68]. In the study, the dorsal-epaxial muscle of rainbow trout exposed to sublethal doses of BaP (1 and 10 ng/L) was sampled using commercially available biocompatible SPME mixed-mode probes in order to detect dose and time dependent alteration in tissue metabolome by case-control model. Being BaP able to affect several metabolic pathways, mainly related to cellular osmotic regulation, energy and lipid metabolism, the results achieved in the study indicated that BaP exposition was able to decrease the number of detected compounds. A different amino acid composition was observed between the three groups: several amino acids were detected free in the control group, whereas only free tryptophan and proline were present in the high-dose exposed group, with a concentration of tryptophan 10 times higher than the control level. Labile compounds, such as arachidonoyl serinol, an endocannabinoid metabolite, were also detected by in vivo SPME: this compound was detected in the high-dose group, probably indicating that BaP affects also the endocannabinoid system. In fact, endocannabinoids are reactive neuroprotective agents, whose dysregulation in the signaling pathway is associated with the inability of the biota to adapt to environmental contaminants exposure. Interestingly, fish exposed to the lowest concentration level of BaP presented significant metabolic pattern changes over the monitored period: the first days they showed features similar to the high-dose exposed group, whereas, after 14 days, similarities with the control groups were observed. This may imply the presence of an adaptation mechanism of the metabolism in response to the presence of pollutants in the surrounding environment.

Bessonneau [60] and Roszkowska [50] have studied the exposome via in vivo SPME monitoring in white sucker (*Catostomus commersonii*) tissues with the final aim of proving that in vivo SPME from fish tissues is suitable for detecting alterations in biota pathways. More precisely, Bessonneau [60] has examined the differences between metabolites detected by ex vivo and in vivo SPME using molecular networking analysis. The in vivo extraction was performed for 20 min by inserting into the dorsal-epaxial muscle of the fish a stainless steel blade coated by 5 μm C_{18} particles, immobilized using polyacrylonitrile-C_{18} (PAN-C_{18}). Ex vivo analysis followed the same procedure sampling non-homogenized frozen tissues from euthanized fish. Analyte identification and networking were performed by ultra performance-liquid chromatography-high resolution mass spectrometry (UPLC-HRMS) and UPLC-MS/MS using molecular networking software. Although most of the identified molecules were endogenous substances, four analytes, namely 4-methoxycinnamic acid, 1-hydroxybenzotriazole, diethylphthalate, and phenoxybenzamine were recognized as exogenous compounds, used in formulation of cleaning products, cosmetics and pharmaceuticals. Globally, 16% of the nodes were only detected by in vivo SPME sampling, whereas 21% were obtained only using ex vivo SPME sampling. The compounds detected only by in vivo SPME were both endogenous and exogenous substances, characterized by chemical instability and/or reactivity: for example, the detected cinnamic acids are prone to auto-oxidation during sample transportation and storage. The species observed only by ex vivo extraction are mainly produced by bacterial and enzymatic metabolism of the degraded tissue. Therefore, in vivo SPME allows the monitoring of labile species, avoiding the detection of biodegradation products.

Roszkowska has applied in vivo SPME to perform non-lethal sampling of white sucker to monitor the response to the exposition of contaminants from sites upstream, adjacent and downstream a development region of oil sands [50]. PAN-C_{18} coated blades were used for SPME in order to extract both hydrophilic and hydrophobic compounds from fish tissues. The UPLC-HRMS analysis resulted in the identification of several classes of toxic compounds present in fish muscles, including pesticides, aliphatic and aromatic hydrocarbons, phthalates, mycotoxins, plasticizers, pharmaceuticals and organometallic compounds. Overall, the results demonstrated that fish collected in the sites closely associated with oil sands production and downstream exhibited altered metabolic profiles compared with the control group, collected upstream from the production site. The uptake of toxic compounds resulted in several alteration of lipid metabolism, including glycerophospholipid metabolism, fatty acid activation and de novo lipid biosynthesis, phosphorylation, energy dysregulation and inflammatory states. The in vivo PAN-C_{18} SPME extraction allowed also the monitoring of labile and unstable compounds, present at trace levels in fish tissues, such as endocannabinoid metabolites. A parallel study has been performed to examine whether tissue exposome monitored in vivo could detect significant induction of CYP1A1, a gene involved in the biotransformation of toxic compound into more polar substances via oxygenation [51]. The study investigated small molecules associated with CYP1A1 induction to identify both contaminants inducers of the gene and explore the induction mechanism. The in vivo SPME was proposed in order both to capture unstable and labile compounds like highly reactive oxygen species (ROS), antioxidants and oxygenated derivatives of cholesterols, and to rapidly stabilize short-living metabolites, preventing their oxidation during storage.

Multivariate data analysis (partial least squares-discriminant analysis) and false rate discovery were applied to process data acquired by SPME-UPLC-HRMS. The metabolome changes associated with CPY1A1 induction highlighted that 182 features were significant in female suckers, whereas only 119 were significant in male fish. The results demonstrated that 12 metabolic pathways were involved in fish response to CYP1A1 activation. Since this gene is involved in the oxygenation of toxic compounds to facilitate their elimination, modification in the concentration levels of ROS and anti-oxidants was expected. In female white sucker, increases in the levels of antioxidants and depletion of short-lived oxygenated metabolites were observed: the endogenous antioxidant cellular content was increased as a response to the production of ROS in order to maintain cell redox status and homeostasis. In male suckers, a significant oxidative stress was detected with a depletion of the cellular pool of antioxidants and a decrease in the levels of endogenous pro-oxidants oxysterols. The differences reported between male and female fish exposome could be or sex-specific or related to variability in terms of chemical exposures. Several exogenous compounds were also identified in fish tissues, but strong inter-individual variability was present in cases fish, possibly due to a different exposure in the ecosystem. Among the different omics sciences, lipidomics is gaining increasing interest with the identification of hundreds of novel lipids involved biological transformations: apart from their role as structural components and energy reservoirs, lipids are also intermediates of cellular pathways [10,69].

Roszkowska has developed an in vivo SPME-UPLC-HRMS method using biocompatible SPME mixed-mode probes for untargeted lipidomics profiling of muscle tissue in living rainbow trout [59]. Samples collected from the same sampling group were stored at −80 °C for 1 year and analyzed by both SPME-LC-HRMS and solid-liquid-extraction-liquid chromatography-high resolution mass spectrometry (SLE-LC-HRMS). By in vivo SPME, 845 features were detected in the 100–500 *m/z* range, 30% of which were annotated as lipid species, divided in three main groups: fatty acids, sterol lipids and glycerolipids. The ex vivo SPME analysis of stored muscle samples showed remarkable differences in lipid composition compared to the in vivo analysis, revealing lipidome profile alterations. The SPME analysis of ex vivo samples resulted in a general 10-fold decrease in the number of detected features and the appearance of higher molecular mass lipids, formed by binding reaction of the previously unbound lipids during sample storage. Spectra obtained by using SLE-UPLC-HRMS method from homogenized fish muscle samples were characterized by the presence of lipid compounds with high molecular masses (up to 900 *m*/z). These compounds were identified as high-abundant lipids, such as sterols and glycerophospholipids, released from both cellular membrane and intracellular environments due to the use of organic solvent mixtures. Therefore, they did not represent the unbound fraction of lipids present in living system, which could be detected only by in vivo SPME.

Deng and coworkers [21,70] have used biocompatible surface-coated probe nanoelectrospray-high resolution mass spectrometry (BSCP-nanoESI-HRMS) for in vivo lipidomics study of widely used model organisms in ecotoxicology like *Daphnia magna*, zebrafish (*Danio rerio*), zebrafish eggs and eukaryotic cells. The main advantage of this approach relies on the rapid, microscale and in situ analysis of complex biological samples. The biocompatible microsampling probe, presenting a probe-end diameter of few micrometers, was obtained by coating a tungsten probe with n-octadecyldimethyl[3-(trimethoxysilyl)propyl]-ammonium chloride (DMOAP) and chitosan. The stationary phase was chosen to interact with both the major lipid species (hydrophobic chain of glycerolipids, glycerophospholipids, sphingolipids and fatty acyls) by the C_{18} group and with the phosphate/hydroxyl/carboxyl groups by the quaternary ammonium ion via ion-exchange adsorption. Chitosan was used since chitosan-based materials are nontoxic, highly biocompatible, non-immunogenic and suitable for in vivo investigations. In addition, it was possible to prevent the absorption of large biomolecules onto the SPME surface. The optimization of the extraction parameters was performed by in vivo lipid analysis of zebrafish. Analysis was performed in positive ion mode since most of the lipids were detected as $[M + Na]^+$ and/or $[M + K]^+$ ions, whereas only a few signals from fatty acids were obtained in negative ion mode. The developed BSCP-nanoESI-HRMS method was compared with conventional direct infusion shotgun MS lipidomics by analyzing tissue extracts. A similar lipid profile was obtained, even though differences in the relative signal intensities were observed. The effectiveness of the coating extraction was demonstrated by sampling zebrafish tissues using uncoated probes, resulting in weaker MS signals. Coating stability was assessed by performing the extraction multiple times using the same probe. No decrease in peak intensity was observed and carryover effect of the coated fiber resulted negligible. The lipid species detected by BSCP-nanoESI-HRMS method were identified via LIPID MAPS structure database. Analysis of zebrafish dorsal-epaxial muscle led to the identification of 137 lipid species excluding isomers, i.e., 57 triradylglycerol (TAG) species, 33 phosphatidylcholine (PC) lipids, 28 phosphoglycerols (PGs), 10 ceramide-1-phosphates (CerPs), 3 fatty acids, (FAs), 2 diradylglycerols (DAGs), 2 cholesteryl esters (CEs), 1 monogalactosyldiacylglycerol (MGDG), and 1 phosphtatidylinositols-ceramide (PI-Cer). The lipid profile of single zebrafish eggs was also obtained: the most intense ions were identified as PC(16:0/18:1) and PC(16:0/22:6) lipids, whereas the signal intensities of many TAGs were much lower compared with those of zebrafish muscle. Principal component analysis (PCA) analysis was applied, showing that zebrafishes and their egg cells were clearly separated into two clusters and the major loadings were attributed to TAGs. Despite the developed method proved to be suitable for the detection of lipid species in living tissues, the accurate location of the C=C bond within the fatty acid chains could not be unambiguously assigned. In addition, isomers could not be differentiated due to the lack of a chromatographic separation. To solve the discrimination of C=C lipid isomers, online Paternò-Büchi (PB) reaction has been proposed [70]. Benzophenone was used as reagent to obtain high reaction efficiency with the methanol/chloroform solvent mixtures. In addition, the use of benzophenone compared to other PB reactants such as acetone results in 182 Da mass increased product ions, which could be easily discriminated from the original ions in the MS spectrum. In order to promote PB reaction, UV irradiation was performed before spray formation (Figure 6).

The identification of C=C lipid isomers was obtained by collision induced dissociation (CID): when CID was performed to the PB ions, C=C diagnostic ion pairs, namely $[M + O]^+$ and $[M + C_{13}H_{10}]^+$, having a mass difference of 150 Da, were produced. The identification of the C=C position alongside the fatty acid chain was based on the *m/z* shift of the CID induced PB product ions compared to the original [PB + M + H]⁺ parent ion. The proposed technique allowed a relative quantitation of C=C location isomers. Finally, in vivo analysis of lipidome of zebrafish was performed to identify C=C isomers, obtaining a detailed lipid profile.

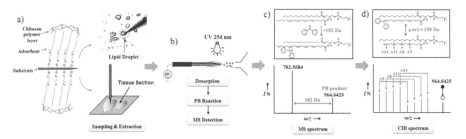

Figure 6. Schematic diagrams for development of a surface-coated probe nanoelectrospray-high resolution mass spectrometry (SCP-PB-nanoESI-HRMS) method. (**a**) A biocompatible surface-coated SPME probe toward lipids was applied for in situ and microscale sampling and extraction of lipids from lipid droplet or biological tissue. (**b**) Desorption, Paternò-Büchi (PB) reaction, and MS detection. (**c**) MS spectrum for unsaturated lipid with PB reaction. (**d**) collision induced dissociation (CID) spectrum for determination of lipid C=C locations and isomers. Reprinted with permission from [70].

One of the major drawbacks of the traditional SPME fiber for in vivo applications is the flexibility and the fragility of the silica core, limiting direct sampling of animal tissues. Poole et al. [42] developed a miniaturized device able to directly puncture robust sample matrices, such as the skin of top-level predator fish, by applying the sorbent coating onto a recession of a stainless steel support, thus protecting the edges of the coating during both puncture and recession steps. The device presents maximum surface area of sorbent per unit of puncture hole diameter, thus maximizing the extraction phase surface area (2.9 times more surface area than traditional nitinol-based bio-SPME fiber). The recessing coating was made by HLB particles suspended in a PAN glue, selected because of their biocompatibility and high extraction capabilities towards a wide variety of polar and nonpolar compounds. In order to demonstrate its robustness and facilitate sampling, the SPME recessed coating needle was also incorporated into custom projectiles, fired by unmodified airsoft guns. The device was tested to extract xenobiotic compounds from wild muskellunge (*Esox masquinongy*). The use of SPME projectiles demonstrated that the rapid puncture of fish scales provided a uniform and more repetitively successful sampler administration, reaching the underlying muscle tissue. This test demonstrated that the developed device was able to extract bioaccumulated and bioconcentrated anthropogenic compounds in a top-level predator. SPME-LC-HRMS analysis resulted in the tentative identification of 35 compounds belonging to pesticides, drugs, phytochemicals, lipids and metabolites.

Another major difficulty in untargeted LC-MS analysis is the presence of redundancy peaks, namely co-eluted peaks, multi-charge ions, adducts, neutral loss, isotopologues, and fragments ions that could result in statistical bias with multiple comparisons. Yu has proposed [67] the GlobalStd algorithm based on paired mass distances (PMD) to remove redundancy peaks from raw LC-MS data and to select independent peaks for further structure/reaction directed analysis. PMD are defined as distance between two masses or mass to charge ratios and this data analysis is based on the identification of unique defect values between analytes in order to identify homologous series or substitution reactions, clustering the compounds that present a similar structure or reactivity. Unknown PMD transitions could be obtained relying on the statistical properties of the LC-MS peak profile. By using this approach, both known and unknown compounds belonging to adducts, neutral loss, the same homologous series, or biochemistry reaction relationship could be identified. The filtered data can be subsequently studied for semi-qualitative or quantitative statistical analyses considering the compounds as a group, thus bypassing the need for identification of each peak present in the raw LC-MS data. The developed method was applied for the in vivo SPME-LC-MS analysis of wild rainbow trout. A total of 1459 peaks was obtained as raw dataset, reduced by the GlobalStd algorithm to only 277 independent peaks, which were imported for subsequent structure directed analysis.

All these studies evidenced that in vivo SPME is a valuable analytical tool for the real time monitoring of target analytes and metabolome profiling of living organisms. This approach was successfully applied for monitoring the uptake, metabolism and elimination of xenobiotic compounds from different fish species. In addition, it allowed the study of exposome directly from living organisms, resulting in the sampling of labile and reactive species, while avoiding the detection of compounds related to tissue sample degradation processes.

An overview of the discussed applications is reported in Table 2.

Table 2. Summary of applications of in vivo SPME for fish tissues.

Analyte	Matrix	Coating	SPME	Detection Technique	LOQs (ng/g)	RSD%	Ref.
OCPs and OPPs	Tilapia/pomfrets muscle	PDMS	Homemade stainless-steel fibers	GC-MS	1.8–15.5	<21.4	[45]
PCPs	Trout muscle	C$_{18}$	Commercially available fibers	GC-MS	5–70	<35.5	[43]
SMs	Tilapia muscle	PDMS	Homemade stainless steel fibers	GC-MS	3.0–13.2 (LODs)	<34.3	[44]
Anesthetics	Tilapia muscle	PDMS	Homemade stainless steel fibers	GC-MS	1.7–9.4 (LODs)	<10.8	[36]
FQs	Pufferfish muscle	C$_{18}$-PAN	Homemade stainless steel fiber	LC-MS/MS	1.0–4.6	<16.1	[46]
TTX	Pufferfish muscle	PS@PDA-GA	Electrospun stainless steel fibers	LC-MS/MS	7.3	<12.1	[63]
Pharmaceuticals	Tilapia muscle	PS@PDA-GA	Electrospun stainless steel fibers	LC-MS/MS	1.1–8.9	<14.3	[14]
Acidic pharmaceuticals	Tilapia muscle	C$_{18}$@GO@PDDA/PANI/pNE	QF	LC-MS/MS	0.80–28.1	<11.5	[37]
Pharmaceuticals	Tilapia muscle	Al$_2$O$_3$@PLCL/pNE	Electrospun stainless steel fibers	LC-MS/MS	0.55–17.8	<15.6	[38]
Acidic pharmaceuticals	Tilapia muscle	CNT@PPY@pNE	Homemade stainless steel fibers - electrosorption device	LC-MS/MS	0.40–0.83	<9.5	[39]
Abs	Tilapia muscle	MIL-101(Cr)-NH$_2$	QF	LC-MS/MS	0.6–3.7	<14.5	[40]
Antidepressant	Tilapia brain/muscle	Polyelectrolyte microcapsules dispersed in silicone rubber	Homemade stainless steel fibers	LC-MS/MS	-	<7.1	[41]
Untargeted BaP metabolomics	Trout muscle	Biocompatible mixed-mode	Commercially available fibers	LC-HRMS	-	-	[66]
Untargeted fish exposome	White sucker muscle	PAN-C$_{18}$	Homemade coated blades	UPLC-HRMS UPLC-MS/MS	-	-	[60]
Untargeted metabolomics	White sucker muscle	PAN-C$_{18}$	Homemade coated blades	UPLC-HRMS UPLC-MS/MS	-	-	[50]
Untargeted CYP1A1 exposome	White sucker muscle	PAN-C$_{18}$	Homemade coated blades	UPLC-HRMS UPLC-MS/MS	-	-	[51]
Untargeted lipidomics	Trout muscle	Biocompatible mixed-mode	Commercially available fibers	LC-HRMS	-	-	[59]
Untargeted lipidomics	Zebrafish muscle	Biocompatible chitosan-based	Homemade coated tungsten probes	nanoESI-HRMS	-	-	[21]
Untargeted lipidomics	Zebrafish muscle	DMOAP/chitosan	Homemade coated tungsten probes	nanoESI-HRMS	-	-	[70]
Untargeted analysis	Wild muskellunge muscle	HLB/PAN	Recessed homemade SPME device	LC-HRMS	-	<21	[42]

- Not declared.

4. In Vivo SPME Extraction of Plant Tissues

The conventional analytical process for the determination of a variety of analytes in plant tissues involves several steps due to the general complexity of the matrix [71]: in fact, solvent extraction and clean-up are usually required for the elimination of interfering compounds prior analysis [72]. Ex vivo analytical methods might introduce variability, potentially induce degradation of compounds of interest during sample preparation and alter both the spatial distribution and the natural content of investigated compounds in biota. These two aspects lead to an overall reduction of representativeness of analytical outcome [73], making metabolomics and tracing studies in different plant compartments hard to accomplish accurately.

The need for representative information regarding the actual composition and the dynamics of xenobiotics and biomolecules in plants has led to the development of a variety of in vivo analytical and extraction methods. Compared with other sampling techniques like microdialysis, in vivo tissue collection and biosensors, SPME offers the advantage of a low cost and simple device [44,71,73–75]. This technique allows the efficient and non-exhaustive extraction of the analytes by inserting the fiber directly in plant tissues with minimum disturbance of the living system. As a further advantage, this technique can be easily hyphenated with chromatography [74]. Nowadays, in vivo SPME is widely applied to study the uptake kinetics of agrochemicals, pesticides, pharmaceuticals and other emerging contaminants (e.g., synthetic musks) and their bioconcentration in plant compartments, defined as the absorption of xenobiotics from the surrounding environment [76]. Therefore, it can be used to perform food safety assessment by comparing detected concentrations with minimum residue limits.

Very recently, Shi et al. [74] have used in vivo SPME coupled with GC-MS for the quantitation of two fungicides, i.e., Y13149 and Y12196, in mung bean (*Vigna radiata*) sprouts. For this purpose, a polystyrene/graphene@silica (PS/G@SiO$_2$) fiber was fabricated via electrospinning and calcination. The coating materials were chosen due to their dimensional structure, rugged surface, superior mechanical and thermal stability. The method was optimized and validated by analyzing water spiked with analytes, demonstrating linearity in the 0.3–100 µg/L range, LODs in the low µg/L range and good precision with RSDs within 12.1%. The average recoveries were 99% and 71% for Y13149 and Y12196, respectively. PS/G@SiO$_2$ SPME fiber was compared with PS/G fiber and with two commercially available fibers, i.e., 85 µm carboxen/polydimethylsiloxane (CAR/PDMS) and 7 µm PDMS in terms of extraction performance, showing higher extraction efficiency toward Y12196, whereas Y13149 resulted to be better extracted using 7 µm PDMS fibers. Fungicides bioaccumulation was assessed directly in mung bean sprouts by inserting the PS/G@SiO$_2$ SPME fiber using a cannula into the stems at 2.0 cm depth and kept in place for 10 min at room temperature. Afterwards, the fiber was extracted and rinsed with water, dried and placed in the GC injector for the analysis. Results showed that the concentration of both analytes increased until day 9, thereafter a decrease was observed. Different plant compartments were also sampled to assess whether there was any difference in spatial distribution of xenobiotics. As a result, fungicides concentration was higher at 3 cm from the roots when compared to 7 cm distance, due to the higher lipid content.

In vivo tracing of other classes of xenobiotics was extensively studied by Chen and Qiu's group mainly using homemade PDMS-coated stainless steel fibers [12,44,77,78].

OCPs and OPPs have been investigated in different compartments of malabar spinach (*Basella alba*) through in vivo SPME [78]. A sampling rate-SPME (SR-SPME) coupled with the GC-MS method was successfully validated and applied for the in vivo tracing of OCPs (namely, endosulfan, hexachlorobenzene, dichlorodiphenyltrichloroethane, aldrin and mirex) and OPPs (namely, parathion-methyl, propetamphos, fenthion, quinalphos and profenofos). In particular, uptake and elimination kinetics were studied, and several parameters including BCFs, distribution concentration factors (DCFs) and transpiration stream concentration factors (TSCFs) were calculated based on in vivo analytical outcome. Spinach plants were grown hydroponically with nutrient solution spiked with the proper mixture of analytes for the uptake study and, right after, with clean nutrient solution for the elimination study. In vivo sampling was carried out by piercing the interested plant organ with a needle and then inserting the fiber at 1.5 cm depth (Figure 7); fiber was held in place for 20 min, cleaned with water and addressed for GC-MS analysis.

Figure 7. In vivo SPME sampling in different organs (leaf, stem and root) of living malabar spinach plant with custom-made PDMS fibers. Reprinted with permission from [78].

OPPs were accumulated faster, while OCPs resulted to be more persistent and less inclined to be eliminated from *B. alba* roots. In stems and foliage similar uptake kinetics and persistence were observed for both classes of analytes. A positive correlation between calculated BCFs and hydrophobicity was demonstrated for all the analytes except fenthion. Overall, the accumulated concentration halved within 4 days after the uptake experiment was concluded. From DCFs it was possible to infer that these two classes of pesticides tend to be more accumulative in roots due to the high lipid concentration. Lastly, hydrophobicity and solubility did not show any clear relationship with TSCFs, suggesting that more complex physiological phenomena are involved.

OPPs have been traced with an in vivo sampling rate-solid phase microextraction-gas chromatography-mass spectrometry (SR-SPME-GC-MS) approach in cabbage (*Brassica parachinensis*) and aloe (*Aloe barbadensis*) [12]. Moreover, in vivo SPME coupled with LC-MS/MS was used for the investigation of fenthion metabolites. Pesticides were administrated to *B. parachinensis* through a nutrient solution via hydroponic cultivation. *A. barbadensis* was cultivated in soil and OPPs were directly sprayed on aloe foliage. The in vivo sampling was performed as reported previously for the tracing study. The validated method reported LODs in the 0.07–2.07 µg/kg and 0.40–1.80 µg/kg range for aloe and cabbage, respectively. Regarding the uptake and the elimination of OPPs from cabbage, analytes were traced in leaves: within 7 days, the concentration of propetamphos, quinalphos and profenofos reached a maximum, whereas a similar behavior was not observed for parathion-methyl and fenthion. For the elimination experiment, the half-lives of the analytes were found to be within the 1.3–5.7 day-range. The accumulation of OPPs in aloe leaves peaked in 8 or 12 h depending on the analyte and a fast elimination was observed after 60 h after the exposure to polluted water. For the investigation of fenthion metabolism in aloe, fibers were desorbed in methanol under agitation and, after the addition of an internal standard, the extract was addressed to LC-MS/MS analysis. In both plants, fenthion resulted to be barely accumulated, whereas its metabolite fenthion-sulfoxide continued to accumulate until 100 h after the exposure.

In vivo SPME has been used also to evaluate whether multi walled carbon nanotubes (MWCNTs) affect the accumulation/elimination process of environmental contaminants i.e., OCPs, OPPs, pyrethroid insecticides and PCPs in mustard (*Brassica juncea*) leaves [77]. For this study, a SR-SPME(PDMS)-GC-MS method was used. Three groups of mustard plants were grown under controlled conditions and watered with tap water spiked with a mixture of all the investigated analytes: different amounts of MWCNTs were added to assess their effect on the uptake and elimination of contaminants (0; 1 and 10 mg/L). It was found that the groups exposed to 1 and 10 mg/L MWCNTs accumulated 10–30% and

20–160% respectively more contaminants compared to the control group. On the other hand, whereas a positive correlation was found between the amount of MWCNTs added in nutrient solution and the analyte concentration in plant tissues, it was observed that as the amount of MWCNTs increased, the accumulation rate constants (k_a) decreased. This behavior was explained taking into account that a longer period of time is needed for the in vivo contaminant concentration to reach a plateau: after the adsorption of the analytes onto MWCNTs, analytes are slowly released. Regarding the depuration capability of *B. juncea*, no differences were observed in the elimination of accumulated analytes between the MWCNTs groups and the control group.

Synthetic musks are an emerging class of xenobiotics which caused severe concern in health and environmental safety since they are able to interact with the endocrine system. This class of analytes has been monitored via in vivo SPME in both tilapia and aloe (*Aloe chinensis Baker*) without any fish or plant sacrifice [44]. Regarding the aloe study, SPME sampling was carried out in both leaves and roots at a depth of 1.4 cm and with a sampling time of 10 min. The concentration of all the investigated compounds in aloe leaves plateaued after the third day of exposure, whereas for roots it took only one day. A rapid clearance was observed in both plant compartments: for aloe foliage, the half-lives for all the compounds of interest were between 0.6–0.7 days, whereas for roots the concentration of absorbed SMs halved in less than 12 h after exposure. BCFs calculated for aloe roots were two orders of magnitude higher compared to those obtained for the leaves for all the analytes. This was consistent with the average lipid content: SMs were found to be more likely to be accumulated in high-lipid plant compartments such as roots. Since chemicals in plants needs to reach the leaves from the root cortex, bioaccumulation in aloe leaf is less efficient, with BCFs at least three orders of magnitude lower than those found for tilapias.

The same research group successfully quantitated different pharmaceuticals in *B. alba* stems and in tilapia (*O. mossambicus*) by using a custom made sulfonated Al_2O_3@PLCL/pNE SPME fiber [38]. The validated SPME-LC-MS/MS method provided LODs in the 0.02–8.02 µg/kg range for *B. alba*, demonstrating linearity within 2–3 orders of magnitude up to 5 mg/kg. Both intra- and inter-fiber precision were also satisfactory, with RSDs within 9.9% and 15.6%, respectively. The extraction from *B. alba* was carried out by piercing the stems and holding the fiber in place for 10 min. The fiber was then desorbed in methanol under agitation; thereafter, internal standard was added before addressing the solution to LC-MS/MS analysis. In order to test method accuracy, all the analytes were quantified performing a classical LE from ex vivo samples. No differences were found between the concentration determined with both SPME-LC-MS/MS and LE-LC-MS/MS methods in tilapia and *B. alba*. Regarding *B. alba*, sulfafurazole could only be detected using the in vivo SR-SPME technique, thus demonstrating the best performances of the in vivo method with respect to the ex vivo one.

Along with xenobiotics, phytohormones and carbohydrates represent other two important classes of analytes of biological interest. Such endogenous compounds are involved in a variety of regulation and pathological processes [72,75].

In this context, Fang et al. [72] have developed a proper SPME coating for the extraction of plant regulators (salicylic acid and three of its derivatives—SAs), i.e., acetylsalicylic acid, 4-methyl salicylic acid and 3-methyl salicylic acid, in aloe leaves with the final aim of monitoring stress levels in plants. For this purpose, C_{18}@GO@PDDA coated quartz fibers were fabricated. C_{18}@GO@PDDA were dispersed in DMF with PAN to form a slurry and coated with a pNE layer to ensure biocompatibility. The sampling rate-solid phase microextraction-liquid chromatography-photodiode array detector (SR-SPME-LC-PAD) method was optimized by analyzing homogenized aloe leaves spiked with the analytes and investigating the effect of extraction and desorption time, pH and desorption agitation speed. The extraction performance of C_{18}@GO@PDDA SPME fiber was compared with those achieved by the commercial 85 µm PA and 65 µm PDMS/DVB, showing higher extraction efficiency toward all the investigated analytes. The validated method provided LODs in the 1.8–2.8 µg/L range and linearity within 3 orders of magnitude. Good intra- and inter-fiber precision were obtained, with RSDs within 8.4% and 9.3%, respectively. The four salicylic acids were also quantified using a classical LE-LC-PAD method: no difference (α = 0.01) was found between the analytical outcomes, thus ensuring the accuracy of the in vivo SR-SPME-LC-PAD method. The method was used to monitor the investigated compounds over time in aloe plants in order to evaluate whether the presence of cadmium, used as stress agent, produced detectable variation in salicylic acids profile over time. As a result, SAs concentration in Cd-stressed group peaked within 16 h. The control group was used to assess the impact of the injuries on plant leaves, made by inserting the SPME fiber: the concentration for all the investigated analytes increased within 6 h but less dramatically in respect to the Cd-stressed group. Thereafter, SAs levels decreased slowly and returned normal within 12 h.

Thin core-sheath electrospun nanofibers with pure PANI sheath and polystyrene core (PS-PANI CSEF) compressed into tiny bars have been applied for in vivo extraction of phytohormones gibberellin A3 (GA3), gibberellin A7 (GA7), jasmonic acid (JA), abscisic acid (ABA) and p-hydroxycinnamic acid (p-HCA) in aloe by LC-MS/MS [73]. The proposed extraction material was biocompatible, characterized by a fast mass transfer rate and large extraction capacity to ensure fast equilibrium extraction and high sensitivity. In vivo extraction was carried out by inserting the PS-PANI CSEF bars in aloe leaves at 3 mm depth for 20 min. Method validation provided LODs in the 0.06–3.1 µg/L range, demonstrating linearity within three orders of magnitude. Good precision and accuracy were obtained, with RSDs always below 13% and recovery rates (RR%) in the 98–110% range. In order to assess suitability of the developed method for the quantitation of acidic phytohormones in aloe foliage, both in vivo and ex vivo methods were applied. GA3 was the only undetected compound using the in vivo extraction, whereas GA3 and GA7 resulted undetectable with the classic ex vivo LE-LC-MS/MS method, thus demonstrating the clear advantages of the developed in vivo approach. Moreover, the in vivo method allowed the detection of the analytes with a spatial resolution of about 3–8 mm^3, whereas the LE method consumed about 60 mg of leaf tissue, without providing any spatial resolution.

Carbohydrate detection in aqueous media, biofluids and tissues is challenging due to the high affinity of these compounds toward water. Owing to its capability of interacting with diols in a rapid and reversible way, phenylboronic acid functionalized MWCNTs, using PAN as binder has been proposed by Chen et al. to develop a custom-made SPME probe (Figure 8) for carbohydrate detection in biofluids and semisolid biotissues [75]. Preliminary tests in phosphate buffer solution showed the specificity of the developed probe toward glucose, chosen as a model compound, even in presence of other interfering compounds normally present in biological samples. The developed probe was used for the extraction of carbohydrates from *B. alba* by inserting it at an average depth of 1.5 cm with the aid of a cannula needle. Thereafter, the probe was withdrawn and desorbed in acetic acid. Finally, the extracted solution was derivatized for GC-MS analysis. Glucose, mannose, galactose and rhamnose were successfully detected in *B. alba* and aloe in 12 h. Finally, MALDI-TOF-MS analyses proved the absence of macromolecules absorbed onto the probe.

Further studies have been conducted by the same research group on the specific monitoring of glucose using a boronate affinity-molecularly imprinted polymer (BA-MIP) biocompatible probe [79]. The presence of boronate acid monomer in the proposed coating played a pivotal role in increasing SPME selectivity due to the unique pre-self-assembly between glucose and boronic acid creating glucose specific memory cavities. A reduced interference from mannose and galactose was observed, whereas commercially available C$_{18}$ and PDMS fibers were not able to extract glucose. Finally, glucose was successfully in vivo extracted from aloe foliage. Again, MALDI-TOF-MS analysis proved the absence of other interfering macromolecules.

Besides targeted analytical chemistry, in vivo extraction techniques play a fundamental role also in untargeted analytical chemistry. In metabolomics, in which the structure and the abundance of a plethora of compounds found in living organisms are accurately investigated, it is extremely important to avoid analyte degradation or the generation of misleading artifacts, which mainly occur during the sample preparation step [80]. Considering also that in plants gene expression is mainly connected with endogenous compounds, DI-SPME might be the technique of choice for investigating plant metabolites directly in vivo [81].

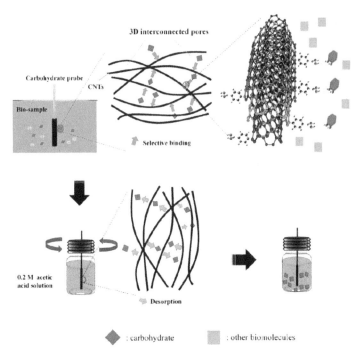

Figure 8. Schematic representation of the carbohydrate recognition onto the developed phenylboronic acid functionalized-carbon nanotubes (CNTs) probe. Reprinted with permission from [75].

In 2016, Musteata et al. successfully used SPME for the in vivo investigation of nonvolatile metabolites in Amazonian plants using UPLC-MS/MS analysis [71]. In this study, a custom-made SPME coating was tested: SPME devices were prepared by coating stainless steel wires with commercially available silica i.e., reverse phase (RP)-amide-C_{16} and pentafluorophenyl-propyl-bonded phase (HS-F5), respectively. Both the coatings were chosen owing to their mechanical resistance and fast equilibration with the sample due to the high surface area of the material. (RP)-amide-C_{16} is characterized by a stable amide embedded polar group able to enhance both the extraction of polar compounds and wettability. HS-F5 coating is able to interact with a wide range of analytes via dispersive, dipole-dipole, π-π and charge transfer interactions, thus being suitable for the extraction of polar and basic compounds. Preliminary investigations on a smaller sample of plants in Hawaii (*Psychotria viridis*, *Diplopterys cabrerana* and *Banisteriopsis caapi*) proved the superior extraction capability of HS-F5 for untargeted analysis. In vivo sampling on Amazonian plants was performed by inserting the probes under the bark of each plant and holding them in place for 30 min. Ex vivo LE-UPLC-MS/MS analyses were also performed with the aim of comparing the number of unique signals obtained by using both extraction approaches. Although the total number of compounds extracted by the in vivo procedure was lower than that obtained by using the ex vivo extraction, SPME-UPLC-MS/MS provided 27% exclusive signals. PCA on data obtained by in vivo extraction revealed significant differences among species belonging to the same genus, despite the investigated organisms were similar according to DNA analysis. Finally, considering the 30 min in vivo extraction time compared to the several hours required to prepare the samples via ex vivo approach, in vivo SPME-UPLC-MS/MS method was unequivocally less time-consuming with respect to LE method.

In the same year, apple (*Malus domestica* fruit) metabolome has been investigated by Risticevic et al. [81] with the aim of evaluating the changes in the metabolic fingerprints in response to fruit maturation. A PDMS overcoated commercial 50/30 μm DVB/CAR/PDMS fiber coupled with two-dimensional gas chromatography-time of flight mass spectrometry (GC×GC-TOF-MS) was devised. As for fiber coating, the use of PDMS overcoating allowed reducing fiber fouling damage of DVB-based coatings when placed in direct contact with complex matrices, thus guaranteeing matrix-compatibility while retaining the original coating sensitivity toward the analytes of interest. Sample collection was carried out by inserting three probes perpendicularly respect to the fruit stem at a 3 cm depth with two different sampling configurations. The results achieved after 60 min sampling, revealed significant differences in terms of method precision: in the case of sampling design 1, RSDs of about 22.0% were obtained considering 357 metabolites, whereas with sampling design 2, RSDs of 37.1% were calculated on 111 metabolites. A negative correlation was found between metabolite molecular weight and precision: larger RSDs were attributed to high molecular weight compounds. Precision of the two sampling designs was also evaluated using a homologous series of esters as model compounds: sampling design 1 provided poor precision regarding the determination of high molecular weight compounds, whereas with sampling design 2 lower RSDs values were obtained. Using a total of 40 compounds ex vivo HS-SPME was also performed for comparison purposes obtaining a median RSDs of 13.6%; however in vivo sampling addressed issues related to the stability of labile and hydrophobic metabolites encountered in HS-SPME. Furthermore, PCA on data obtained from in vivo analysis of apples at two different maturation stages showed a good separation between the groups, thus demonstrating the capability of the in vivo DI-SPME-GC×GC-TOF-MS metabolomic platform to provide representative data useful for staging the maturation level of fruits.

An overview of the discussed applications is reported in Table 3.

Table 3. Summary of applications of in vivo SPME for plant tissues.

Analyte	Matrix	Coating	SPME	Detection Technique	LOQs	RSD%	Ref.
Fungicides	Mung bean sprouts	PS/G@SiO$_2$	Homemade stainless-steel fibers	GC-MS	0.06–0.08 µg/L	<12.1	[74]
OCPs and OPPs	Malabar spinach roots/stem/leaf	PDMS	Homemade stainless steel fibers	GC-MS	0.09–4.10 ng/g	<57.7	[78]
OPPs	Cabbage stem—aloe leaf	PDMS	Homemade stainless steel fibers	GC-MS and LC-MS/MS	0.07–2.07 ng/g	<12.5	[12]
OCPs, OPPs, pyrethroid insecticides and PCPs	Mustard leaves	PDMS	Homemade stainless steel fibers	GC-MS	0.1–34.8 ng/g (LODs)	-	[77]
SMs	Aloe leaf/roots	PDMS	Homemade stainless steel fibers	GC-MS	3.0–13.2 ng/g (LODs)	<34.3	[44]
Pharmaceuticals	Spinach stem	Al$_2$O$_3$@PLCL/pNE	Electrospun stainless steel fibers	LC-MS/MS	0.05–26.7 ng/g	<15.6	[38]
SAs	Aloe leaf	C$_{18}$@GO@PDDA	QF	LC- PAD	6.1–9.3 µg/L	<9.3	[72]
Acidic phytohormones	Aloe leaf	PANI	Nanofiber bars	LC-MS/MS	0.06–3.1 ng/mL	<13	[73]
Carbohydrates	Aloe leaf—Malabar spinach stem	Phenylboronic acid functionalized MWCNTs	QF	GC-MS	0.12 µmol/L (LODs)	-	[75]
Glucose	Aloe leaf	BA-MIP	Miniaturized stainless steel wire	GC-MS	0.7 µmol/L	-	[77]
Nonvolatile phytochemicals	Amazonian plants	RP-amide-C$_{16}$-HS-F5	Commercially available fibers	UPLC-MS/MS	-	-	[71]
Nonvolatile metabolome	Apple	PDMS overcoated DVB/ CAR/PDMS	Overcoated Commercially available fibers	GC×GC-TOF-MS	-	<15 (50% of the detected compounds)	[81]

- Not declared.

5. In Vivo SPME Extraction of Cells and Simple Organisms

In vivo extraction and detection of compounds of biological and environmental interest from small living organisms and single cells is a challenging task due to reduced sample dimension, but it is of paramount importance to give an insight in microsize processes. In this context, ambient MS provides a straightforward strategy for direct analysis of individual organisms and single cells under ambient conditions [82,83].

In 2015, Deng et al. [22] investigated the presence of perfluorinated compounds (PFCs) in individual *Daphnia magna*, small organisms widely used as a model in ecotoxicology, and its egg cells using 2 μm thin tungsten needles coated with DMOAP for SCP-nanoESI-HRMS. Perfluorooctanesulfonic acid (PFOS) and perfluorooctanoic acid (PFOA) were chosen as model compounds. *D. magna* was exposed to water spiked with both PFOS and PFOA at a concentration of 10 μg/L. Different exposure time were investigated: (i) 3-day exposure was used to assess whether or not bioaccumulation phenomenon occurred equally among 28 different individuals; (ii) different samples within 10-day were collected to study the accumulation kinetics; (iii) 3-day exposure was used to investigate the analyte distribution within *D. magna* body. Organisms and egg cells were sampled with the aid of a three-dimensional micromanipulator by inserting the probe at 50 μm depth and holding it in place for 60 s. The method was optimized and validated using spiked *D. magna* juice as a matrix, demonstrating linearity over two orders of magnitude and providing LODs in the low μg/L range. Intra- and inter-probe precision were satisfactory, both below 11%. Regarding the bioaccumulation study, it was found that among 28 individuals, the accumulated concentration of both analytes in 3 *D. magna* was significantly higher with respect to other 25 investigated individuals. Bioaccumulation kinetic study showed that both PFOS and PFOA were rapidly accumulated within 3 days after reaching a steady-state for the investigated individuals. Finally, different compartments of *D. magna,* namely head, abdomen, back, tail and egg cells were successfully sampled to assess analyte distribution: the highest detected concentration of both analytes was observed in abdomen, whereas the lowest in egg cells, thus suggesting that the risk of bioaccumulation can be transferred from the mother to offspring.

D. magna was used as a model organism in a further study [21] in which in vivo lipidomic was performed using a the previously cited biocompatible SCP-nanoESI-HRMS method. Lipidomic investigation resulted in detection of high intensity signals for lipid species in the 700–950 *m/z* range. Similar compounds were detected in different compartments, observing an overall concentration decrease in abdomen, back, head and tail, respectively. A total of 152 lipid species excluding isomers were identified belonging to different classes, i.e., 80 TAGs, 28 PCs, 15 phosphatidic acids (PAs), 11 PGs, 6 MGDGs, 5 wax esters, 3 phosphatidylethanolamines (PEs), 2 FAs, 1 CerP and 1 sulfatide (SHexCer). The sodium/potassium adduct signals of TAGs and PCs were mostly detected (Figure 9a–d). To clearly visualize the distribution of the lipid species, the most abundant compounds i.e., TAG (16:0/16:4/18:3) and PC (16:0/18:3) were selected as representative for imaging (Figure 9e). The high concentration of TAGs in abdomen was attributed to their accumulation in viscus.

Lipidomic investigation has been also conducted in single cells of the eukaryotic cell line HepG,2, but poor signals were observed. Therefore, lipidomic study was performed on a pool of about 100 HepG2 cells, resulting in abundant lipid signals stable up to 40 s. A total of 60 lipids (excluding isomers) were detected including 38 PCs, 9 PGs, 4 lysophosphatidylcholines, 3 sphingolipids SpLs, 1 SHexCer, 1 PA, 1 phosphatidylethanolamines-ceramide, 1 PE, 1 lysophosphatidylethanolamine and 1 CE. Most biological membranes are constituted by these PCs, thus explaining their high abundancy in the lipidome profile.

An overview of the discussed applications is reported in Table 4.

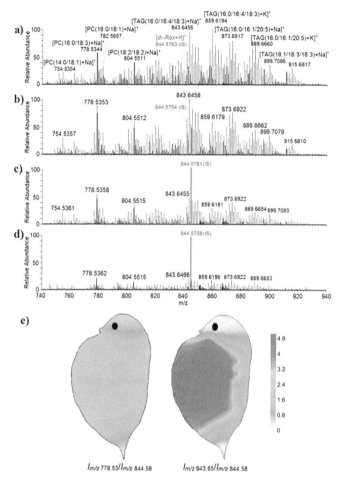

Figure 9. Biocompatible surface coated probes (BSCP)-nanoESI-HRMS spectra for analysis of the
(**a**) abdomen, (**b**) back, (**c**) head, and (**d**) tail of individual *Daphnia magna*. (**e**) Distribution of
phosphatidylcholine (PC) (16:0/18:3) and triradylglycerol (TAG) (16:0/16:4/18:3) in *Daphnia magna*.
d7-Rox was used as internal standard, added into the spray solvent at 50 ng/mL. Sodium/potassium
adduct signals of TAGs and PCs: TAG (16:0/16:4/18:3) (*m/z* 843.6456 [M + Na]$^+$ and *m/z* 859.6194
[M + K]$^+$), TAG(16:0/16:1/20:5) (*m/z* 873.6917 [M + Na]$^+$ and *m/z* 889.6660 [M + K]$^+$), TAG(18:1/18:3/18:3)
(*m/z* 899.7086 [M + Na]$^+$ and *m/z* 915.6817 [M + K]$^+$), PC(16:0/18:3) (*m/z* 778.5344 [M + Na]$^+$) PC(16:0/18:1)
(*m/z* 782.5657 [M + Na]$^+$), PC(18:2/18:2) (*m/z* 804.5511 [M + Na]$^+$), and PC(14:0/18:1) (*m/z* 754.5354
[M + Na]$^+$). Reprinted with permission from [21].

Table 4. Summary of applications of in vivo SPME for small organisms and single cell.

Analyte	Matrix	Coating	SPME	Detection Technique	LOQs (ng/mL)	RSD%	Ref.
PFOS and PFOA	*Daphnia magna*	DMOAP	Homemade coated tungsten probes	nanoESI-HRMS	0.06–0.09	<10.4	[22]
Untargeted lipidomics	*Daphnia magna*—eukaryotic cell	Biocompatible chitosan-based	Homemade coated tungsten probes	nanoESI-HRMS	-	-	[21]

- Not declared.

6. Conclusions

In vivo SPME is an emerging technique allowing for the rapid, low cost, non-invasive and sensitive determination of both exogenous and endogenous compounds in living systems. The use of miniaturized devices for in vivo SPME can minimize adverse effects commonly present when tissue sampling is performed by ex vivo procedures, allowing the direct analysis of different body areas with high spatial resolution. All the protocols presented in this survey proved to be particularly suitable for evaluating the temporal variation in the profile of analytes as a consequence of the capability of performing repeated sampling over the time on the same living organisms or cells without animal/plant sacrifice.

The development of novel biocompatible coatings plays a pivotal role in the diffusion of in vivo SPME both for targeted and untargeted analysis. In the first case, new materials able to provide high selectivity toward specific analytes have been designed, whereas in the latter case coatings characterized by enhanced extraction capabilities toward a wide range of both hydrophobic and hydrophilic compounds have been proposed. Additional advantages in terms of increased surface area and controlled porous structure can be obtained by adding to the commonly used polymeric substrates 3D structured materials like MOFs or carbon nanotubes.

Finally, the use of portable instruments and hyphenation with sensitive techniques like ambient mass spectrometry will increase the applicability of in vivo SPME allowing the implementation of ex vivo SPME protocols for in vivo applications. In this context, the analysis of larger cohort of samples and short-living and labile compounds will provide valuable information about the health of ecosystems, biological processes and toxicological effects.

Author Contributions: N.R., F.F., F.B., M.C.: Literature review, writing and revisions. All authors have read and agree to the published version of the manuscript.

Funding: This research received no external funding.

Acknowledgments: This work has benefited from the equipment and framework of the COMP-HUB Initiative, funded by the 'Departments of Excellence' program of the Italian Ministry for Education, University and Research (MIUR, 2018–2022).

Conflicts of Interest: The authors declare no conflicts of interest.

References

1. Reyes-Garcés, N.; Gionfriddo, E.; Gómez-Ríos, G.A.; Alam, M.N.; Boyacı, E.; Bojko, B.; Singh, V.; Grandy, J.; Pawliszyn, J. Advances in Solid Phase Microextraction and Perspective on Future Directions. *Anal. Chem.* **2018**, *90*, 302–360. [CrossRef] [PubMed]
2. Bojko, B.; Pawliszyn, J. In vivo and ex vivo SPME: A low invasive sampling and sample preparation tool in clinical bioanalysis. *Bioanalysis* **2014**, *6*, 1227–1239. [CrossRef] [PubMed]
3. Gómez-Ríos, G.A.; Mirabelli, M.F. Solid Phase Microextraction-mass spectrometry: Metanoia. *TrAC Trends Anal. Chem.* **2019**, *112*, 201–211. [CrossRef]
4. Gómez-Ríos, G.A.; Reyes-Garcés, N.; Bojko, B.; Pawliszyn, J. Biocompatible Solid-Phase Microextraction Nanoelectrospray Ionization: An Unexploited Tool in Bioanalysis. *Anal. Chem.* **2016**, *88*, 1259–1265. [CrossRef]
5. Ahmad, S.; Tucker, M.; Spooner, N.; Murnane, D.; Gerhard, U. Direct ionization of solid-phase microextraction fibers for quantitative drug bioanalysis: From peripheral circulation to mass spectrometry detection. *Anal. Chem.* **2015**, *87*, 754–759. [CrossRef]
6. Piri-Moghadam, H.; Ahmadi, F.; Gómez-Ríos, G.A.; Boyacı, E.; Reyes-Garcés, N.; Aghakhani, A.; Bojko, B.; Pawliszyn, J. Fast Quantitation of Target Analytes in Small Volumes of Complex Samples by Matrix-Compatible Solid-Phase Microextraction Devices. *Angew. Chem. Int. Ed.* **2016**, *55*, 7510–7514. [CrossRef]
7. Filipiak, W.; Bojko, B. SPME in clinical, pharmaceutical, and biotechnological research–How far are we from daily practice? *TrAC Trends Anal. Chem.* **2019**, *115*, 203–213. [CrossRef]
8. Roszkowska, A.; Miękus, N.; Bączek, T. Application of solid-phase microextraction in current biomedical research. *J. Sep. Sci.* **2019**, *42*, 285–302. [CrossRef]

9.   Zhang, Q.-H.; Zhou, L.-D.; Chen, H.; Wang, C.-Z.; Xia, Z.-N.; Yuan, C.-S. Solid-phase microextraction technology for in vitro and in vivo metabolite analysis. *TrAC Trends Anal. Chem.* **2016**, *80*, 57–65. [CrossRef]

10. Reyes-Garcés, N.; Gionfriddo, E. Recent developments and applications of solid phase microextraction as a sample preparation approach for mass-spectrometry-based metabolomics and lipidomics. *TrAC Trends Anal. Chem.* **2019**, *113*, 172–181. [CrossRef]

11. Xu, J.; Chen, G.; Huang, S.; Qiu, J.; Jiang, R.; Zhu, F.; Ouyang, G. Application of in vivo solid-phase microextraction in environmental analysis. *TrAC Trends Anal. Chem.* **2016**, *85*, 26–35. [CrossRef]

12. Qiu, J.; Chen, G.; Zhou, H.; Xu, J.; Wang, F.; Zhu, F.; Ouyang, G. In vivo tracing of organophosphorus pesticides in cabbage (Brassica parachinensis) and aloe (Barbadensis). *Sci. Total Environ.* **2016**, *550*, 1134–1140. [CrossRef] [PubMed]

13. Bessonneau, V.; Zhan, Y.; De Lannoy, I.A.M.; Saldivia, V.; Pawliszyn, J. In vivo solid-phase microextraction liquid chromatography-tandem mass spectrometry for monitoring blood eicosanoids time profile after lipopolysaccharide-induced inflammation in Sprague-Dawley rats. *J. Chromatogr. A* **2015**, *1424*, 134–138. [CrossRef] [PubMed]

14. Xu, J.; Huang, S.; Wu, R.; Jiang, R.; Zhu, F.; Wang, J.; Ouyang, G. Bioinspired Polydopamine Sheathed Nanofibers for High-Efficient in Vivo Solid-Phase Microextraction of Pharmaceuticals in Fish Muscle. *Anal. Chem.* **2015**, *87*, 3453–3459. [CrossRef] [PubMed]

15. Gao, D.; Wang, D.D.; Zhang, Q.; Yang, F.Q.; Xia, Z.N.; Zhang, Q.H.; Yuan, C.S. In Vivo Selective Capture and Rapid Identification of Luteolin and Its Metabolites in Rat Livers by Molecularly Imprinted Solid-Phase Microextraction. *J. Agric. Food Chem.* **2017**, *65*, 1158–1166. [CrossRef]

16. Goryńska, P.Z.; Chmara, K.; Goryński, K.; Paczkowski, D.; Harat, M.; Bojko, B. A new strategy for brain tumour metabolomic analysis. *Med. Res. J.* **2018**, *3*, 15–22. [CrossRef]

17. Lendor, S.; Hassani, S.A.; Boyaci, E.; Singh, V.; Womelsdorf, T.; Pawliszyn, J. Solid Phase Microextraction-Based Miniaturized Probe and Protocol for Extraction of Neurotransmitters from Brains in Vivo. *Anal. Chem.* **2019**, *91*, 4896–4905. [CrossRef]

18. Bessonneau, V.; Boyaci, E.; Maciazek-Jurczyk, M.; Pawliszyn, J. In vivo solid phase microextraction sampling of human saliva for non-invasive and on-site monitoring. *Anal. Chim. Acta* **2015**, *856*, 35–45. [CrossRef]

19. Gionfriddo, E.; Boyacl, E.; Pawliszyn, J. New Generation of Solid-Phase Microextraction Coatings for Complementary Separation Approaches: A Step toward Comprehensive Metabolomics and Multiresidue Analyses in Complex Matrices. *Anal. Chem.* **2017**, *89*, 4046–4054. [CrossRef]

20. Huang, S.; Chen, G.; Ye, N.; Kou, X.; Zhu, F.; Shen, J.; Ouyang, G. Solid-phase microextraction: An appealing alternative for the determination of endogenous substances-A review. *Anal. Chim. Acta* **2019**, *1077*, 67–86. [CrossRef]

21. Deng, J.; Li, W.; Yang, Q.; Liu, Y.; Fang, L.; Guo, Y.; Guo, P.; Lin, L.; Yang, Y.; Luan, T. Biocompatible Surface-Coated Probe for in Vivo, in Situ, and Microscale Lipidomics of Small Biological Organisms and Cells Using Mass Spectrometry. *Anal. Chem.* **2018**, *90*, 6936–6944. [CrossRef]

22. Deng, J.; Yang, Y.; Xu, M.; Wang, X.; Lin, L.; Yao, Z.P.; Luan, T. Surface-Coated Probe Nanoelectrospray Ionization Mass Spectrometry for Analysis of Target Compounds in Individual Small Organisms. *Anal. Chem.* **2015**, *87*, 9923–9930. [CrossRef] [PubMed]

23. Pellenburg, H.; Graumans, M.H.F.; Droge, S.T.J.; Hermens, J.L.M.; Booman, I.J. Direct tissue sampling of diazepam and amitriptyline using mixed-mode SPME fibers: A feasibility study. *Forensic Chem.* **2016**, *1*, 51–57. [CrossRef]

24. Anzillotti, L.; Marezza, F.; Calò, L.; Andreoli, R.; Agazzi, S.; Bianchi, F.; Careri, M.; Cecchi, R. Determination of synthetic and natural cannabinoids in oral fluid by solid phase microextraction coupled to gas chromatography/mass spectrometry: A pilot study. *Talanta* **2019**, *201*, 335–341. [CrossRef] [PubMed]

25. Vasiljevic, T.; Singh, V.; Pawliszyn, J. Miniaturized SPME tips directly coupled to mass spectrometry for targeted determination and untargeted profiling of small samples. *Talanta* **2019**, *199*, 689–697. [CrossRef] [PubMed]

26. Bianchi, F.; Riboni, N.; Carbognani, P.; Gnetti, L.; Dalcanale, E.; Ampollini, L.; Careri, M. Solid-phase microextraction coupled to gas chromatography–mass spectrometry followed by multivariate data analysis for the identification of volatile organic compounds as possible biomarkers in lung cancer tissues. *J. Pharm. Biomed. Anal.* **2017**, *146*, 329–333. [CrossRef] [PubMed]

27. Castro, Ó.; Trabalón, L.; Schilling, B.; Borrull, F.; Pocurull, E. Solid phase microextraction Arrow for the determination of synthetic musk fragrances in fish samples. *J. Chromatogr. A* **2019**, *1591*, 55–61. [CrossRef]

28. Hassani, S.A.; Lendor, S.; Boyaci, E.; Pawliszyn, J.; Womelsdorf, T. Multineuromodulator measurements across fronto-striatal network areas of the behaving macaque using solid-phase microextraction. *J. Neurophysiol.* **2019**, *122*, 1649–1660. [CrossRef]

29. Reyes-Garcés, N.; Diwan, M.; Boyacı, E.; Gómez-Ríos, G.A.; Bojko, B.; Nobrega, J.N.; Bambico, F.R.; Hamani, C.; Pawliszyn, J. In Vivo Brain Sampling Using a Microextraction Probe Reveals Metabolic Changes in Rodents after Deep Brain Stimulation. *Anal. Chem.* **2019**, *91*, 9875–9884. [CrossRef]

30. Wang, D.D.; Gao, D.; Huang, Y.K.; Xu, W.J.; Xia, Z.N. Preparation of restricted access molecularly imprinted polymers based fiber for selective solid-phase microextraction of hesperetin and its metabolites in vivo. *Talanta* **2019**, *202*, 392–401. [CrossRef]

31. Roszkowska, A.; Tascon, M.; Bojko, B.; Goryński, K.; dos Santos, P.R.; Cypel, M.; Pawliszyn, J. Equilibrium ex vivo calibration of homogenized tissue for in vivo SPME quantitation of doxorubicin in lung tissue. *Talanta* **2018**, *183*, 304–310. [CrossRef] [PubMed]

32. Zhang, J.; Rector, J.; Lin, J.Q.; Young, J.H.; Sans, M.; Katta, N.; Giese, N.; Yu, W.; Nagi, C.; Suliburk, J.; et al. Nondestructive tissue analysis for ex vivo and in vivo cancer diagnosis using a handheld mass spectrometry system. *Sci. Transl. Med.* **2017**, *9*. [CrossRef] [PubMed]

33. Van der Oost, R.; Beyer, J.; Vermeulen, N.P. Fish bioaccumulation and biomarkers in environmental risk assessment: A review. *Envrion. Toxicol. Pharmacol.* **2003**, *13*, 57–149. [CrossRef]

34. Streit, B. Bioaccumulation of contaminants in fish BT - Fish Ecotoxicology. In *Fish Ecotoxicology*; Birkhäuser Basel: Basel, Switzerland, 1998; pp. 353–387, ISBN 978-3-0348-8853-0.

35. Walczak, M.; Reichert, M. Characteristics of selected bioaccumulative substances and their impact on fish health. *J. Vet. Res.* **2016**, *60*, 473–480. [CrossRef]

36. Huang, S.; Xu, J.; Wu, J.; Hong, H.; Chen, G.; Jiang, R.; Zhu, F.; Liu, Y.; Ouyang, G. Rapid detection of five anesthetics in tilapias by in vivo solid phase microextraction coupling with gas chromatography-mass spectrometry. *Talanta* **2017**, *168*, 263–268. [CrossRef]

37. Qiu, J.; Chen, G.; Liu, S.; Zhang, T.; Wu, J.; Wang, F.; Xu, J.; Liu, Y.; Zhu, F.; Ouyang, G. Bioinspired Polyelectrolyte-Assembled Graphene-Oxide-Coated C18 Composite Solid-Phase Microextraction Fibers for in Vivo Monitoring of Acidic Pharmaceuticals in Fish. *Anal. Chem.* **2016**, *88*, 5841–5848. [CrossRef]

38. Qiu, J.; Chen, G.; Zhu, F.; Ouyang, G. Sulfonated nanoparticles doped electrospun fibers with bioinspired polynorepinephrine sheath for in vivo solid-phase microextraction of pharmaceuticals in fish and vegetable. *J. Chromatogr. A* **2016**, *1455*, 20–27. [CrossRef]

39. Qiu, J.; Wang, F.; Zhang, T.; Chen, L.; Liu, Y.; Zhu, F.; Ouyang, G. Novel Electrosorption-Enhanced Solid-Phase Microextraction Device for Ultrafast in Vivo Sampling of Ionized Pharmaceuticals in Fish. *Envrion. Sci. Technol.* **2018**, *52*, 145–151. [CrossRef]

40. Mondal, S.; Xu, J.; Chen, G.; Huang, S.; Huang, C.; Yin, L.; Ouyang, G. Solid-phase microextraction of antibiotics from fish muscle by using MIL-101(Cr)NH 2 -polyacrylonitrile fiber and their identification by liquid chromatography-tandem mass spectrometry. *Anal. Chim. Acta* **2019**, *1047*, 62–70. [CrossRef]

41. Xu, J.; Wu, R.; Huang, S.; Yang, M.; Liu, Y.; Liu, Y.; Jiang, R.; Zhu, F.; Ouyang, G. Polyelectrolyte Microcapsules Dispersed in Silicone Rubber for in Vivo Sampling in Fish Brains. *Anal. Chem.* **2015**, *87*, 10593–10599. [CrossRef]

42. Poole, J.J.; Grandy, J.J.; Yu, M.; Boyaci, E.; Gómez-Ríos, G.A.; Reyes-Garcés, N.; Bojko, B.; Heide, H.V.; Pawliszyn, J. Deposition of a Sorbent into a Recession on a Solid Support to Provide a New, Mechanically Robust Solid-Phase Microextraction Device. *Anal. Chem.* **2017**, *89*, 8021–8026. [CrossRef]

43. Ocaña-Rios, I.; Peña-Alvarez, A.; Zuñiga-Perez, I.; Loeza-Fuentes, E. Trace analysis of UV filters and musks in living fish by in vivo SPME-GC-MS. *Anal. Bioanal. Chem.* **2019**, *411*, 3209–3218. [CrossRef] [PubMed]

44. Chen, G.; Jiang, R.; Qiu, J.; Cai, S.; Zhu, F.; Ouyang, G. Environmental fates of synthetic musks in animal and plant: An in vivo study. *Chemosphere* **2015**, *138*, 584–591. [CrossRef] [PubMed]

45. Xu, J.; Luo, J.; Ruan, J.; Zhu, F.; Luan, T.; Liu, H.; Jiang, R.; Ouyang, G. In vivo tracing uptake and elimination of organic pesticides in fish muscle. *Envrion. Sci. Technol.* **2014**, *48*, 8012–8020. [CrossRef]

46. Tang, Y.; Xu, J.; Chen, L.; Qiu, J.; Liu, Y.; Ouyang, G. Rapid in vivo determination of fluoroquinolones in cultured puffer fish (Takifugu obscurus) muscle by solid-phase microextraction coupled with liquid chromatography-tandem mass spectrometry. *Talanta* **2017**, *175*, 550–556. [CrossRef]

47. Lv, Y.Z.; Yao, L.; Wang, L.; Liu, W.R.; Zhao, J.L.; He, L.Y.; Ying, G.G. Bioaccumulation, metabolism, and risk assessment of phenolic endocrine disrupting chemicals in specific tissues of wild fish. *Chemosphere* **2019**, *226*, 607–615. [CrossRef]

48. Valdés, M.E.; Huerta, B.; Wunderlin, D.A.; Bistoni, M.A.; Barceló, D.; Rodriguez-Mozaz, S. Bioaccumulation and bioconcentration of carbamazepine and other pharmaceuticals in fish under field and controlled laboratory experiments. Evidences of carbamazepine metabolization by fish. *Sci. Total Environ.* **2016**, *557–558*, 58–67.

49. Song, X.-Y.; Chen, J.; Shi, Y.-P. Different configurations of carbon nanotubes reinforced solid-phase microextraction techniques and their applications in the environmental analysis. *TrAC Trends Anal. Chem.* **2017**, *86*, 263–275. [CrossRef]

50. Roszkowska, A.; Yu, M.; Bessonneau, V.; Ings, J.; McMaster, M.; Smith, R.; Bragg, L.; Servos, M.; Pawliszyn, J. In vivo solid-phase microextraction sampling combined with metabolomics and toxicological studies for the non-lethal monitoring of the exposome in fish tissue. *Environ. Pollut.* **2019**, *249*, 109–115. [CrossRef] [PubMed]

51. Vincent, B.; Jennifer, I.; Mark, M.; Richard, S.; Leslie, B.; Mark, S.; Janusz, P. In vivo tissue sampling using solid-phase microextraction for non-lethal exposome-wide association study of CYP1A1 induction in Catostomus commersonii. *Environ. Res.* **2016**, *151*, 216–223. [CrossRef] [PubMed]

52. Gobas, F.A.P.C.; Wilcockson, J.B.; Russell, R.W.; Haffner, G.D. Mechanism of biomagnification in fish under laboratory and field conditions. *Environ. Sci. Technol.* **1999**, *33*, 133–141. [CrossRef]

53. Landrum, P.F.; Fisher, S.W. Influence of Lipids on the Bioaccumulation and Trophic Transfer of Organic Contaminants in Aquatic Organisms. In *Lipids in Freshwater Ecosystems*; Springer: New York, NY, USA, 1999; pp. 203–234.

54. Croteau, M.N.; Luoma, S.N.; Stewart, A.R. Trophic transfer of metals along freshwater food webs: Evidence of cadmium biomagnification in nature. *Limnol. Oceanogr.* **2005**, *50*, 1511–1519. [CrossRef]

55. OECD. *Guidance Document to OECD TG 305-2nd Draft*; Oecd: Paris, France, 2016; pp. 1–116.

56. Vallecillos, L.; Borrull, F.; Pocurull, E. Recent approaches for the determination of synthetic musk fragrances in environmental samples. *TrAC Trends Anal. Chem.* **2015**, *72*, 80–92. [CrossRef]

57. Dimpe, K.M.; Nomngongo, P.N. Current sample preparation methodologies for analysis of emerging pollutants in different environmental matrices. *TrAC Trends Anal. Chem.* **2016**, *82*, 199–207. [CrossRef]

58. Miller, T.H.; Bury, N.R.; Owen, S.F.; MacRae, J.I.; Barron, L.P. A review of the pharmaceutical exposome in aquatic fauna. *Environ. Pollut.* **2018**, *239*, 129–146. [CrossRef] [PubMed]

59. Roszkowska, A.; Yu, M.; Bessonneau, V.; Bragg, L.; Servos, M.; Pawliszyn, J. Tissue storage affects lipidome profiling in comparison to in vivo microsampling approach. *Sci. Rep.* **2018**, *8*, 1–10. [CrossRef]

60. Bessonneau, V.; Ings, J.; McMaster, M.; Smith, R.; Bragg, L.; Servos, M.; Pawliszyn, J. In vivo microsampling to capture the elusive exposome. *Sci. Rep.* **2017**, *7*, 44038. [CrossRef]

61. Zhang, X.; Oakes, K.D.; Wang, S.; Servos, M.R.; Cui, S.; Pawliszyn, J.; Metcalfe, C.D. In vivo sampling of environmental organic contaminants in fish by solid-phase microextraction. *TrAC Trends Anal. Chem.* **2012**, *32*, 31–39. [CrossRef]

62. Ouyang, G.; Oakes, K.D.; Bragg, L.; Wang, S.; Liu, H.; Cui, S.; Servos, M.R.; Dixon, D.G.; Pawliszyn, J. Sampling-rate calibration for rapid and nonlethal monitoring of organic contaminants in fish muscle by solid-phase microextraction. *Environ. Sci. Technol.* **2011**, *45*, 7792–7798. [CrossRef]

63. Chen, L.; Qiu, J.; Tang, Y.; Xu, J.; Huang, S.; Liu, Y.; Ouyang, G. Rapid in vivo determination of tetrodotoxin in pufferfish (Fugu) muscle by solid-phase microextraction coupled to high-performance liquid chromatography tandem mass spectrometry. *Talanta* **2017**, *171*, 179–184. [CrossRef]

64. Háková, M.; Chocholoušová Havlíková, L.; Solich, P.; Švec, F.; Šatínský, D. Electrospun nanofiber polymers as extraction phases in analytical chemistry—The advances of the last decade. *TrAC Trends Anal. Chem.* **2019**, *110*, 81–96. [CrossRef]

65. Wild, C.P. Complementing the genome with an "exposome": The outstanding challenge of environmental exposure measurement in molecular epidemiology. *Cancer Epidemiol. Biomark. Prev.* **2005**, *14*, 1847–1850. [CrossRef] [PubMed]

66. Roszkowska, A.; Yu, M.; Bessonneau, V.; Bragg, L.; Servos, M.; Pawliszyn, J. Metabolome Profiling of Fish Muscle Tissue Exposed to Benzo[a]pyrene Using in Vivo Solid-Phase Microextraction. *Environ. Sci. Technol. Lett.* **2018**, *5*, 431–435. [CrossRef]

67. Yu, M.; Olkowicz, M.; Pawliszyn, J. Structure/reaction directed analysis for LC-MS based untargeted analysis. *Anal. Chim. Acta* **2019**, *1050*, 16–24. [CrossRef] [PubMed]

68. IRIS. *I.R.I.S. Toxicological Review of Benzo [a] pyrene [CASRN 50-32-8]*; IRIS: Washington, DC, USA, 2017.

69. Sethi, S.; Brietzke, E. Recent advances in lipidomics: Analytical and clinical perspectives. *Prostaglandins Other Lipid Mediat.* **2017**, *128*, 8–16. [CrossRef] [PubMed]

70. Deng, J.; Yang, Y.; Liu, Y.; Fang, L.; Lin, L.; Luan, T. Coupling Paternò-Büchi Reaction with Surface-Coated Probe Nanoelectrospray Ionization Mass Spectrometry for in Vivo and Microscale Profiling of Lipid C=C Location Isomers in Complex Biological Tissues. *Anal. Chem.* **2019**, *91*, 4592–4599. [CrossRef]

71. Musteata, F.M.; Sandoval, M.; Ruiz-Macedo, J.C.; Harrison, K.; McKenna, D.; Millington, W. Evaluation of in vivo solid phase microextraction for minimally invasive analysis of nonvolatile phytochemicals in Amazonian plants. *Anal. Chim. Acta* **2016**, *933*, 124–133. [CrossRef]

72. Fang, X.; Chen, G.; Qiu, J.; Xu, J.; Wang, J.; Zhu, F.; Ouyang, G. Determination of four salicylic acids in aloe by in vivo solid phase microextraction coupling with liquid chromatography-photodiode array detection. *Talanta* **2018**, *184*, 520–526. [CrossRef]

73. Wu, Q.; Wu, D.; Guan, Y. Polyaniline sheathed electrospun nanofiber bar for in vivo extraction of trace acidic phytohormones in plant tissue. *J. Chromatogr. A* **2014**, *1342*, 16–23. [CrossRef]

74. Shi, Z.; Chen, D.; Chen, T.T.; Wei, G.; Yin, C.Y.; Xu, H.; Yang, G.F. In vivo analysis of two new fungicides in mung bean sprouts by solid phase microextraction-gas chromatography-mass spectrometry. *Food Chem.* **2019**, *275*, 688–695. [CrossRef]

75. Chen, G.; Qiu, J.; Xu, J.; Fang, X.; Liu, Y.; Liu, S.; Wei, S.; Jiang, R.; Luan, T.; Zeng, F.; et al. A novel probe based on phenylboronic acid functionalized carbon nanotubes for ultrasensitive carbohydrate determination in biofluids and semi-solid biotissues. *Chem. Sci.* **2016**, *7*, 1487–1495. [CrossRef] [PubMed]

76. Zenker, A.; Cicero, M.R.; Prestinaci, F.; Bottoni, P.; Carere, M. Bioaccumulation and biomagnification potential of pharmaceuticals with a focus to the aquatic environment. *J. Envrion. Manag.* **2014**, *133*, 378–387. [CrossRef] [PubMed]

77. Chen, G.; Qiu, J.; Liu, Y.; Jiang, R.; Cai, S.; Liu, Y.; Zhu, F.; Zeng, F.; Luan, T.; Ouyang, G. Carbon Nanotubes Act as Contaminant Carriers and Translocate within Plants. *Sci. Rep.* **2015**, *5*, 15682. [CrossRef] [PubMed]

78. Qiu, J.; Chen, G.; Xu, J.; Luo, E.; Liu, Y.; Wang, F.; Zhou, H.; Liu, Y.; Zhu, F.; Ouyang, G. In vivo tracing of organochloride and organophosphorus pesticides in different organs of hydroponically grown malabar spinach (*Basella alba* L.). *J. Hazard. Mater.* **2016**, *316*, 52–59. [CrossRef] [PubMed]

79. Chen, G.; Qiu, J.; Fang, X.; Xu, J.; Cai, S.; Chen, Q.; Liu, Y.; Zhu, F.; Ouyang, G. Boronate Affinity–Molecularly Imprinted Biocompatible Probe: An Alternative for Specific Glucose Monitoring. *Chem. Asian J.* **2016**, *11*, 2240–2245. [CrossRef] [PubMed]

80. Gorrochategui, E.; Jaumot, J.; Lacorte, S.; Tauler, R. Data analysis strategies for targeted and untargeted LC-MS metabolomic studies: Overview and workflow. *TrAC Trends Anal. Chem.* **2016**, *82*, 425–442. [CrossRef]

81. Risticevic, S.; Souza-Silva, E.A.; DeEll, J.R.; Cochran, J.; Pawliszyn, J. Capturing Plant Metabolome with Direct-Immersion in Vivo Solid Phase Microextraction of Plant Tissues. *Anal. Chem.* **2016**, *88*, 1266–1274. [CrossRef]

82. Bianchi, F.; Riboni, N.; Termopoli, V.; Mendez, L.; Medina, I.; Ilag, L.; Cappiello, A.; Careri, M. MS-Based Analytical Techniques: Advances in Spray-Based Methods and EI-LC-MS Applications. *J. Anal. Methods Chem.* **2018**, *2018*, 1–24. [CrossRef]

83. Duncan, K.D.; Fyrestam, J.; Lanekoff, I. Advances in mass spectrometry based single-cell metabolomics. *Analyst* **2019**, *144*, 782–793. [CrossRef]

MDPI

St. Alban-Anlage 66

4052 Basel

Switzerland

Tel. +41 61 683 77 34

Fax +41 61 302 89 18

www.mdpi.com

Separations Editorial Office

E-mail: separations@mdpi.com

www.mdpi.com/journal/separations

Ingram Content Group UK Ltd.
Milton Keynes UK
UKHW052243040423
419479UK00004B/129

9 783039 369287